Everything but the Girl

Shaun C. Hawkins

For Dan Gallagher,
a cherished friend

Table of Contents

Introduction

honeymoon junkie *(hŭn'ē-mūn' jŭng'kē) n., slang* - a rare psychological disorder and addiction, most typically affecting men, and used as a defense mechanism to only remain in a relationship long enough to enjoy the "honeymoon effect" before departing for greener, well-manicured pastures.

* * *

What is traditionally supposed to be the happiest moment, the zenith, in a young couple's relationship? The easy answer is the honeymoon, typically between seven and fourteen days of unending bliss. It usually occurs in some remote tropical paradise, completely devoid of the stressfulness of everyday life. The fantasy of being surrounded by nature's breathtaking seascapes and an army of well-trained servants lets the couple feel nothing but unwavering joy. Inevitably, the honeymoon ends, and like the grim reaper, check-out time arrives. The tanned couple returns to their home or apartment carrying a mountain of luggage and feeling the burden of work, commuting, deadlines, taxes and surviving the challenges ahead. The honeymoon is officially over.

Every relationship begins with an abundance of positive energy. If it didn't, why would there ever be a second date? In the early stages of exploration and discovery, the male and the female are hastily searching for and pinpointing each other's positive attributes, accumulating them like kindling for a wildfire. This joyful stage of ecstasy eventually detonates and petty imperfections become magnified. This phenomenon often increases at a much faster rate for the male than the female. While she clings to hope for the relationship, the male often searches for the fire escape.

But that early stage of the relationship building process is most often quite enjoyable for the male. There is no bickering or silly discord. It is a honeymoon high that can last for a few weeks, a month, sometimes even longer. And just like any drug, the more you experience it the more you desperately want to take a hit.

I confess to unwillingly becoming a honeymoon junkie. I was tainted by the emotional pain of divorce and separation from what I loved the most, my daughter. The heartache mixed with the ruthlessness of Wall Street and dating in Manhattan generated a combustible situation. Every time a relationship began to exhibit even the tiniest signs of complexity, a chemical imbalance was triggered and a frantic search for the exit ensued. It was an easily repeatable pattern, but like most addicts I was oblivious to the carnage that I left in my tumultuous wake.

I finally did fall in love but had become so comfortably numb that I didn't even recognize it until it was much too late. The damage was irreparable. It was maddening and so I exercised my only option. "The best way to get over a woman is to turn her into literature" is a quote from a controversial twentieth century writer, Henry Miller. For me, no truer words had ever been spoken. I put pen to paper and created *Honeymoon Junkie: Everything but the Girl*. It is a story of heartache, tragedy, erotica, scandal and humor that morphs into a therapeutic journey for a man who teetered on the brink of emotional bankruptcy, but it also chronicles the escapades of a guy who enjoyed a shit load of fun before he stared into the abyss.

1

Worlds Colliding

Easter Sunday April 8, 2007 2:34AM

It was an ordinary Saturday night in the energetic and frolicsome borough of Manhattan. A hint of springtime warmed the post-midnight air and I was overbearingly giddy about my new apartment in Soho, the trendiest neighborhood on an island that gorged on chic. I was also ecstatic about confirmed travel reservations for my annual pilgrimage to Louisville for the Kentucky Derby in May. It was the best of times and I was enjoying my age of foolishness. As the cab pulled onto West 16th Street, I discreetly checked my watch. I was wrapping up my evening with Lindsay, an incredibly beautiful and delightful Southern belle raised on a farm in rural Alabama. She exceeded the legal limit on southern charm and we were concluding our first date, sort of. I had randomly met Lindsay three weeks earlier at a birthday party for someone neither of us really knew.

Lindsay was painfully genuine in a city that typically discouraged and even punished such realness. She emitted radiant warmth that flowed from her illuminating smile. She wasn't tainted by the dark side of Manhattan, unlike some of the bitter, angry, and opportunistic women that stocked the singles shelves like cartons of outdated, sour milk. Initially I wasn't convinced that I should pursue a physical relationship with Lindsay. Grooming her to play the role of my wing woman was a tantalizing proposition given her magnetism and her enchanting allure.

I instructed the cabbie to leave the meter running as I escorted Lindsay to her door and gave her the obligatory double peck on each cheek. I'm not sure why, but somehow the European-style air kiss had become part of my repertoire. I once laughed at its phoniness and thought it was just a mainstay of the metro-sexual calling card. It was one of the glaring indications that I had over-stayed my welcome in Manhattan. I was doing it instinctively, like some flamboyant fashion designer from Milan.

After Lindsay entered the safety of her lobby, I hopped in the cab and whipped out my cell phone to respond to a late night "booty text". There was a full moon that night and the wolves were howling. I had two missed calls along with a second booty text. I was being solicited by a psychotic Venezuelan stripper named Rosa, and another woman I had recently spent some time with, Samantha. The dual demand was undeniably flattering yet inherently dangerous.

Samantha was a professional chef with a small roster of upscale clients. She was taking advanced classes at a culinary school somewhere in East Buttfuck, New Jersey. She lived in a studio apartment in a brand new doorman building on the western fringe of Chelsea, and she was the epitome of high maintenance. Whenever I spent time with her, she would test the limits of my tolerance with her whiny requests, annoying quirkiness, and brazen demands. She had been spoiled rotten by some previous boyfriends, and like the quintessential bratty child, she pouted when things were not done according to her precise specifications. The air of entitlement ingrained in her psyche was at once laughable and disturbing.

I had just moved to a quaint one-bedroom on Sullivan Street in Soho, a neighborhood as popular with the locals as it was with the upscale international tourists. It offered incredible charm with tree-lined streets, sidewalk cafés, exclusive retailers, and even a kiddy pool. Where else could you find a Sevens Jeans, Diesel for Kids, Dolce & Gabbana, a basketball court, and a great pizza shop where they filmed a scene from *Men in Black* all on the same block?

Samantha had sent me a booty text disguised as an innocent inquiry about my new pad. She claimed to be wrapping up drinks with a girlfriend at a lounge near my block and was wondering if she could check out the apartment. I knew she had at least two ulterior motives. Since it was almost three o'clock in the morning, she obviously hoped to get naked, but also wanted to inspect my place to see if it was worthy of her meaningless approval. I was hoping she would be underwhelmed by its small size or displeased by the lack of an elevator, two common attributes of any Soho apartment.

Samantha was all about the accessories—an ice-cold, fourteen-carat bitch. What was a guy's address? What kind of car did he drive? Where did he summer? How successful was he? And that could only be measured one way—the Benjamins in his wallet and how generous he was at doling them out. She was so blatantly obvious it was at best insulting and at worst despicable. So why was I still with her? Why was I torturing myself? At first she exhibited some endearing qualities, but they became overshadowed by her dark side. I was just dragging my feet on an exit strategy. I wanted to plot a graceful departure with an unbreakable "let's be friends" clause. I always tried to adhere to the axiom "never burn a bridge" unless it was completely unavoidable.

The cab pulled onto Houston Street and my cell phone began vibrating. I assumed it was Samantha calling to confirm I was physically at the apartment, because God help me if I made her wait outside for ten seconds! It was actually an incoming call from Rosa, the voluptuous Venezuelan stripper whom I had stopped seeing a few months earlier. She was determined to remain in my life, or at a minimum, occasionally crawl into my cozy and familiar bed. She had sent three text messages earlier which I had neglected. When she sent a fourth just before I dropped off Lindsay, I quickly typed that I was in Miami for the weekend, hoping that would end her tireless pursuit until Monday. I hit the ignore button on my cell, but she countered with redial and called me again. I wanted to shut my phone off, but I knew Samantha would call to confirm that I was prepped and ready for her red-carpet entrance.

I arrived at the apartment and quickly began tidying up because I figured Samantha would inspect my new pad like a Gestapo officer. Predictably, she called, pretending to forget my address and the apartment number. Five seconds later the doorbell rang and I buzzed her in. I still had a few minutes because Samantha was going to have to tackle five flights of stairs. It was one more thing Samantha was going to complain about, but it also helped build my case for us not to see each other any more. It sounds ridiculously petty, but trust me, by the time she reached the fifth floor she would be thinking, "Fuck this shit… I'm not dating a guy without an elevator."

I opened the door as Samantha was trudging up the last five stairs, a pained and annoyed grimace plastered all over her face. Suddenly another female figure with long, jet black hair came barreling around the corner at the bottom of the stairwell. It was a classic case of worlds colliding, a bachelor's worst nightmare. Nothing disturbs the natural balance of the universe with greater magnitude than when your current girlfriend crosses paths with your old girlfriend, especially on your doorstep at three o'clock in the morning. It was a potential Armageddon that was impossible to defuse.

Samantha heard the racket and glanced back as Rosa started up the last set of stairs with reckless abandon, pointing her finger and yelling something in Spanish that I am sure was profanity. She looked like a bull in a china shop. I tugged Samantha up the last few stairs and positioned her behind me in the doorway.

"What the hell are you doing here? Go home. You are fucking *loca!*" I said sternly.

"I knew you no in Miami. You no tell truth. Who dis girl? Dis your new *mamacita*? Dis Sandy?" asked Rosa in broken English.

I stood in the doorway with my arms crossed berating Rosa for being an uninvited guest and acting like a psychopathic stalker. I asked her how the hell she got inside my building.

"I let her in," Samantha chimed in. "She was standing at the door when you buzzed me in. I assumed she lived here."

I started to close the door in Rosa's face, but I knew with her fiery temper and her persistence she would inevitably throw a tantrum in my hallway and wake up half the building. It was almost 3:00AM so I was trapped—I had no choice but to let her in.

The three of us sat in the living room staring at each other in an awkward moment of deafening silence. Samantha stood up and began inspecting my kitchen as she quizzed me.

"So...what's the explanation here?"

I introduced Samantha to Rosa and explained that I had briefly dated the crazy, intrusive Latina before I met her. I then told Samantha how Rosa had been calling my cell at all hours of the night, sending nasty text messages, stalking me, and now breaking into my building. I further explained that I had abruptly dumped Rosa shortly after meeting her, and that Rosa was obviously having a difficult time accepting her dismissal.

Rosa hastily interrupted, "Tell her the time three week ago. Tell wha' happen in you *apartamento.*"

Samantha snickered, "Yeah, tell me about it. I'm curious. This ought to be good."

I reminded Samantha about a Sunday afternoon three weeks prior when I had asked if she would help me with some packing for my move. Predictably she declined to help, claiming she had to study. Samantha vaguely recalled the conversation. Rosa had randomly called an hour later and asked what I was doing. When I told her I was packing she offered to help. After four hours of laboriously wrapping items and stuffing boxes we ordered some food for delivery. Rosa offered me a massage and eventually coerced me into the break-up sex she had been denied three months earlier.

As I finished the story I felt my cell phone vibrate. I glanced down and was ecstatic to see a text message from Lindsay. She said she had a fantastic time and looked forward to having brunch with me on Sunday afternoon. I just had to figure out a way to get these two crazy women out of my apartment so I could get a decent night's sleep. Samantha caught me sneaking a peek at my phone and tried to swipe it from my hand. As the smug grin gradually evaporated from my face I asked myself, "What the hell am I doing?" Why was I wasting my time dating a girl who made me miserable, and why was I allowing a psychotic Venezuelan to linger in my life? My vice wasn't gambling, drugs, or alcohol, but it was beginning to control and derail my life. It was a rare moment of self-reflection, and I felt helpless and pathetic.

Samantha was not thrilled to hear about our fornication. In a perverse way I was happy; this unplanned testimony would undoubtedly end my nauseating and lame relationship with her. The bad news was this ham-fisted exit meant the friendship clause I was angling for would be denied. Samantha's ego had been severely deflated and her staunch exterior was crumbling.

She lashed out, "What do you have to say for yourself?"

I shrugged my shoulders and offered a genuine apology, but I couldn't resist tossing in, "I guess you should've helped me pack."

Samantha got up, grabbed her coat, and exchanged phone

numbers with Rosa just to torment me. She left in disgust, but I felt a tremendous sense of relief as the door closed.

One gone, one to go. Now my task was to get Rosa the hell out of there. She clung to the "I drink too much—no make me drive" plea. She knew how to manipulate my disdain for drinking and driving, so I graciously offered her the pull-out couch. In the wee hours of the morning Rosa slithered into my bed undetected. Suddenly I was awakened by the sensation of a warm and unfamiliar wetness. I was groggy and disoriented, but soon realized that Rosa had wet my bed.

I was irate and shouted, "What the fuck? Are you fucking kidding me?"

She was tearfully apologetic, offering to take my urine soaked bedding to the dry cleaner on the corner. Rosa was painfully embarrassed and begged me to forget the incident as I escorted her and my drenched sheets to the door.

I was beginning to realize that my sanity hinged on a relaxing brunch with Lindsay! How the hell had I allowed my personal life to decay to this embarrassing state of utter chaos and shallowness? I desperately needed a change and stability in my life.

Thursday December 22, 1994 8:14PM 🕗

The madness all began twelve years earlier as my wife and I cruised east on the Merritt Parkway in Connecticut with our three-and-a-half-year-old daughter sleeping peacefully in her car seat. We were heading to Maine for Christmas, but stopping in Boston for the night at the Ritz in Back Bay. I was spending Friday in Goldman Sachs' Boston office to acquaint myself with our regional institutional sales team. My wife and baby girl would leave in the morning and I would travel to Maine by bus that evening. I had no idea how this three-and-a-half hour car ride to Boston would alter the course of my life forever.

We had been living in a nice two-bedroom apartment in the

quaint town of Harrison, less than a mile from the prestigious Westchester Country Club. We had moved there in August after I had completed my MBA at Cornell so I could begin my quest for fortune at Wall Street's premier firm, Goldman Sachs. Cornell sat on the peak of a steep hill overlooking Lake Cayuga in the picturesque college town of Ithaca, New York. My wife was a country girl at heart and had grown quite fond of Ithaca during our two-year stay.

My wife and I had had an auspicious beginning when we first met in 1984. I was seventeen, had just graduated high school, and was preparing to attend Cornell on an academic scholarship in the fall. My wife was a tall, skinny sixteen-year-old preparing for her senior year of high school. My friends and I had crashed a party at her house that June. One of the guys in our crew was friendly with my wife's family and knew that her parents were out of town for the weekend. He was a six-foot-four, two-hundred-and-thirty pound football player and had promised her folks that he would stop by the party to make sure there were no shenanigans or unruly guests. I was actually with a girl named Lisa that evening. My introduction to my wife-to-be was an uneventful encounter. The only noteworthy highlight was probably when I accidentally mispronounced her name.

My wife and I had a few chance encounters throughout our college years, but our conversations were never more than a brief greeting. She had dated a hockey goalie for almost five years. I vaguely knew him through an old friend so when I bumped into her I always inquired, "How's Timmy doing?"

In July of 1989 I was home on vacation visiting my folks in Maine, enjoying the beach all day, and hanging with my high-school drinking buddies at night. I was getting sauced with Mikey at a hole-in-the-wall bar called Eric's in the Old Port. My future wife strolled in and she looked absolutely stunning. It was quite a transformation from the tall, gawky girl I had met five years ago. She was much sexier and sophisticated, maturing from a tomboyish simplicity to a strikingly beautiful woman. I was awestruck by her piercing light-blue eyes that contrasted sharply against her olive complexion and her perfectly shaped, jet-black eyebrows. I couldn't believe it was the same girl.

As usual, I began the conversation by asking about Timmy. I was shocked when she indicated that their relationship was finished. I shrugged off their break-up as fleeting and insisted that they would get back together. After she spent an hour convincing me that she wasn't going to reunite with Timmy, I opportunistically asked her to dinner. She accepted and we scheduled a date for Sunday evening. It was Friday night and I initially offered to take her out on Saturday. She just smirked.

"Sorry buddy, but I already have a date for Saturday night."

But she said it in a way that was endearing and playful, not cocky or arrogant. It was conclusive evidence that she was eager to move forward after spending five years with the puck-head goalie.

We enjoyed a simple dinner at a new brick oven pizzeria in South Portland. I drove her home afterwards and I remember it vividly as she exited my car, strolling in a care-free mood up the driveway toward the back porch. The evening had been magical. It was bizarre that I felt so comfortable with her, as if we had been dating for years. I felt invigorated. As I backed out of the driveway in my new Honda Prelude I remember saying to myself, "There goes the girl I'm going to marry." I can't explain it, but I just knew. I was about to turn twenty-three and couldn't believe I was having matrimonial thoughts.

Eighteen months later, on a crisp January evening, I faced a standing room only crowd at a small Episcopal church in Cape Elizabeth. I nervously stood at the altar in the flickering candlelight and boldly said, "I do." My life was moving at hyperspeed.

Monday August 1, 1994 7:31AM

Game day arrived and I began my dream job. I had been hired in January as an Associate in the Equities Division of Goldman Sachs. Goldman was a private partnership and the undisputed envy of Wall Street. Everyone wanted to work there, but so few did. The firm was stubbornly lean, but famously profitable. It was considered the Harvard of the Street: a place with a brutally tough interview and admission process, but where you learned from the best and the brightest in the business.

Goldman had created a culture of success that was unmatched both on Wall Street and in corporate America. Few Goldman professionals left the firm unless it was time to retire, or for an opportunity to help humanity with their accumulated wealth. Occasionally, a high-profile partner resigned to answer the country's call as a civil servant. Examples include two former senior partners, Robert Rubin and Hank Paulson, who each served as the Secretary of the Treasury under Presidents Clinton and Bush. And former senior partner Jon Corzine, who was a U.S. Senator and Governor of New Jersey.

The move to Harrison was purely to accommodate my wife. She had grown up in Maine and loved the tranquility. Our two years in Ithaca were the happiest years of our marriage probably because of its remote and peaceful setting. She loved the clean crisp air, the simple layout of the town, and the friendliness of the people. She felt safe. When I landed the job at Goldman, whose headquarters were located at the southern tip of the Manhattan, I had begged my wife to try living in the city.

"Not a chance in hell," was her response.

She despised New York without giving it a chance and longed for the simplicity of life in Maine. She worried about safety issues for herself and our daughter. After three months at Goldman she was begging me to move back to Maine and become a teacher and a high-school football coach. It sounded lovely. What about the sixty grand in student loans I had just accumulated?

Like so many before me, I had arrived on Wall Street with the lofty goal of a seven-figure paycheck. She knew it was the dream, and in the early stages of our relationship had fallen in love with my intense motivation and goal-oriented qualities. I think she soon realized that if she convinced me to leave so early in my burgeoning career, I might harbor resentment towards her for squashing our goals and forcing me to abandon my dream. I promised that we would only live in Manhattan for a few years because I wanted our daughter to experience a more traditional suburban upbringing.

"Why wait? Let's get familiar with suburbia now," was her hasty response.

I realized it was an argument that I had no chance of winning. And by accepting this seemingly small defeat, I was tacking on another two hours of commuting each day to my grueling routine. But it was a sacrifice I was willing to make for my wife's happiness.

Goldman was a tough place to be a trainee. There was enormous pressure to perform even the most menial tasks with precision and timeliness. The training program was downright militaristic in structure and format. We had an instructor who thrived on emulating an unforgiving and emotionless drill sergeant. He was Gunnery Sergeant Hartman in Stanley Kubrick's *Full Metal Jacket* with Ferragamo suits and a profanity-free vocabulary. He thrived on humiliation. There were severe consequences when someone fucked up, sometimes for the individual, and sometimes for all hundred of us. The bottom line was: never be late, never make excuses, and never make shit up.

The honeymoon of becoming a Goldman trainee abruptly ended ten minutes into the first day of classes. After the pleasantries of introductions and congratulating us for being the 'best of the best', our instructor asked the Harvard MBA's to raise their hands. About fifteen arms proudly extended skyward, each with a smug grin as if to say, "That's right, my shit don't stink." One of the freshly minted HBS pukes was selected and asked to come up front.

"Go fetch me a Coke!" he was ordered as he was handed a fresh dollar bill.

The class giggled at first and then stared in silent awe as Mr. Crimson exited the room. The instructor didn't miss a beat and resumed his segment reviewing our August schedule on the overhead projector. When the Harvard guy returned he set the Coke down on the lengthy table up front and slithered quietly back to his seat. The instructor turned around and looked at the Coke.

He paused and then furiously stared at the trainee, "What am I supposed to drink it out of?"

The Harvard guy was a bit flustered, but then promptly scampered out into the hallway. He soon returned with a clear glass, and once again set it on the table before tiptoeing to his seat. The instructor turned, and it was *déjà vu.*

He paused, stared, and in a thunderous voice inquired, "What? No ice?"

The poor HBS guy was now beet-red and seemed near tears. Humor had quickly turned to fear amongst all of us. Although no one was ever forced to march around the hallway with their pants pulled down around their ankles while simultaneously sucking their thumb, the lesson was loud and clear.

The training program lasted from the stifling heat of August until the middle of December. In mid-December we would be dispersed to our final destination, a product desk or a department, where we would embark on our fruitful careers. Those four-and-a-half months were extraordinarily stressful and intense. The curriculum was structured to be a mental boot camp. The firm was having an excruciatingly bad year because of some unanticipated rate hikes by the Federal Reserve during 1994. The fixed-income department was positioned on the wrong side of the interest rate trade and the firm was going to suffer an unprofitable year. The translation was a decrease in partner capital accounts to keep the firm afloat. And for the professionals and managing directors who were not partners, it meant they would not be getting paid what they deserved.

Suffice it to say no one was thrilled when they saw one hundred eagle-eyed, perky trainees stampeding onto the trading floor each afternoon. Our group became affectionately known as "overhead", meaning that we represented nothing more than a non-revenue-producing cost center. The numerous executives who came to lecture us always assured the group that the training program was off limits with regard to cost-cutting. In mid-November that promise was conveniently abandoned as ten of our underperforming classmates were dismissed in an effort to cut expenses. But it was hard to classify anyone as underperforming since we hadn't done anything yet.

It was the first of many falsehoods I would hear from these respected titans of finance. Was there any integrity on the Street? It was especially alarming to experience these fabrications at a place that harped on ethics and preached integrity as much as Goldman Sachs.

As Dan Akroyd's character said in the movie *Trading Places*, "Take no prisoners in the pits. It's either kill or be killed."

It was a brutal introduction to the reality of Wall Street, a street that ironically begins at the East River and ends at the Trinity Church graveyard!

My typical day consisted of rising at precisely 5:00AM. After a shower and a shave I would suit up in the game day uniform: a tailored Hickey Freeman suit, a freshly laundered white shirt, and Hermes tie. We only had one car so I would walk a mile to the train station to catch the 5:55AM train. I would read the Wall Street Journal religiously each morning on the Metro North train into Grand Central. Once there I would head downstairs to the subway and catch the 4 or the 5 train express to the Bowling Green station downtown. We had to be in our seats at 7:30AM sharp. My trip took about an hour and twenty minutes leaving me a fifteen minute cushion.

Two hours and forty minutes of commuting each day was brutal, but sacrifice and compromise were part of the marriage contract and I wanted to keep my wife happy. I convinced myself that the extra commute time gave me an opportunity to gain an edge on my fellow trainees. I often utilized the time on the Metro North train to study the reams of material being tossed at us on a daily basis. We had standardized tests, industry licensing exams, bond math, economic modeling theory, etc. At times it seemed overwhelming, but we all counted down the days until mid-December.

After work ended at 5:00PM there was always something to attend. There were social events, team dinners, and classes. It was rare that I ever arrived home before 8:30PM. I was usually completely exhausted and could barely muster the energy to read my little girl a bedtime story. Half the time I would fall asleep before even finishing that evening's children's book. I was always asleep by 10:30PM.

The worst day of the week was Friday. Our training class was required to gather in our oversized meeting room at 5:30PM to be grilled on what had happened in the markets that week. These sessions were mandatory and usually lasted until at least 8:00PM in order to completely disrupt any weekend plans. This was particularly disturbing for my single classmates during the sun-drenched month of August.

Thankfully, by Christmas my time as a trainee was almost complete. As the holidays approached I was about to embark on my real career. The ride up the Merritt Parkway was quick and easy on that fateful Thursday evening. There was barely a car on the road. We crossed the Charter Oak Bridge in Hartford and took I-84 east towards the Mass Pike in Sturbridge. During the trip we had listened to some music and talked about Christmas presents for various family members. Once we reached the Mass Pike there was an eerie and awkward silence for about fifteen miles.

I looked over at my wife and asked, "What's wrong? Is something bothering you?"

She glanced back at our daughter still sound asleep in her car seat. She turned and looked at me with some tears and some swelling in her eyes as she inhaled a deep breath.

"We're not coming back after Christmas," she uttered softly.

And just like that my life was in complete disarray and there was nothing I could do to stop it. It was a feeling of complete helplessness. I was paralyzed by the severity and the implications of those six simple words.

"What do you mean? Do you want to stay in Maine through New Year's?" I asked, pretending that I misunderstood what she meant.

She shook her head, "We're going to live with my parents."

I became silent and looked at her in disbelief. She explained how she had agonized about her decision, describing how difficult it was to find the courage to make a stand. She claimed grave concern about the effect this would have on our daughter, but didn't want our precious little angel to be raised in a stressful and loveless marriage. I tried to convince her that she was making a colossal mistake and I pleaded for her to give us a chance. I promised her that my job was going to have a more manageable schedule. I told her we could try marriage counseling. I begged her to rethink her decision.

As we approached the outskirts of Boston I realized that my attempts to get her to reconsider were futile. I couldn't stop the recurring questions spinning through my head. What was I going to do? How will my little girl handle this? How did I fail at marriage? Is it too late to save it?

I realized I had been engrossed in my career. I also realized I was woefully unprepared and ill-equipped for bachelorhood. I had lived with my wife for four years and dated her for a year-and-a-half; I had spent almost a quarter of my life with this woman. I had expected to spend fifty more years with her "in good times and in bad". We had taken a vow in the presence of God, "till death do us part". Didn't that mean anything? My grandparents had been married for sixty years and my parents for thirty. Divorce was not an option in my family. What was I going to do? What could I do?

After about six months of pleading and trying to reunite with my wife, I finally accepted the idea that she was steadfast in her decision and would not be returning to New York or to me. She was convinced our union was destined to remain a loveless marriage and claimed we both deserved better. She accused me of being motivated by my daughter's absence as the sole reason I was clinging to the hope of reconciliation.

The pain of coming home every night to an empty apartment in Harrison was excruciating. Some nights I would walk into my daughter's room, inspect her stuffed animals, her toys, her overflowing bookcase, and then just flop onto the floor and cry like a baby. Around the same time American Airlines used to air an ad of a plane mechanic strolling past a gate inside the terminal to remind himself of the importance of his job. He watched a little girl clutching her stuffed animal and pumping her wobbly legs as she sprinted to greet her Daddy. It always caused me to spew tears like a broken fire hydrant.

It was without question the most difficult and lonely time in my life. Here I was, blessed with an amazing child, an Ivy League MBA, working for the best firm on Wall Street, in perfect health, and I was consumed by misery and filled with depression. I had been an over-achiever, successful in all my life's endeavors, but I felt like a complete failure. My burdensome pride prevented me from even admitting to the world that my marriage had crumbled. I was living a lie, too ashamed and too proud to share my plight with anyone.

I kept hoping I could patch things up with my wife, so for six months I quietly maintained a façade at the office that everything was fine at home. I didn't want anything in my personal life to distract or impede my professional progress. I stayed focused on performing my job as an institutional sales trader at a high level, and regarded work as therapeutic. The markets and the trading desk were so consuming and intense that I never had time during the day to contemplate how miserable I actually felt. It was a welcomed distraction. My depression faded and morphed into jaded bitterness. I was becoming increasingly angry with my wife for quitting on me and on us. I still couldn't comprehend why she had abandoned me and conveniently transferred the blame by labeling her a quitter.

I upheld the mirage of a happy family unit until July of 1995 when I finally divulged to my boss what was happening in my personal life. The lease on the Harrison apartment expired at the end of the month so I had decided to make the transition to Manhattan. It no longer made sense to spend so much time commuting to work. I contacted an old fraternity brother who lived on the Upper East Side to gain his insights on the apartment search. Coincidentally, he had a cousin who owned a small studio on East 78th Street. She had purchased the shoebox-sized apartment when she was still single, but got married, moved to the suburbs, and kept the unit as a rental property.

The current tenant was scheduled to leave on July 28th so I stopped by one evening to give the place a quick inspection. It was ridiculously small, but perfect in one major way—it was cheap. The rent was $750 per month. It was a one-room studio with a single window, no view, and on the third floor of an old walk-up building. It was about 250 square feet, just big enough for a twin bed, a small desk, a dresser, and one chair. The bathroom was a disaster; everything worked, but the sink, the toilet and the bathtub were all at least fifty years old. But I didn't care. My rationale was the same one embraced by many young Manhattan residents. I planned to spend eighty percent of my time in the apartment with my eyes closed, so who cared how big it was or what it looked like.

Sunday July 30, 1995 1:11PM

I enlisted the help of my cousin Charles, and we moved my simple furnishings into my new digs. I am still indebted to Charles as it was a hot, humid Sunday and took quite an effort to pack, transport, unload and store all my crap.

Moving to the Big Apple was symbolic. In essence I was conceding that there was no chance to reconcile with my wife. But it had an even bigger meaning to which I was completely oblivious. Manhattan isn't just one of the five boroughs in New York City—it's a lifestyle. I had no idea it was the beginning of a raucous and addictive ride that would last for over a decade.

Seven months prior to the big move I had been a slightly nerdy, out-of-shape husband and father, content with my life in suburbia. The highlight of my weekend was something as simple as taking my daughter to a pumpkin farm in Connecticut, enjoying a hay ride decked out in my LL Bean flannel shirt, or visiting the neighborhood playground to play on the swings. I was a galaxy away from stud status in appearance and attitude.

I wore goofy horn-rimmed glasses that were too big for my face. My body was soft and chubby because I had barely exercised in over a year. My wardrobe was boring because most of it had been selected by my wife. I was a universe away from looking the part of a chick magnet, but that was by design. I was a married father. I wasn't trying to attract attention from other women. I had no desire to be confronted by unnecessary temptation.

Now I was a single, twenty-nine-year-old guy, living in

the Big Apple, and trying to build a successful career on Wall Street. I had no idea I was about to embark on a titanic cruise that most men can only dream of navigating. I never imagined the places I would go, the people I would meet, or the outrageous shit I would do; places and things that I used to lay awake and dream about as a middle-class kid growing up in Maine. The events, the people, and the parties began to happen instantaneously. I got the impression that I was being seduced by the city from the moment I moved to the Upper East Side, but it was a seduction I welcomed with open arms. I felt alive, renewed, and invigorated.

I was initially intimidated by the single lifestyle. Manhattan is not an easy place to be single, even when you are totally unencumbered. Try meeting a smoking hot, twenty-four-year-old woman in New York City, telling her that you have an ex-wife, a four-year-old kid, a negative net worth, and then inviting her to your shoebox apartment. Once you get her there, she has the pleasure of climbing up three flights of stairs, sitting in your one lousy chair, and peeking out your only window with a fabulous view of a brick wall. Would you want to date that guy or bring him home to meet the parents? I quickly became disheartened and discouraged because I telepathically heard the words "baggage" or "damaged goods" rattle through the mind of every girl I met.

I had hoped to conquer and master the legendary Manhattan nightlife, but the social scene had changed radically since my college days in the '80's. I felt like I had been in suspended animation for eight years. The clothes, the music, the clubs, and the female attitudes were all much different than I had remembered during my brief stint in bachelorhood. What was the story with the velvet rope drama and the "Are you on the list" bullshit? Who devised the asinine concept of "bottle service" at nightclubs? It was a two-hundred-dollar cover charge in disguise for single dopes like me who arrived at a trendy spot without gorgeous females. Wasn't the idea of going there to meet girls? How did I know I was supposed to "bring sand to the beach"? And where do you find the sand? Did I have to rent them too, adding one more expense to a night out? No hot babes in tow, no bottle service, no entry. It was the mantra of the doorman at any exclusive club.

I always believed that the "bottle service" requirement will bite one of these hot clubs in the ass someday. Especially in a place like Southampton where late night driving occurred on unfamiliar, winding, dimly lit back roads. I could just envision someone getting into an accident and pointing to the door policy as the source of their involuntary intoxication. Requiring two guys to purchase two full bottles of hard alcohol to gain admittance could easily be construed as over-serving your patrons. Would any bartender allow someone to pony up to his bar and polish off a whole bottle of vodka without shutting him off or calling him a cab? Maybe a bad economy will alter this silly practice before something more tragic beckons a re-evaluation of a flawed policy.

I spent most of my twenties with my ex-wife, so "my game", "my rap", and "my mojo" were way beyond rusty. But it was a new beginning and I felt challenged by my rebirth. It was time to trade in the flannel shirts, upgrade from the LL Bean tags to Zegna labels, and replace my oversized, dorky, horn-rimmed glasses with undetectable contact lenses. My wardrobe and my appearance desperately needed a complete makeover if I was going to have a fighting chance of surviving in the concrete jungle. The dating game was full of seasoned, experienced veterans just waiting to pounce on a timid rookie like me. For the males, it was Darwinism with a wallet.

I was anxious to start this new phase of my life after spending the previous five years attending graduate school, playing the role of husband, and lovingly changing crap-filled diapers. However, I could not predict that I would become a serial dater, and then morph into a "honeymoon junkie" as I patrolled Manhattan's canyons of glass and steel, searching for the perfect female companion. I was determined there would never be a second ex-wife in my life. The next "I do" would be my last!

Everything that follows is unequivocally true. The names have been changed to protect the guilty, and to avoid any backlash in our overly litigious society. Step aboard and fasten your seatbelt as I share some anecdotes from a sampling of my dating experiences. I hope you enjoy the ride because I sure as hell did!

2

Birth of the Honeymoon Junkie

I have always been an extremely competitive guy and desperately wanted to figure out how to win at the dating game in New York. The city was legendary for its toughness, resiliency and grittiness, and finding an intimate partner in the Big Apple would require all three. I had mourned the disintegration of my marriage for seven months. It was time to exit the pity party and raise some hell. New York was overflowing with intelligent, attractive women from all over the world.

I was ready to attack Manhattan like gangbusters, but there were some barriers including time. I didn't have the capacity or the desire to ever be out foolishly late on 'school nights'. Thursday was the only night I ever considered staying out late, and late meant 1:00AM, a shabby effort by New York's standards. Unfortunately, any place that was worth fighting to get into on a Thursday was practically empty at 12:30AM. The cool crowd typically rolled in around 1:30AM, about the time my head was hitting the pillow. It was uncanny how they all arrived in unison, like a shift change at a steel mill. Did they get an email or a memo? And if so, who sent it? I eventually figured out it was the promoters who were the driving force behind all the party scene coordination.

By September of '95 I recognized the need to polish off years of accumulated rust and rediscover my swagger. In college I had done my utmost to achieve stud status, often fancying myself as a BMOC. I marketed myself as the handsome football star living in the best fraternity house at Cornell. It was the best house in terms of aesthetic beauty, location, and most importantly, the quality of its membership. I dated an All-American cheerleader from southeast Florida, a beautiful girl with an athletic body achieved through years of competitive diving. Many upper classmen had taken a swing at her and struck out weakly.

I urgently needed to find the confident BMOC that had once lurked within. But even if I reconnected with him, Manhattan was the cultural and financial center of the universe. The playing field was infinitely more difficult than being a football toting, beer swilling, frat boy sheepishly roaming through an unsophisticated, rural college town. Manhattan was the big leagues; it was "The Show" in baseball vernacular. Dating was a brutal endeavor in the Big Apple that hinged on charm, wit, money, and the proper pedigree. I was smart enough to know that it would require a lot of precious time and effort to master the process and refine the skill set.

Time was a major impediment because of the intense requirements of my job and my responsibilities as a father. I had to be at my desk by 7:15AM every day without exception. I viewed my seat on the Goldman trading floor as a lottery ticket, so there was no way I would do anything to jeopardize its inherent value. There were fifty people who wanted my job, and they wanted it tomorrow. That meant no monkey business, no late nights, no drugs, and no hangovers, or the "Irish flu" as they call it on Wall Street.

I also spent many weekends visiting my daughter in Maine, a monotonous five-hour drive from New York. She was only four-years-old and I felt it was imperative that I spend as much time with her as possible. It was an impressionable period in her life and I already felt guilt stricken that she had to cope with the awkwardness and the confusion of divorce at such a tender age. And I missed her like crazy! I was determined to be a good father so I had limited time to dedicate to this new world of bachelorhood. I had to learn quickly and needed some crib notes. I had to be resourceful and hoped to leverage someone else's battle-tested expertise. Why reinvent the wheel? There was little time for trial and error, and thirty was knocking on my door.

The first guy I enlisted was a trusted co-worker who had been with me in the trenches as a Goldman trainee. Steve Kiley and I had formed a solid friendship during the rigorous training program, always looking out for one another. We even resembled each other physically, which confused the hell out of the drill sergeant. We had the same build, wore the same goofy glasses, and even had the same hair color and style. We strategically sat next to each other in class because we knew it created uncertainty for our instructor.

He had once pointed directly at me and said, "Steve Hawkins, what happened in the currency market yesterday"?

The whole class cackled in a reserved manner. Quickly realizing his mistake, he pointed to Steve and said, "Shaun Kiley, why was oil so weak today?"

Now the class erupted in a chorus of laughter. Our fearless leader had smoke billowing out of his ears. He hated laughter, particularly at his own expense. When Steve and I sat next to each other we were safe. The gunnery sergeant feared a repeat of his prior miscue.

Steve and I were also destined for the same product desk performing the same job for different clients. In the first few months of living in the city he was my savior. He invited me to some parties, introduced me to some single guys and gals, and shuttled me around to some Manhattan hot spots. Steve was plugged in and became my first wingman, but he had one unbreakable flaw. While every wingman must be an expert at the famed Houdini maneuver, disappearing to enhance your partner's game, Steve abused the tactic and often exited the scene to advance his own agenda.

Except for his propensity to vanish, Steve was a phenomenal wingman. He was thirty-two years old and had never really come close to being married, playing the field aggressively and masterfully since his college days. He could walk into an environment and assess the talent situation in sixty seconds. Although he often lacked patience, he was efficient whenever he was "out on the hunt" or "trolling late night with chum". We never wasted time lingering in a place that wasn't either target-rich or lacked at least one all-star prospect. We evaluated everybody in trader terminology, which evolved into a crude and boorish code.

"I'm a buyer of the gal with the knee high boots and I'm a seller of the blond with the pancake ass" are examples of the impromptu scouting report Steve would summarize after performing a "fly-by" at some arbitrary bar. He was like a CIA operative always scrutinizing and critiquing the female assets in the room. A top rating would be, "I'm going to have to file on the brunette in the miniskirt." The translation was that Steve was such a huge buyer he would have to register ownership papers with the SEC because his investment stake exceeded five percent. It was a tad juvenile and reminded me of my college days, minus the brutally offensive nicknames like Lily Monster, A-Train or Jaws.

The worst rating a girl could receive would be, "I'm a short seller of the chick with the goofy librarian glasses" or even worse, "I can't get a locate on the blond wearing the Auburn t-shirt." In trader parlance, "getting a locate" referred to a process where a trader must locate a stock; in other words, he must find someone willing to lend the stock before selling it short since he doesn't actually own it. When a stock is heavily shorted it becomes difficult to find shares available for lending, therefore, one cannot get a locate. This comment represented the bottom, something as low as whale shit, when directed at anyone. And it wasn't always related to appearance or limited to females. The no locate reference was bestowed upon any girl who exhibited stupidity, arrogance, or a miserable personality. Or any guy who was just a complete douche bag!

Steve had been living the bachelor life in Manhattan for twelve months by the time I arrived in August. He was an admitted serial dater and sometimes he would double-book. One night he got caught halfway to home in the middle of a botched squeeze play. He scheduled dinner with a girl named Susan and then told Cristina he would be home later after a client outing. Cristina and Steve had been on a few dates so he absentmindedly invited her to meet him at his place at ten o'clock. Around noon that day he left instructions with his doorman to provide Cristina with the key if she arrived before him. Susan exceeded his expectations, and in his blind enthusiasm he invited her to his place for a night cap. Upon entering the apartment, Cristina was sitting on the couch watching television. Steve froze like the proverbial "deer in the headlights". Cristina instantly assumed control of the situation.

She smiled at Steve and said, "Seth left the key for me. Do you know where he is? That idiot was supposed to be here an hour ago."

Cristina then got up to leave and with a shit eating grin said, "Tell your roommate he really fucked up tonight. I was going to rock his world." And she left.

When I heard that story I absolutely fell in love with Cristina. How could you not? She had to be the coolest chick in Manhattan to handle the situation that smoothly. About a year later, I did take her out on a date. She was an Ivy League bombshell who worked for billionaire Ronald Perelman. I still remember picking her up for a date at his multimillion-dollar townhouse on East 63rd. The first floor served as Perelman's New York office and he had original Lichtenstein paintings hanging on the wall. A few years later Cristina dated and was engaged to Steve's roommate, Seth. How bizarre?

Steve rented a great apartment near Columbus Circle in a building where a fast-rising comedian named Adam Sandler also lived. He worked at Goldman and had an MBA from Northwestern so he was armed with the right pedigree. He attended college on a golf scholarship, and if there is one thing that Wall Street is obsessed with besides making money, it's golf. Many managing directors would rather play golf with a good foursome than enjoy a hedonistic threesome with Pamela Anderson and Jenna Jameson. Sadly, I'm not kidding.

Steve also had the luxury of choosing from a posse of good wingmen when he went out on the town. Nothing is more crucial to navigating the choppy waters of Manhattan than a good wingman. I later discovered the only thing better is a dedicated and well-trained wing woman. I learned many techniques from Steve. I befriended some of his wingmen. He helped me backfill the void that had been created while I was married and suspended in dating hibernation for almost seven years.

I was beginning to understand what worked and what didn't when talking to single women in Manhattan. I had never realized what a sheltered, well-fed house cat I had become living in suburbia. Although I still listened to U2, Springsteen, and the Rolling Stones, I forced myself to become familiar with music genres such as hip-hop, techno, and house. I started wearing a lot of black clothing and fancy designer labels that I could barely pronounce. I had never realized how essential men's footwear could be to a woman in Manhattan. I began to understand the dialogue and the protocol.

I soon learned that living on the Upper East Side was a statement about my personality. I had arbitrarily chosen to live there based on a friend's recommendation and because it was dirt-cheap. I had no idea that women would "size me up" based on my neighborhood. After a trip to the West Coast I decided to get physically fit and joined a gym. I once loathed running on a treadmill but quickly became addicted. I was a recreation of Forrest Gump—just a running fool!

After four months in Manhattan I was experiencing a metamorphosis. My confidence slowly returned and I accepted my new role as a bachelor even though I never wanted to audition for the part. Steve was instrumental in accelerating my learning curve.

Work was going extraordinarily well as evidenced by some seven-figure block trades in Archer Daniels Midland. It was the kind of trade that was almost unprecedented for a first-year sales trader, generating about half-a-million dollars in commissions in one day. It served as an instant validation of my sales skills and ability. I even got an "atta boy" pat on the back and a handshake from one of the senior partners. The firm was having a decent year which meant my first bonus in December would be a generous one. After my wife pocketed our puny pile of assets in the divorce decree, I would finally have a few bucks in my bank account and could stop living from paycheck to paycheck.

Saturday November 18, 1995 7:30PM ⌚

Steve invited me to a house party on Park Avenue South near Union Square on a drizzling Saturday night. It was a decent party with a good looking crowd of young professionals in their mid-twenties. Steve had cornered an attractive young girl who had shiny, thick, black hair. Steve loved to chase the blonds, so I found it somewhat peculiar that he was spending so much time laying his rap on this girl. Eventually he waved me over and introduced me. She was stunning with a perfect porcelain complexion, light eyes, and a warm smile. Her name was Cassie and her outfit included some ritzy accessories which screamed a wealthy upbringing. Steve excused himself and left us to explore the typical rundown of questions.

Cassie was from Winnetka, an affluent suburb north of Chicago located on the lake. I had lived in Chicago briefly after graduating from college so I knew about her hometown and how it reeked of money. Steve had trained me well. I could inspect the clothing and the jewelry to make numerous and often accurate assumptions. I had never cared about a girl's financial status, and based upon the experience with my ex-wife, I preferred a girl who was dirt-poor. Frugality was something I practiced, but it is a difficult habit to impose on someone accustomed to unlimited monetary resources.

My ex-wife had been born into a wealthy, conservative, aristocratic family. Her lineage included a distant great-grandfather who was a high-ranking officer in the War of 1812. The U.S. had limited funds so her distant grandfather was compensated for his patriotic service with a massive land grant in upstate New York. She had another distant great-grandfather who was a Governor of New Hampshire and a signer of the U.S. Constitution. The old governor's mansion, Langdon House in Portsmouth, still bears his name. I remember strolling into her grandparent's home in Bar Harbor, a magnificent property with a brook, a private beach, and sweeping ocean views. I sat on an antique chair in the living room and looked up in amazement at a picture of President Franklin D. Roosevelt with the inscription, "To Betsy, Love Frank". My wife's grandmother had grown up next door to the Roosevelt family in Hyde Park, New York.

What little I knew about most of my earliest relatives was that they had clawed, scratched and begged their way to America from places like Cork, Ireland and Odessa, Ukraine. The movie *Titanic* used to make me imagine that Leonardo DiCaprio's character depicted my great grandfather, and Kate Winslet's character represented my ex-wife's great grandmother. It symbolically captured how she and I were from opposite backgrounds. I needed a soul mate who was "tired, poor, and from the huddled masses".

Cassie had graduated cum laude from Northwestern and was attending Columbia's MBA program. She was exceptionally bright and intensely focused on her school work. I was enamored with her from the outset. She was intelligent, beautiful and abundantly classy. Probably the only thing I didn't like was that she appeared to be filthy rich! I was worried that she was spoiled and I didn't have the patience or the resources to tolerate a demanding, rich bitch. She was also twenty-three, which fit perfectly within Steve's rulebook. His guideline regarding age was computed with some basic algebra, "half your age plus seven". I was almost thirty which meant a twenty-two-year-old was right in my wheelhouse. The age gap was another oddity because before dating my-ex wife no previous girlfriend had ever been more than two years younger than me.

When Steve reappeared he sensed a cozy rapport building between me and Cassie so he pulled a Houdini. Cassie and I left the party and shared a cab to the Upper East Side. As fate would have it, she lived in a one bedroom high-rise on the corner of East 79th and 1st Avenue. Her building was a mere two hundred yards from my cubbyhole on East 78th. I asked her if she wanted to meet on Sunday and watch some NFL games. Cassie looked at me as if I was nuts.

"Wow, I'm impressed. You're not going to pull that forty-eight hour crap on me," she said.

I honestly had no clue what she meant so I responded, "No. What's that?"

She explained to me that the "New York dating rules" dictated that there was a forty-eight hour waiting period before you could call someone you had just met. It was one of many rules crafted by some lame-ass dipshit and its purpose was to give the appearance that you were either too busy with your career or your social calendar. I smugly told Cassie that I played by my own rules, which I think she found endearing.

After our Sunday rendezvous for some NFL action at a local joint, I walked her to the door and gave her a kiss good night. I asked Cassie to dinner on Tuesday and she agreed, but with the disclaimer that she needed to get an accounting project finished. Two weeks later we were dating, or so I thought. Our status wasn't clear to me. We were spending a lot of time together, but we never had an actual conversation about dating each other. This was new territory. Besides my wife, I hadn't had a steady girlfriend since my senior year of college. Back in the dark ages, before the internet, cell phones, and satellite television, you had the conversation and agreed upon exclusivity. Cassie and I never had that discussion, but I felt uncomfortable even broaching the subject. It seemed as if labeling someone as your girlfriend or boyfriend had become passé. I didn't want to alienate Cassie or risk the embarrassment of looking like a rookie.

Our awkward relationship continued for a few months. Cassie spent most evenings working on her studies and then would walk over to my apartment around ten and spend the night. I had to be up every morning at six o'clock sharp. I will never forget the routine that she used to perform that still makes me laugh. Every morning when I would emerge from the bathroom wrapped in my wet towel, my bed would be freshly made to perfection, and Cassie would be fully dressed while lying on top of the bed, hands behind her head, and propped up by the duvet pillows resting against the headboard. She would watch me dress for work with a "cat that swallowed the canary" smile plastered on her face. She did this every morning without fail!

We were having a lot of fun every other weekend. After pulling my own version of the Houdini one weekend, I had to confess to Cassie about my unique situation. I was worried that a twenty-three year-old would not be able to cope with an ex-wife, much less a four-year-old child. I was highly confident that Cassie had never dated anyone with either of those challenges. Amazingly, she completely understood and loved the fact that I had been married, and that I was a dedicated father.

I was stunned by her maturity and annoyed with myself for underestimating Cassie. Her response was so refreshing that I prodded her to explain why. She made it sound so abundantly simple. It was gratifying to hear her explain to me how being married meant I wasn't afraid of commitment, and how having a daughter made me a more desirable man. She single-handedly changed my perspective and helped me realize that my daughter and my divorce were attributes, not deterrents, in pursuing a new relationship. Her explanation made me feel better about myself than I had in a long time. Cassie made me feel vibrant and confident, and I am forever indebted to her for her thoughtfulness.

Cassie was dead right regarding my daughter. She was the part of my life that I was most proud of—she did make me a more attractive man on an emotional level. I had experienced adolescence sequestered in locker rooms and surrounded by an excess of testosterone and male chauvinism. It extracted a toll on my personality, and sometimes my awareness of women's emotional needs was severely lacking. Thankfully, my daughter changed all of that the first time I held her. I had a whole new perspective on women and gender equality. It was God's wake-up call, and I revel in the irony that many former teammates, who were notoriously chauvinistic, all have daughters.

Cassie was also enormously beneficial as my social chairwoman. I was usually exhausted by the time Friday evening approached. The work week was mentally and physically draining. I never wanted to waste much effort thinking about weekend plans. Cassie was always happy to set the agenda. She loved to read the *New York Times* or *New Yorker* magazine and uncover a new restaurant or a fun lounge with live music. She helped me discover different parts of the city by dragging me to neighborhoods that I never frequented. We experienced new eateries on the Lower East Side and in Hell's Kitchen. She discovered cool, obscure spots in the West Village and Tribeca.

Cassie broadened my horizons in art and fashion. She had worked as an intern for an emerging and talented designer named Cynthia Rowley. She was well-versed in many art genres guiding me on weekend excursions to the Metropolitan Museum of Art, the MoMA, and the Guggenheim. Cassie's father owned original works by Gerhard Richter. I was initially clueless about what that meant, but later realized how wealthy her family was and became less interested. I hesitated to pursue anyone with clouded vision—someone backstopped against a trust fund. I had already been down that bumpy road. I wanted someone who would take a chance on me, "for richer or for poorer".

In late January Cassie and I enjoyed an extended weekend cooped up in her apartment as thirty-six inches of snow piled up in the Blizzard of '96. But as winter gradually segued into spring I felt like a transition was occurring in my relationship with Cassie. The newness had evaporated and our routine was becoming as stale. Throughout the winter I had encouraged her studious habits, but now I would get irritated whenever school work affected our schedule. She was getting annoyed with my continued absence on weekends when an event or a fun party occurred. It was becoming obvious to both of us that the honeymoon was ending after four months of relative bliss.

Saturday March 16, 1996 2:33PM

I was attending a New York Knicks matinee with a hedge fund client. It was St. Patrick's Day weekend and I had injured my hand playing basketball that morning. One section over from our seats two hot blonds had been blatantly checking us out for the entire game. As the game ended and we headed for the exit, I strategically paced myself to time our arrival at the tunnel. I made some trivial comment about the game to initiate a conversation with the taller one. She and her friend were giddy to chat with us as we slowed to a crawl shuffling down the ramp under the arena seats. Her name was Jillian and she immediately gave me her pager number. She told me to page her later and suggested that the four of us should all go out. Who was I to argue?

My client had a serious girlfriend, so after the girls disappeared from earshot he told me that I would need a pinch hitter for him. He had chatted briefly with Jillian's friend but heeded a warning.

"I can tell this chick is a fucking wild one!"

Steve was only a cab ride away and would be more than happy to ride shotgun with a big-breasted, hot blond for the evening. I waved goodbye to my client and quickly located a pay phone near the exit of Madison Square Garden. I dialed Steve to apprise him of the situation. He called it a code red and urged me to come to his apartment pronto. I obliged, and once there, we set our strategy for the night.

My hand was still throbbing so I wrapped it in some ice before dialing Jillian's pager. A few minutes later, Steve's phone rang and it was Jillian. I told her to grab her friend and head over to Steve's apartment for a few pre-game cocktails before hitting a highly-touted house party. She asked if my friend was still with me. I had no choice but to tell a white lie. Steve ran to the corner store to make sure we had plenty of mixers to compliment his fully stacked bar. I was hopeful that Jillian's friend would be the lay-up that my client thought she would be because I still owed Steve a major assist for his role in my relationship with Cassie.

Jillian and her friend Michelle arrived at Steve's apartment forty-five minutes later. Michelle was noticeably upset when I pretended that my client had just left.

The second she met Steve, Michelle dizzily asked, "Who

just left?"

Her intentions were palpable; I could see it plainly in her eyes. Steve was headed for an interesting evening and I couldn't wait to hear the recap. The four of us had a fun night except for me dragging around a plastic bag full of ice for my wounded hand. The throbbing had escalated to extreme pain so the only remedy was to keep my hand numb.

We hit a house party, a swanky lounge, and a small club in Soho. At that point Steve and Michelle headed back to his place. Jillian and I forged on to one last stop. Felix was jam-packed but Jillian knew the bartender and got served instantly. When she handed me my beer she looked at the palm of my hand and saw three shades of purple.

"Finish your beer. I'm taking you to a hospital. You live upper east, right? Cornell Medical Center is close to your apartment."

I stared at my hand and realized she was right. It looked pretty nasty.

Sunday March 17, 1996 3:58AM

By the time we arrived at the emergency room it was almost four o'clock in the morning. They were busier than a McDonald's in Times Square offering free burgers on New Year's Eve. St. Patty's was their busiest day of the year. The examining doctor put a temporary splint on my hand and directed us to wait near a bed behind a curtain.

Two hours later Jillian and I were curled up asleep on the bed in each other's arms when we were awakened by another doctor. He ordered x-rays and filled out a prescription for some pain killers. I was half drunk and half awake, but thought the doctor looked familiar.

"Hey Doc, is your first name Tom?" I asked.

He was initially puzzled but then glanced at my paperwork

and realized how I knew him. Tom was a senior at Cornell in my frat when I was a pledge peon. Now he was in his second year of residency. On an island with millions of people, even the borough of Manhattan can become an unbelievably small place.

Tom instructed me to come back tomorrow and he would reset a proper cast for my hand. Jillian found a Duane Reade, filled my prescription, escorted me home, tucked me in my bed, and kissed me good night. When I awoke that Sunday afternoon I found a sweet note and her phone number on my desk. Jillian was an all-star and I couldn't wait to see her again.

I called her Sunday to thank her for a great Saturday night and for taking care of my hand. She was glad I called and invited me to a restaurant opening on Tuesday night. The party was over-the-top with mouth watering menu samples, an open bar, and a crowd full of "beautiful people." Jillian seemed to know most of the partygoers and introduced me to half the room. At one point in the evening I whispered in her ear.

"What exactly is it that you do?"

She laughed and whispered back, "I'm a drug dealer and these are my best clients."

I gave her a look that said you must be kidding but I'm not one hundred percent sure.

"Just kidding—I work for *Condé Nast*."

I shook my head as if I knew what that meant and then responded, "Still no help." She chuckled again at my cluelessness.

"Sy Newhouse. *Condé Nast*, the big magazine publisher. You know. *Vogue*. *Vanity Fair*. *GQ*. I work for *Gourmet*."

I felt ignorant for not knowing what *Condé Nast* was, but now it all made sense. I now understood why Jillian was at this party and why she knew everybody. I also recognized her unlimited potential as someone who could be the "key-master" in helping me unlock the mystery of the nightlife scene. The magazine crowd was plugged into the fashion world, the entertainment business, and the high-end retailers through Madison Avenue. Those industries were all fighting for exposure in the trendy magazines and spent lavishly to promote their products. Being at *Gourmet* meant Jillian had carte blanche at every restaurant in town because a good or bad review could make or break any restaurant in the cutthroat business of satisfying Manhattan's discerning foodies.

Jillian knew this, and she knew how to leverage the power of her business card. She was incredible. She fraternized with club owners, doormen, top restaurant owners, and their rock-star chefs. Sometimes she was invited to multiple events in the same evening. If there was a list, she was on it. If we were hungry and wanted to dine at a top restaurant without a "resi", it was never a problem. She had mind-boggling energy, someone who could go all night and function on three hours of sleep the next day. And she loved to walk. She traipsed all over Manhattan, seldom taking a cab, and acting as if the subway didn't exist. She was 5'9"and thin, but her legs were rock solid from all that walking. She never went to the gym, claiming she didn't have time to get all sweaty, so walking was her exercise.

Jillian grew up on a horse farm in Princeton, New Jersey and had attended the University of Maryland. She loved Terrapin basketball and the New York Knicks. She loved to brag about her uncle-by-marriage, Gordon Gund, the blind owner of the Cleveland Cavaliers. She was in a sorority at Maryland and ran around the city with the coolest group of six girls I ever met in Manhattan. They were all good looking, smart, fashionable, and so much fun. They all got along well and avoided the drama that most girls seemed to thrive on in New York. Although I was unofficially with Jillian, I soon grew to love them all. I was constantly parading around the city with Jillian and a subset of her "Gang of Six". They all took an immediate interest in my daughter and always asked about her, especially after weekends in Maine. It was as if I had a new girlfriend who had five close sisters. And when I toured with them I felt like I was "The Man".

Steve was impressed with Jillian's crew. The bad news was he was off limits because he had hooked up with Michelle, who had lived up to expectations and rocked his world that first Saturday night. It was fascinating to me to finally realize that I could have amazing friendships with women without any sexual tension. Although Jillian and I had become intimate, her gang joined the list with Steve as my new drinking companions.

The next four months were a whirlwind. I was constantly out with Jillian and the girls and meeting a never-ending stream of new people. The summer arrived and I had signed up for my first summer share house in Newport with three other guys. Steve invited me down to Avalon and Stone Harbor one weekend in June. Jillian and her posse were locked in to the Hamptons for the summer.

It was an amazing summer that included a week long vacation in Newport with my daughter. We ate breakfast every morning at the Ocean Breeze Café on Thames and that remains our Newport spot. By Labor Day my head was spinning from all the weekend travel: Maine, Jersey Shore, Hamptons, Rhode Island, and weddings in upstate New York and Boston. The memory of being a married suburban guy was fading fast. I began to realize from hanging out with Cassie and Jillian that I was just scratching the surface. They were the tip of the iceberg. There were so many great women to meet and adventures to take. This bachelor gig was really becoming addictively fun!

3

Quarterback Sneak

Jillian had taken the train down to Princeton to spend time with her Mom and brother. The Gang of Six was missing in action that weekend. There weren't many single guys that I had known in college still living and playing in Manhattan. One of my fraternity pals, Jessie Webster, had been living with his girlfriend for a year, which meant I hardly ever saw him. His gal was away for the weekend so he organized a boy's night out. Jessie recruited some younger Cornell guys from our fraternity to join us, including a former tight end named Jake. I had met Jake when he was a senior and captain of the football team in '92 as I was beginning my first semester of business school at Cornell.

Jake was originally from White Plains in Westchester County. He was a slightly chubby, freckled, red-headed guy with a large frame, a big smile, and an unquenchable thirst for beer. In a nutshell he was your prototypical college fraternity knucklehead and football player and resembled our crew. He was three years out of Cornell and worked in the fixed income department at J.P. Morgan. I hadn't seen him in a while and was happy to have him joining our merry band of misfits for the evening.

Saturday May 4, 1996 8:21PM ©

Jessie had signed us up for a private party hosted in a defunct church that was being remodeled on Central Park West. The pews had been removed providing room for dancing and the altar was transformed into a makeshift stage where a DJ spun some tunes. The owners were trying to generate some income while the church was being renovated. We entered the party and clustered in a huddle as we surveyed the crowd.

My confidence level was running high as my eyes landed on the top prize of the evening. I announced to the boys that there was a superstar at three o'clock sitting all by her lonesome on a pew against the wall. I was becoming the master at identifying the prettiest woman in a large gathering. The boys glanced over to check her out and were impressed with my keen, quick eye for talent.

One of the boys commented, "Wow, she looks like Pamela Anderson, minus the fun bags".

She was definitely a knockout, but I couldn't figure out why she was sitting alone. She was such easy prey, like a wounded gazelle that had drifted from the pack. As I took one step to go offer her some company, a six-foot-four, strapping young stud that looked like Garçon from *Beauty and the Beast* sat down and held her hand. I wasn't surprised; a girl with her stellar appearance rarely attended these events solo as there were too many vultures circling.

I took one step back to rejoin the huddle and heard a voice barely rise above the music, "I know her."

My ears perked up as if I had just heard rolling thunder.

I quickly responded, "Who said that?" wondering who in our crew knew the Pamela Anderson clone.

Shockingly, the culprit was the chubby and fiery red-head, Jake. I hastily waved him over to where I was standing, looked him square in the eyes, and jokingly told him he had one task, and one task only that evening.

"You have to find a way to introduce me to her before this evening is over. Are you up for the challenge? Can you handle the directive?" I asked in a half-assed militaristic attempt to motivate Jake.

"No problem buddy," he shot back.

"At some point, the boyfriend will have to go to the men's room. He can't take her in there with him. That will be our opportunity to strike," I said.

"I'll keep an eye on the situation," Jake responded as he chuckled at my intense resolve.

Twenty minutes later I was deep in conversation with a marginally attractive brunette. She was definitely buying my rap when I felt a firm tug on my arm, almost yanking it out of my shoulder socket. Jake was a six-foot-three, two-hundred-fifty pound dude. He flashed me a look and without speaking a word, I knew it was game time!

Jake dragged me across the floor as I meagerly attempted to give the stunned brunette the one second signal with my index finger. It probably looked like a kidnapping from her vantage point. The blond bombshell was sitting in the identical spot where I had first noticed her.

As Jake and I approached I whispered, "How did you say you knew her?"

He told me she grew up near him and attended an all-girls high school. I could easily tell she was one of those girls that every guy within a five town radius knew about. She was way too good-looking to have skated through high school undetected.

Jake understood there was limited time for an introduction. A male's trip to the bathroom is roughly a two minute ordeal unless he is there for "the deuce". Jake played his role as the intermediary like a wily veteran. He introduced me with a flurry of compliments to ease any anxiety this girl may have been feeling. I could tell by her muted reaction that she knew

Jake, but not well.

Her name was Jacqueline and I tried to be brief in my comments and questions. I just wanted to gather basic information about her before Prince Charming returned from the urinal. The first question was standard operating procedure. I had to qualify what the relationship was between her and Garçon.

As I had anticipated he was her boyfriend. What I did not anticipate was that he was the starting quarterback for the New York Giants. Now, there is healthy competition, and there is unfair advantage. In boxing there are various weight classes because a 160-pound middleweight has no chance against a 240-pound heavyweight. I was a thirty-year-old, divorced father, barely earning six figures, and living in a decrepit studio on the Upper East Side. How in the hell could I compete with a twenty-four-year-old golden boy millionaire quarterback who started for the New York Football Giants?

I was just stupid enough or arrogant enough to think that I could. Besides, I had convinced myself that Dave Brown wasn't that good and wouldn't hold onto the job for long. I was knowledgeable about football and recognized that he was an interim solution to the Giants post-Phil Simms quarterbacking woes. He had attended Duke, so when the Giants sacked his ass, he still had a worthwhile degree to scribble on his resume.

Jake listened to our conversation while maintaining a honed eye on the men's room door. I would've asked Jacqueline for her cell phone number, but in 1996 hardly anybody even had a cell phone. Cell technology and reliable networks were still evolving; pagers were the most common form of instantaneous communication. I didn't own a cell or a pager, so whipping out a device and asking for the digits wasn't an option.

I soon felt the sharp nudge of Jake's elbow in my back and knew it was time to wrap things up. Adhering to the rules of etiquette, I didn't want to be blatantly flirting with Mr. Brown's gal directly upon his return. Every guy knows that when you attend a party with a smoking hot date such as Jacqueline, the hawks will swoop down with precision from their perch the moment you abandon her side. One just has to be confident and secure enough to let the other challengers take their feeble turn in the ring. Mr. Brown was unwise in not bringing a wingman to protect his dazzling girlfriend from an all-out assault like ours. It was the quarterback's tactical error and I was only too happy to exploit his poor decision-making and make the interception.

There is an old proverb among sales people in the business world: if you stand second in enough lines you will eventually move to the front. I felt a positive vibe from Jacqueline that night. It wasn't ragingly strong, but I still saw a tiny twinkle in her eye. I just hoped I would someday get a chance to move up to the pole position in her lengthy line of suitors. Luckily, the opportunity arrived quicker than expected.

Saturday August 17, 1996 8:44PM ◷

I was attending a charity event at Belcourt Castle in Newport. I had happily agreed to rent a summer share house with two guys from Boston and a New York friend I had met through Steve. It was a three bedroom condo off Thames Street near downtown. The summer had been outrageously fun, my first full summer as a single guy. One of the Boston roomies owned a demolition business and was very entertaining, a witty Irish kid who loved to drink and uncovered the humor in everything. He kept us laughing and drinking all summer. I had achieved a full recovery from the anguish of my divorce.

The charity event was the White Party, a highly anticipated social event each summer in Newport for over a decade. I was impressed with the venue and the crowd. After being there for an hour and getting liquored up with the boys, I decided to drift into the grand dining room, which had been emptied of its priceless antique furniture and converted into a dance floor. As I studied all the ladies' dance moves, my eyes were uncontrollably drawn to a sensuous blond standing with a friend against the far wall.

I couldn't believe my good fortune. It was Jacqueline wearing a white cocktail dress and sporting a savage late summer tan. She was with a cute friend, and after observing them for a few minutes, it was obvious that neither one of them had a date. My new housemate from New York was walking towards me so I grabbed him by the arm and quickly explained it was time for his wingman audition. I needed someone to occupy Jacqueline's adorable friend.

As we approached the two ladies, Jacqueline's facial expression ever so slightly suggested that she vaguely remembered me and a faint smile pierced her lips. I reintroduced myself and she readily recalled our first introduction.

"So how do you know Jake?" she asked.

"We were fraternity brothers at Cornell."

"I barely know him but I think he went to an all-boys Catholic school near me."

She told me she graduated from Boston College and her brother had played football there. She seemed relieved when I told her about my football career at Cornell because she loved athletic men. I asked her about the guy she was with when I met her in May, pretending to be ignorant.

"Who? Oh, Dave...he's no longer in the picture," she responded.

It was music to my ears as I promptly twirled Jacqueline onto the dance floor. If you stand second in line, the opportunity to move up inevitably presents itself. Tonight was my shot at the title belt!

I didn't leave Jacqueline's side the whole evening. My friend did his best to occupy Jacqueline's friend, but they were not interested in each other. Her friend, Simone, eventually joined us and I felt like Hugh Hefner, parading around the opulent castle with two elegant women, one on each arm. Simone and I struck a chord with each other and we both sensed that a rewarding friendship might lie ahead. Sometimes you instantly click with someone, and there is no better endorsement for a guy than the approval of a girl's best friend. The best friend often plays the role of the gatekeeper. If she declares you as the key master, you're in good standing and it opens the door to endless possibilities. Simone and Jacqueline made quite a pair, feeding off each other's energy and wittiness. Simone was the gregarious, comedic, crazy one, whereas Jacqueline garnered more attention but was conservative and subdued. Jacqueline preferred to relax and let the action come to her.

At the end of the event we piled into a BMW convertible driven by Dave, who was the owner of the prestigious Viking Hotel. We ended up in the Viking Presidential Suite for a kick-ass after party. The night concluded with me giving Jacqueline a good night kiss and a firm commitment for dinner in Manhattan on Monday night. Jacqueline even lived near me on the Upper East Side which was a welcome convenience.

I met Jacqueline at a Tex-Mex joint called Canyon Road on First Avenue. It was my neighborhood go-to place for a first date. It had all the qualifications that your go-to joint required as a bachelor in Manhattan. The food was good, the prices were moderate, the décor was tasteful, and the crowd was always nice-looking and energetic. Moderate prices are the critical attribute for a guy's go-to eatery. Not all first dates go smoothly, so why pay exorbitant prices for someone who may not get a second invitation? Canyon Road hosted practically every first date I scheduled during the eighteen months in my jail cell sized studio on East 78th Street.

Jacqueline and I were amazingly compatible and I think her brother was probably a vital ingredient. Jacqueline seemed to understand my quirks and my sports analogies so well. One cannot participate in an activity like football for twelve formative years and not retain most of its residue. My ex-wife understood me in a similar manner. Her younger brother had been a D1 college hockey player. Having experienced adolescence with their athletic brothers in the house provided both her and Jacqueline with a different perspective on men. I'm sure they both had the displeasure of observing their brother's crude behavior, witnessing crass friends in action, or hearing the machismo ring loudly throughout their tales of female conquests.

Jacqueline had been raised in an upscale town in Westchester County where her father was a dentist and her brother was a local high school football legend. And Jacqueline had always been tagged as the unofficial "belle of the ball" everywhere she went. She was the respectable girl from a prestigious parochial school that every guy wanted to take to the prom, the girl that every guy wanted to bring home to meet Mom. She was gorgeous, intelligent, personable, and courteous. She was blessed with one of those personalities where everyone wanted to be her friend. It was a rare quality in Manhattan, but when you found a girl who had "it", you felt like you had struck gold. Our dinner at Canyon Road was a success. Even though neither of us said anything declaring us a couple, it was implied that we were now dating.

The next two months were packed with fun. Simone was a social butterfly and often included Jacqueline and me in her busy event calendar. We spent many Thursday nights at an Upper East Side hot spot called Dakota, which was conveniently co-owned by another one of my fraternity brothers. As October crawled closer to Halloween I received some conflicting news from my superiors at Goldman Sachs.

The good news was that the firm wanted me to transfer to the Boston office. I would be responsible for a more important account package, so professionally it was a tremendous opportunity. It was an even bigger home run in my personal life.

It meant being only one hundred miles away from my sweet little angel who was living in Maine. For the prior twenty-two months I had been taking buses, Amtrak, the Delta Shuttle, or driving three hundred miles twice a month just to see my little girl. Sometimes I would come home from work on Friday and be so exhausted that I would take a power nap, go to the gym to get energized, and leave New York around nine o'clock at night to begin the five hour drive just to enjoy a measly thirty-six hours with my kid.

The traveling was wearing on me. I knew it and Goldman knew it. The firm aptly understood that a happy employee was a productive employee. The Boston sales trading desk was woefully understaffed and an unacceptable amount of business was slipping through the cracks while they struggled to kowtow and genuflect to the eight-hundred-pound gorilla in the equity business, Fidelity. My transfer to Boston was viewed by the big brass as a no-brainer, a win-win situation. Former Under Secretary to the Treasury, Robert Steel, ran the Equities Division and called me into his office to deliver the news.

The bad news was that I would be leaving all my New York friends behind. I had only moved into Manhattan in July of 1995, but I had amassed a potpourri of new friendships, mostly females, during my short tenure. Unfortunately I knew I didn't feel strongly enough about Jacqueline to attempt a long-distance relationship across the Northeast corridor. I always sensed her hesitation and personal struggle about pursuing a serious relationship with a divorced father. I could have dated her until December and then dropped the bomb, but that would have been cruel and selfish. I decided to tell her about the coming relocation even though I knew it would most likely end our three month romance. The silver lining was my budding friendship with Simone.

Fast forward and here is where things quickly get weird. I had been living in Boston for nine months and had just completed another fun-filled summer of debauchery in Newport. It was late September of 1997 and I received an unanticipated phone call at my office from Jake at J.P. Morgan. I hadn't seen him in quite awhile and had only spoken to him twice since the night he introduced me to Jacqueline. Jake had been seriously dating a girl named Sophie for eighteen months when I left New York so I figured he was calling to tell me he was engaged. I couldn't have been more right or more wrong at the same time. Jake informed me that he and Sophie had split up at the beginning of the year and that he had begun dating Jacqueline. I was shocked and then he dropped an even bigger bombshell; he and Jacqueline were engaged and wanted to invite me to their spring wedding.

This was a bizarre twist of events. The guy who had introduced me to Jacqueline had dated her, was now engaged to her, and wanted to invite me to their nuptials. It was another one of those *Twilight Zone* moments. I asked Jake if he had run the idea by Jacqueline. I wasn't convinced she would want my smiling face sitting in a pew witnessing her wedding. I couldn't imagine her being too excited about having any old boyfriends at her wedding. And I couldn't fully understand why Jake was so enthusiastic about having me attend either. I sure as hell didn't invite any of my ex-wife's former boyfriends to my wedding. Who does that? I thought he was kidding.

A nicely decorated invitation arrived in February inviting me and a guest to the April wedding. The reception would be hosted at the swanky Westchester Country Club. I still couldn't believe I was invited and was somewhat uncomfortable and apprehensive about attending. But I certainly didn't want to insult Jake and Jacqueline by declining. I also needed a date so I called a girl from southern Connecticut. It was a black-tie gig so I needed an all-star. There would be guys from my fraternity in attendance, but most of them were freshman the year after I had graduated, so they only knew me in name if at all. I had briefly dated a girl in June of 1996 that lived in Rowayton, CT. I hosted her for a few weekends in Newport and we were still good friends. She was the perfect solution; she was smart, stunning, and gregarious. She worked for a Stamford-based hedge fund and graduated at the top of her class from UConn.

Saturday April 25, 1998 3:53PM ©

The wedding and the reception were a lavish production, but every detail was planned with tasteful extravagance. The one drawback was that the bride's mother seemed determined to steal the show according to my date. Her dress, jewelry, hair, and make-up were all extraordinarily elegant. Her grand entrance and snail-paced saunter down the aisle were impossible not to notice. My date disapproved of her attempts to garner the spotlight and overshadow the bride. I half-heartedly agreed with her assessment, but had to admit that Jacqueline's mother was a fine-looking, mature woman.

Jacqueline looked breathtaking as she entered the back of the church. Her father stood sternly at her side, chest thrusting outward, and beaming a proud smile. My eyes swelled up as I couldn't help but imagine that someday it would be me flashing a blinding grin before marching my own beautiful little girl down the aisle. I pictured her dressed in a white flowing gown, her neck wrapped in pearls, and a flower-filled crest lay softly on her head. Jacqueline's demeanor radiated a shy humbleness, as if she were embarrassed by her attractiveness. Her gown was magnificent and her pace was quick as if to avoid the envious gaze and awestruck faces of the congregation.

I just sat in my pew and thought about how I was going to burn in hell. I kept conjuring up naked images of Jacqueline in my head while trying to force myself to end such wicked behavior in the House of God. The more I tried to stop, the clearer the images rushed to the forefront of my memory banks. It was devilishly comedic, yet hauntingly sacrilegious. I was still baffled as to why I was invited.

The reception was a festive celebration. One of our fraternity brothers amused the crowd with a dazzling karaoke rendition of Elvis, complete with full costume, fake sideburns, and rhinestone sunglasses. It was a well-rehearsed act, earning a hysterical response, and was the definitive highlight of the reception. My date was twenty-three, which made her younger than most of Jake's frat boy guests. I sat back and chuckled as they all tried so feebly to impress her. At thirty-two, having been divorced and a father, I felt so much more mature than Jake's twenty-seven-year-old buddies.

Jacqueline and Jake eventually had a baby and Jake accepted a promotion with J.P. Morgan that landed him in Tokyo. But a bank restructuring brought them back to New York City where Jake soon lost his job. The strain of the child, the instability of numerous address changes, and the financial burden of the job loss all weighed heavily on their marriage. Sadly, they were separated by the end of 2005.

During their marriage I had moved back to Manhattan in mid-2000 after accepting a new job with Morgan Stanley. I had become much closer with Jacqueline's best friend, Simone. I accidentally bumped into her everywhere I went each summer whether it was the Hamptons, Nantucket or Newport. When I first moved back to Manhattan, Simone had an entire roster of cute single girls she wanted me to meet. She loved playing Cupid and arranged for me to go out with a former Miss South Carolina, an heiress to an oil empire, and a fashion industry executive, just to name a few.

Wednesday July19, 2006 6:14PM ◷

I was completely unaware of the spiraling downturn that Jacqueline and Jake had suffered. I received a random invitation from Simone to attend a David Yurman product launch hosted on a swanky roof deck in Tribeca. When I arrived I was pleasantly surprised that Jacqueline was among the elegant and fashionable guests. Our conversation switched from a happy reunion to an ugly summation of the prior year. I was saddened to learn of her pending divorce, but even more disappointed at Jake's handling of the situation.

Divorce is almost always unpleasant business. Simone had intentionally invited me to the party thinking I could provide support and advice to Jacqueline. She knew that I had dealt with the process, and that my daughter was about the same age as Jacqueline's son when I faced the ordeal back in 1995. Jacqueline was content using me as a sounding board, but Simone was in Cupid mode, deviously hoping to reignite a romantic spark that hadn't flickered in a decade.

By the end of the evening and after many glasses of wine I was feeling a strange vibe from Jacqueline. Her intentions had shifted from seeking advice to searching for some downright naughtiness. It was a side of Jacqueline that was repressed when I had dated her in 1996. It always amazed me at how quickly women become uninhibited in their thirties. I was flattered, but was unprepared for her suggestive body language and her playful comments. I had just met a girl named Darien in the Hamptons, and although I wasn't sure where that relationship was headed, I knew I wasn't comfortable with the confusing emotions that Jacqueline was feeling. I needed Jacqueline to digest everything that was happening and understand what she wanted.

I saw Jacqueline in some social settings over the next twelve months. Each engagement always involved Simone as the coordinator and chaperone. Simone had also gotten married in June of 2005. We had become such good friends that I had attended her wedding. It was an extravagant affair with the ceremony performed on a manicured lawn overlooking the Atlantic at the Astor Beechwood mansion in Newport. Even as a married woman Simone was still playing Cupid. I was impressed with her determination to try and get us together. A nice idea had become an obsession and she was relentless. It was part of what had made Simone a successful executive in the fashion industry.

Sunday January 13, 2008 9:48PM

Simone achieved her objective. The timing was right, both Jacqueline and I were unattached. I had been unceremoniously dumped in October by an Irish girl from Alabama. Jacqueline had just ditched a thirty-nine-year old guy who had never come close to getting married, which any girl would label a red flag. Jacqueline had grown tired of his indecision and commitment phobia. She didn't want to waste time on someone who was spineless. So after twelve years, a move to and from Boston, a move to and from Tokyo, a failed marriage, job changes, and the birth of a son, Jacqueline and I finally found intimacy on a bitter cold Sunday night in the warm comfort of my Soho bed. Even in the wake of a few sexual escapades, Jacqueline still calls me for advice about men and our friendship remains firmly intact.

4

Plastic Fantastic

My former college teammate and fraternity brother, Jessie Webster, was throwing his bachelor party in Miami. Always looking for an excuse to congregate, a hearty group of my college boys descended upon South Beach for a weekend of debauchery. Most of the guys were married. I had gotten married the earliest, but also held the unwelcome distinction of being the first and only one to get divorced at that point in time.

We all stayed at the Colony Hotel directly on Ocean Drive, just a few steps from the beach and all its splendid silicone implants. The Colony is the quintessential South Beach hotel. In true dedication to the art-deco origins of Miami Beach, its name basked in neon lighting at night and the exterior was painted in a pastel blue color. Whenever someone wants to capture the style and essence of South Beach, the Colony Hotel is usually in the frame, whether it's a postcard, a live television feed, or an iconic movie such as *Scarface*.

Thursday March 21, 1999 5:43PM

The Cornell crew was coming in from all over the country: San Francisco, New York, Chicago, Philadelphia and Boston, among others. It was a blustery, snowy Thursday afternoon and I was traveling from Boston with Greg Riggs and Lance Fitzpatrick. On our way to Logan Airport we discovered our flight had been canceled, but a desperation call to the airline revealed one last USAir flight scheduled to depart Hartford. After intense deliberation, I finally convinced my two buddies that we needed to drive the ninety miles to Hartford. I was determined to make it to South Beach for a Thursday night out on the town. We drove through a blizzard that intensified as we traveled west towards the Berkshire Mountains on the Mass Pike. We pulled up to Bradley International, parked the car, grabbed our luggage, and sprinted to the gate making our USAir flight with about five minutes to spare.

When we finally arrived at the Colony Hotel some of the boys were already out carousing and enjoying South Beach's legendary nightlife. Lance and Greg were exhausted and headed for bed. It was almost 1:30AM so I headed for one of the hottest spots on Collins Avenue called The Living Room. Once inside I found a few of the boys pinned up against the bar. We were all enjoying the fleshy scenery including my married buddy Joe. He was affectionately known in college as the "Italian Stallion". And any girl who loved that dark, rugged Italian look was easily attracted to Joe. He was just shaking his head, saying he was glad to be married, because he wouldn't even know where to begin.

Joe left around 3:00AM, reminding me and another Chicago native, Marcus, that our tee times at Doral were scheduled for 9:05AM sharp. Soon after Joe departed, a twenty-one-year-old "hottie" approached me at the bar, wearing a tiny skirt and a bikini top, fairly standard club clothing for the women in South Beach. She opened the conversation with an overly enthusiastic hello so I asked her to sit next to me at the bar. This girl was being aggressively flirtatious when her half-naked friend unexpectedly appeared and joined in the conversation. I was able to assess the situation without delay. These two girls were working the crowd, and would probably accept drugs or hard currency for services rendered. I decided to play along just for a goof. Once I let the gals know that I understood their gig, I asked how much.

She responded, "Three hundred dollars for me, or four hundred gets you blackjack, 21."

That was slang for the coveted two-on-one experience.

At that point in my life I was thirty-three and could proudly boast that I had never paid for a sexual encounter of any kind. I sat there just imagining the kinkiness that the three of us could perform back at my room in the Colony Hotel.

"What a great package deal. Nice marketing plan," as I checked out their tight and tanned bodies. "I want to meet the idiot who doesn't spend the extra $100 and get the two-for-one special. He'd have to be an absolute moron."

I commended the girls on their ingenious pricing strategy.

I left Marcus at The Living Room shortly after 4:00AM and crawled into my hotel bed, only to be painfully awakened by a loud pounding on my door at 8:01AM. I always enjoyed a round of golf and a few frosty beers with the boys, but I so badly wanted to roll over and go back to sleep. They just wouldn't allow it. Besides, Doral was an annual stop on the PGA Tour and its famed Blue Monster course was patiently waiting to inhale at least a dozen of my best golf balls. I had never played a golf course with more water hazards, and of course, I routinely found them all.

The funniest part of the round occurred while we stood patiently on the tee box of a par three island green waiting for the group in front of us to putt out. Shockingly a man slowly emerged from one of the lagoons dressed in a diving suit from the 1940's, complete with an old cast iron headgear. It felt like a misplaced scene from a horror movie parody. He had been patrolling the bottom of the murky water scooping up a basket full of golf balls. We asked him to stop for some candid photos. He obliged and then nonchalantly descended into the water on the other side of the tee.

Saturday was a perfect beach day so the guys bought a few cases of beer, a Styrofoam cooler, a few bags of ice, and we parked ourselves on a blanket on the beach about one hundred yards in front of the Colony Hotel. I hadn't even been in Miami for thirty-six hours, but I had probably consumed almost two dozen drinks. Today would be no different as the streak continued. Around 2:30PM we were all beginning to look like lobsters in a boiling pot, so we headed back to the hotel and set up camp at a table in front of the hotel adjacent to the sidewalk. We just sat there and watched the nonstop parade of luscious babes stroll by in their high heels, short shorts, and thong bikinis.

And then she walked by on the opposite side of Ocean Drive. The Queen of the Beach was wearing a bright yellow bikini and a see-through white wrap tied to her waist. She was about 5'9", had thick, flowing blond hair, a dark tan, and an absolutely perfect body. Given all the stunning women and all the outrageous bodies that strut up and down Ocean Drive on any given Saturday, it's sometimes difficult to be noticeable, but this girl stopped traffic! There were nine of us at that table and we had been obnoxiously loud all afternoon. The girl in the yellow bikini went to the crosswalk, crossed over to our side of the street and started walking towards the Colony Hotel. I elbowed the guy next to me and it was like a chain reaction right around the table. As she approached you could hear a pin drop as drool was collecting in a few salivating mouths. She walked right past us and into the hotel lobby. I sensed divinity as I looked skyward.

"Thank you God. I can't believe she is staying under the same roof as me," I murmured under my breath.

One of the guys heard me and warned not to get too excited. He said he saw her, two guys, and another girl all checking in together around noontime. I wasn't surprised. I would never have expected that a girl like that was hanging out at the Colony Hotel all by herself. She was incessantly exotic and dripping in sex appeal. I just prayed for an opportunity to see her alone at some point during the remainder of the weekend. That Saturday night, my prayers were divinely answered.

We had a large group for dinner on Saturday night so someone had made a reservation for twenty at the China Grill on Fifth Street. We been seated for about half an hour when I got a hard elbow in the chest from my buddy Rob. He motioned with his head.

"There's your girl," said Rob.

I glanced across the dining area towards the bar area and there she was decked out in an elegant cream-colored dress. It conspicuously accentuated her deep bronze tan and her flowing, thick, platinum blond hair. I kept one eye on her all through dinner. She was seated directly in my sight line, which was fortunate considering the massive size and the complicated angles of the restaurant. There was no hardware on her hand, and her body language indicated that she and her date were most likely in the early stages of their relationship. She spent most of the dinner chatting with her girlfriend. I waited patiently like a hawk on a high perch waiting for some unsuspecting, furry little prairie creature to emerge from the security of its tiny burrow.

Out of the corner of my eye I miraculously discovered my answer. Bathrooms at China Grill were co-ed, meaning the restroom queue was mixed. My devilish scheme was to slide in right behind her if she took a trip to the ladies room. Thirty minutes later my opportunity presented itself. I saw her get up and I observed the waiter point towards the restrooms so I knew where she was headed. I hastily got up from the table, threw my napkin in my chair, and frantically hurried across the room to secure a spot directly behind her in line. It was perfection, a deliciously devious and well-executed plan.

There were about seven people in front of us, so I now had her captive for at least five minutes. I struck up a seemingly innocent conversation and by the time my five minutes expired, Fabianna seemed sincerely interested in my shameless advances. She hesitated when I asked about her cell phone number and instead asked for mine. I wrote it out for her using her lipstick and the back of some other pitiful dude's business card that was lingering at the bottom of her purse. I walked away thinking there was a ten percent chance that she would call. But that was better than zero percent.

We finished up dinner and moved on to some outrageous nightclub. It had all the usual trimmings: mind-numbing music, half-naked cage dancers, pulsating and colorful lighting, and plenty of scantily dressed babes in their twenties all oozing sexiness. The night wore on and our numbers dwindled; the guys were all intoxicated. I think just about everyone was inebriated before we even departed the hotel for dinner, courtesy of our hardcore drinking session in the hot Miami afternoon sun.

The weekend was a tremendous success. Jessie had an absolute blast and the weather was predictably perfect all three days. It was time well spent with a treasured group of guys who were so close in college, but now found ourselves with so few opportunities to all get together. The college crew even got a free meal when one of Jessie's currency broker's from New York got nailed with the China Grill tab in a high stakes game of credit card roulette. It was an extraordinarily amusing weekend, but I was happy to get to the airport on Sunday afternoon and begin the "detox" process.

The next week was humming along at its usual uninterrupted and frenetic pace when I arrived home from work on Thursday. As I entered my apartment I noticed the message light flashing on my answering machine. I played the message and to my surprise, I would have lost that ten to one bet. A sexy Spanish-sounding voice echoed off my twelve foot ceilings.

"I don't know if you will remember me, but this is Fabianna from Florida. I met you last Saturday at China Grill."

I was euphoric, but had to laugh at the "I don't know if you will remember me" part, as if I was going to forget the exotic minx in that bold yellow bikini engraved in my memory banks. When was the next flight to South Florida?

I called her that evening and we enjoyed a lengthy conversation. She lived in Lake Worth, nestled between Ft. Lauderdale and West Palm Beach. My sister lived in Ft. Lauderdale with her husband, so I told Fabianna that I was planning to visit them next weekend. It was a fabrication, but I wanted to see her as soon as possible without appearing impulsive. Acting impetuous would make me look desperate. She agreed to a date the following Friday. I called my sister to ask if she was even going to be home. Waiting for the next eight days to pass was excruciating. I felt like a five-year-old counting the days until Christmas morning. It was still March in the Northeast so the gloomy weather only added to my motivation to see Fabianna again.

The weekend was perfect. The weather was eighty degrees with barely a cloud in the sky. I had two casual dates with the fair-haired Latina bombshell. Friday night we met at a casual restaurant in Boca Raton that attracted a younger, more professional happy-hour crowd. It was the perfect setting for us to chat and get to know each other a little better. Two topics headlined the conversation that night: her job and her heritage. She was a social worker who dealt with troubled youth throughout Broward and Dade County. The job, and the delicate manner in which she explained it, indicated to me her love for children, her compassion for humanity, and her nurturing personality.

Her parents were an unusual mix. Her mother was one hundred percent Polish and her father was one hundred percent Puerto Rican. She had grown up near San Juan and had been living in the United States for about seven years. Her ethnicity explained the thick golden hair, the sultry green eyes, and the perfectly bronzed complexion. It was so rare to see an authentic blond who was able to naturally maintain such a savage tan.

She was twenty-four years old and had already received four wedding proposals. She claimed she was holding out for Mr. Right. In her opinion three of the men viewed her as nothing more than "arm candy" so she barely even considered their insincere proposals. With her outrageously good looks and dazzling figure I could understand their misguided motivation. If a man was searching for arm candy, there was none sweeter than Fabianna. She was so attractive that even I felt the embarrassing stares and the wandering eyes when I was accompanying her anywhere. I am sure random strangers accused me of being an arm candy bandit, but that was just a jealous rationalization.

Friday April 19, 1999 6:33PM

Fabianna flew into Boston's Logan Airport. I was living in a magnificent 1860's brownstone on tree-lined Commonwealth Avenue, two blocks west of The Commons. It was a perfect location. I was about one hundred miles away from my beloved daughter and about a half mile from Fenway Park. What more could I ask for? Fabianna had only been north of Atlanta once, a weekend visit to New York City with some relatives. Everything she knew about Boston was either from a history book, a newscast, or a movie so she was excited for an adventurous weekend.

On Saturday morning I escorted her on an exploratory walk all over the city. We covered Newbury Street, Beacon Hill, Faneuil Hall, and the North End, stopping along the way for coffee, lunch, ice cream and some appetizers on the waterfront. On the way back to the apartment a funny thing happened. The expression "she could stop traffic" took on a completely new meaning. We had just passed Granary Cemetery, the final resting place for Paul Revere, John Hancock and other revolutionary notables. We were about to enter The Commons by Park Street Church when a cab driver became quite enamored with Fabianna in the crosswalk. Apparently he was so fixated on her that he failed to notice the light was still red, drifted into the intersection, and nipped a passing bicycle rider. Fortunately no one was injured, but it reminded me of how atypical she looked amongst my fellow Bostonians. Her Latina heritage and exotic appearance were fairly common in South Florida, but in Boston, men could not help but be flabbergasted.

I had been invited to an engagement party for a Goldman co-worker on Sunday afternoon. We attended the event and once again, Fabianna attracted a little too much attention, especially from the male guests. It was borderline embarrassing and a bit uncomfortable, but the bride-to-be was a girl I never liked much anyway. After being there for about twenty minutes I could almost hear the steam whistling out of her ears. I didn't make the cut for the wedding invitation list and I always knew why. No bride would ever want a girl possessing Fabianna's exotic beauty attending her nuptials. What bride would want to compete with her for attention? I can credit Fabianna with saving me the two-hundred-and-fifty bucks I would have shelled out for a wedding present.

That evening we finished off the weekend with a fabulous meal at a five-star French restaurant called Aujourd'hui in the Four Seasons Hotel. Sadly, I had to deliver Fabianna back to Logan Airport early Monday morning for her flight, but I was heading to Florida again in ten days. She visited Boston four times in April and May including Mother's Day weekend. We journeyed north to Maine to meet my folks.

I arranged for an elegant dinner in Kennebunkport at The White Barn Inn, recipient of the prestigious five diamond award, and perhaps the finest restaurant in New England. Fabianna and I arrived early so I could share some of the scenic Maine coast with her. We even stopped by the Bush compound on Walker Point like a couple of silly tourists and snapped a few pictures. The meal at the White Barn Inn was predictably exquisite. My mother and my grandmother thoroughly enjoyed all the culinary artistry. And I am fairly confident that the male wait staff at White Barn Inn was talking about the blond bombshell for many days to follow.

Friday June 4, 1999 4:44PM

Fabianna landed in Boston for another hectic weekend. Our evening began at Fenway watching an inter-league game between the Red Sox and the Atlanta Braves. We left the game early, Pedro had a commanding 4-1 lead in the 7th inning, and zipped down to Newport for some late night drinks with my good friend, Tony. We rose early Saturday morning, hustled to New London, CT and caught the ferry to Orient Point. We were spending the weekend at Jessie's house in East Hampton. It was so fitting since I had met Fabianna during his bachelor party outing.

We arrived in East Hampton around 10:30AM. Jessie and his fiancé, Malin, gave us a warm welcome. Malin was also a striking blond who was from a quiet coastal town in southern Norway. Faithful to her Viking heritage, she was tall and physically fit. That afternoon we saddled up and rode out to Cyril's clam shack. It was hysterical to watch the crowd as these two golden-haired beauties navigated their way through the jam-packed gravel parking lot. They were both extremely attractive women, but as a pair they were the epitome of double trouble. They each had an unfamiliar, exotic look combined with a swimsuit-model physique. Jessie and I walked a step behind in their shadows and quietly giggled at the crowd's reaction.

Jessie was a skillful cook so he was busy that evening working the grill and preparing dinner. I was in the kitchen carving up some vegetables with Malin while Fabianna was showering.

Malin and I were discussing Fabianna and I wanted to solicit her opinion. As Jessie walked in from the deck he overheard part of our conversation.

"Her breasts are real, right?" he sarcastically blurted out.

I slowly shook my head with a sly smirk.

Malin chimed in with her Norwegian accent, "I don't care. I think she is plastic fantastic."

Jessie and I burst into laughter. Malin had an innocent gaze upon her face, not realizing the humor in her unintentionally rhythmic, but accurate description.

The weekend was a roaring success and I could sense the overwhelming sadness when I took Fabianna to Logan on Monday morning. I told her to cheer up because in two weeks I was taking her to my summer share house in Nantucket. She found some solace in those plans as it represented another unfamiliar place and a new adventure. And I added that we were going to spend an August weekend in Maine. She gave me a big hug and a kiss before hurrying off to her gate.

Fabianna fell in love with Nantucket. She loved everything about the island and I can't say that I blame her. It's the perfect summer retreat, offering a welcoming touch of exclusivity. It's bustling, yet secluded. It's hard to get to, yet easy to stay. Other than living in Back Bay and being within walking distance of hallowed Fenway Park, Nantucket may have been one of the best aspects of life in Boston. We had an intimate conversation on the beach that Saturday as we were both trying to figure out where our relationship was headed. I think deep in my soul I knew she would never be comfortable in the Northeast. There were only four cities where I could perform my job function: Boston, New York, Chicago, and San Francisco. Sadly, Miami was not an option.

There would be one more weekend together in Maine. We enjoyed lobsters and seafood prepared by my mother, affectionately known as Martha Stewart North by her close friends.

I always wished she would open her own little cozy restaurant and share her culinary talents with the world, or at least with her fellow Mainers.

I showed Fabianna more of the picturesque Maine coast. We both sensed our relationship was coming to an abrupt end based on what single people call "being geographically undesirable". It means having a partner who has everything you are searching for in a relationship, except they reside a great distance apart and neither party is willing to compromise their natural habitat. It's a bunch of crap, a lame excuse. If the bond between us had been strong enough, we would have figured out a solution.

I never saw Fabianna again after that weekend in Maine. I lost contact with her, which was unusual. I always tried diligently to remain friendly with all my ex-girlfriends, as long as nothing scandalous or improper had caused the breakup. Why spend time with someone on an intimate level, let them touch your heart, and then not at least have a friendship to reflect such a deep personal investment? It doesn't make any sense, but it took me until I was thirty to figure that out.

My friend from Newport who had met her that summer told me he spotted Fabianna at a restaurant called Bice in West Palm Beach. He said she was sporting some shiny hardware on her ring finger. My guess was that proposal number five stuck. Thanks to the power of Facebook and the global village of the internet, I recently reunited with Fabianna electronically. She is happily married and the proud mother of two children. I always knew she was perfectly suited and destined for the title of Mom.

5

Almost the First Mistress

In the summer of 1996 I was fortunate to participate in a Newport share house. Newport was a nontraditional destination for the Manhattan crowd, but having spent a few weekends there as a single guy in the summer of 1989, I was intimately familiar with what the town offered. It lacked the pretentiousness of the Hamptons, but it was more sophisticated than the Jersey Shore. The New York Yacht Club was domiciled in Newport; competitive sailing dominated the spirit and the identity of the town. The best attribute of Newport was that everything was within walking distance, including the nightlife, a welcomed perk when alcohol was involved. The Hamptons and the Jersey Shore suffered from being too spread out. Driving around the Hamptons from venue to venue or chasing the party was always a buzz kill. Grabbing a bagel, coffee, and a newspaper in the morning could be a forty minute ordeal in the Hamptons. Not fun when burdened with a Sunday morning hangover.

The weekend program in Newport was simple. Friday and Saturday nights were spent eating and drinking somewhere along Thames Street. The upscale crowd ended up at the Candy Store on Bannister Wharf later in the evening. Saturday and Sunday were spent either sunbathing on Second Beach or sailing. Newport was distinctly proud of its nautical traditions, hosting the 1980 America's Cup race. Memorabilia from that event were still proudly displayed all over town. The weekend closed with one of my all-time favorite social events, Sunday afternoon cocktails at Castle Hill. Perched upon a hilltop parcel, Castle Hill was a charming Victorian mansion overlooking the narrow entrance to Newport Harbor. It had been converted into a ritzy Bed & Breakfast, but had hosted this Sunday ritual since the mid-70's.

The grounds around the mansion included a plush, sweeping lawn extending down a gradual slope to the rocky edges of a small cliff overlooking the channel. Every floating vessel departing from or arriving to Newport cruised past Castle Hill's majestic gaze and the fascination of all her patrons. The women donned their best sundresses, applied their expensive cosmetics, and occasionally added elegant accessories such as a hat. The outfits reminded me of the grandeur of the Kentucky Derby. The men dressed sharply as well even though there was no formal dress code. Everyone respected the elegance and honored the splendor of a sunny Sunday afternoon at Castle Hill.

It was always an excellent opportunity to socialize and meet interesting people. Whereas on Friday or Saturday the stylish crowd would be spread across the different restaurants or be drawn to various night life spots, everybody who was anybody headed to Castle Hill on Sunday because it was the only game in town. I met one of the Farrelly brothers on the manicured lawn at Castle Hill. They were the comedy team behind the mega hit movie, *Something About Mary*, and grew up in Rhode Island. I shared drinks with PGA golfer Brad Faxon, another Rhode Island native who reminded me of Shaggy from the *Scooby Doo* cartoon.

The official drink of Castle Hill was the Mud Slide and the crowd was always geographically diverse. Young professionals summering in Newport traveled from Boston, Providence, Hartford, and New York. Everyone partied until around eight o'clock, long enough to witness the glorious sunset across the channel as the sun would dip beneath the treetops of Jamestown and the steel-blue water of Narragansett Bay. By eight-thirty everyone was on the road and heading back to their city.

In the summer of '96 I was steadily grinding out commissions while working in the Equities Division at Goldman Sachs. There was an older guy on the desk who had been a Newport renter for years. Peter was a knowledgeable fellow who lived large and loved to share his outlandish stories and simple wisdom. He was an ex-college football player jam-packed with traditional Wall Street axioms such as "the three F rule", which emphatically stated, "If it flies, floats, or fucks...rent it."

Peter provided me with a detailed roadmap of the Newport landscape. He knew the attributes of every bar and restaurant within a hundred yards of Thames Street. Peter was a tremendous resource, whether I was searching for a hole-in-the-wall to drink cheap beer on a rainy Saturday or a white-glove dinner spot to impress a special female guest. He clued me in on where to go and what to do before Memorial Day weekend arrived. Thanks to Peter's savvy advice, my summer house crew and I were plugged in.

Saturday June 29, 1996 12:31PM

Peter invited me and my house mate over to his place for some afternoon cocktails. Our visit began with a guided tour of his bungalow, which had originally been a carriage house for a manor on Bellevue Avenue. Bellevue was the address for some of the most opulent mansions ever constructed in the United States. Most were built in the late nineteenth century and are now operated as museums. The great industrialists of the Gilded Age, names like Vanderbilt and Astor, were the vast wealth behind the construction of these breathtaking estates and christened with celebrated names such as The Breakers, The Elms and Marble House.

Peter's carriage house had been purchased by a woman with

incredible vision and impeccable interior design skills. Hanging in the hallway were numerous before-and-after pictures of the property, and the transformation was mind-boggling. Each room was like a museum filled with expensive antique furniture, fine china, decorative figurines and all sorts of pricey knickknacks.

After the tour Peter led us out to the pool area where hors d'oeuvres and a stocked wet bar awaited our arrival. At the far end of the pool a goddess rose from the padded lawn chair where she had been sunbathing. As she sashayed around the edge to come greet us, an embarrassing trance consumed me and my friend. This woman was devastatingly beautiful with a perfect figure. She introduced herself as Donna and we must have looked like a couple of five-year-olds meeting Santa Claus for the first time at the mall. I thought I was going to piss my pants.

"I'm pretty sure it moved," my friend whispered in my ear.

"I know mine did," I responded.

Peter was trying not to laugh. He could easily sense how uncomfortable we were as Donna approached. She looked like a supermodel and her dimensions seemed symmetrically perfect to the millimeter. And Peter knew it. As an added bonus, she was so sweet and humble. Most women who looked like Donna were keenly aware of their beauty and often exhibited an unpleasant arrogance that reeked. Sometimes these women would brandish their cockiness as a weapon like a skunk using its putrid stench to ward off enemies. I had occasionally experienced this phenomenon in Manhattan and it was infuriating. I never acted like some obnoxious clown harassing them for a date, a phone number, or some inane conversation. I always behaved like a gentleman.

Donna had grown up in Connecticut and attended Boston College. She worked at a prominent mutual fund company headquartered in Boston and lived in the South End. Peter and Donna had met years ago in Newport, but she was dating someone else at the time. Peter patiently pursued Donna, and eventually earned his chance to date her. But they seemed an odd combination. It was part of the jaw-dropping awe we had felt by the pool. Not only were we stunned by Donna's attractiveness, but equally perplexed by the thought of "why are you dating this guy?" They just didn't seem to fit as a couple.

Their incompatibility became more obvious after sitting by the pool for the next two hours. Peter and Donna were bickering over foolish topics and the tension became almost unbearable. Peter was a hot-tempered control freak who often used his size and fiery temper to intimidate people. He acted like a grade-school playground bully and often spoke to Donna in a condescending manner.

"Cover up your fat ass", he barked as she went inside to refresh our drinks.

I had heard enough demeaning commentary.

I looked at Peter and said, "C'mon bro. Are you shitting me? That ass couldn't be any more perfect."

You could almost see the smoke billowing from Peter's ears. Donna had heard my comment and flashed a thankful, flirtatious smile from the French door entryway just beyond Peter's watchful eye. Peter gave me a cold stare as I sat in my chair. I wondered how badly he wanted to mangle me. My only chance was to heed the advice of the sensei in *The Karate Kid* and "sweep the leg" exposing Peter's surgically repaired knee. Luckily, Peter just sat fuming in his chair and pouted.

My friend and I had witnessed enough foolishness. After Donna refilled our glasses, we pounded our drinks, thanked the host, and left so we could begin preparing for some Saturday night debauchery on Thames Street.

I saw Peter and Donna a dozen times that summer, most frequently at The Cook House or at Castle Hill. Donna was always flirtatious, and Peter just seemed to get more and more annoyed each time I was present. One time she commented that she loved my car, a black convertible Jaguar XJS, and I thought Peter was going to blow a gasket. I couldn't help daydreaming naughty thoughts about Donna, but figured I could never act upon my fantasies. I spent ten hours a day, five days a week within fifteen feet of Peter. Any inappropriate behavior with Donna would have been cataclysmic at work. Donna was attractive enough to make most men ditch their wives, or even change religions, but there was no way in hell I was going to risk losing my seat at Goldman.

Soon after the final Newport sunset on the summer of 1996, an interesting opportunity arose and it meant being closer to Donna. Goldman Sachs asked me if I would be willing to move to Boston's institutional desk. It was an opportunity to cover a more important account package and to be closer to my daughter, who was living in Maine. I accepted the job and moved to an apartment on the first block of Marlborough Street in the desirable Back Bay neighborhood, just steps from the Commons.

Monday January 2, 1997 7:11AM

I eagerly arrived for work on my new desk and immediately fell in love with Boston. I knew plenty of people in the city and in the suburbs to help make the transition seamless. As an added bonus I lived a scant twelve minute walk to hallowed Fenway Park, home of my beloved Red Sox. I couldn't wait for summer; Newport was now an easy eighty minute ride as opposed to the three-and-a-half-hour trek from Manhattan.

A trendy new restaurant had just opened on Columbus Avenue at the edge of the South End neighborhood. It was called Mistral, and its interior resembled the sleek and sultry décor of a sexy South Beach restaurant. It was quite a stretch for Boston, a place where stodgy, mahogany paneled steakhouses were still revered by their old school, nostalgic, cigar-smoking patrons. But Boston was ready for something bold and chic, and Mistral rapidly became a Mecca for the hip local crowd as well as out-of-towners. It was crawling each night with local celebrities and financial types. The place became so popular they hired a doorman to prevent overcrowding in the bar area.

Shortly after Mistral opened, I ran into Donna there. She was all dolled up in a flattering designer dress and as usual, she exuded sexiness. She was on display dining at a center table with a minority owner of the restaurant and a gaggle of stunning, stylish, and slender women. It's a classic restaurant tactic; place the beautiful people at your most visible table as a self-promotional endorsement. One of the women at Donna's table caught my attention. I was dining at a table near the wall, but I was sitting in a spot where Donna could easily see me. Eventually I caught her eye and she decided to come say hello. As I stood to greet her, I unexpectedly received a lengthy hug, a kiss on the cheek, and an invitation to come meet her friends. My dining companions hadn't seen her approaching our table and were in complete awe. A striking goddess had magically appeared and whisked me away.

I spent a few minutes at Donna's table meeting her gorgeous girlfriends and her host, a well-known Boston nightclub impresario. They asked me to join them, and as much as I wanted to accept the invitation, I had to do the right thing. It would have been impolite to ditch my table, but most men would have abandoned etiquette for this flock of hotties. I did make firm eye contact with one of the ladies at the table. She was a tall blond with strong features, and legs that began at her tiny ankles but seemed endless.

When I returned to my table my friends jokingly bowed to me like a God, similar to when a hockey crowd bows to their goalie after making a spectacular save. It was juvenile, but I fully appreciated the gesture. It's comically predictable how American men are universally appreciative and respectful of two things: athletic accomplishments and associations with beautiful women. What if we polled a large sample of American males between the ages of twenty and thirty-five and asked what male celebrity would you most like to spend a night hanging out with? I would wager that Tom Brady and Hugh Hefner would be near the top of that list. I just grinned, enjoyed the phony genuflecting, and prepared for the onslaught of questions I was about to receive concerning Donna.

"How do you know her? Who is she? Where does she live?"

"Does she have a sister? Does she have a twin sister? Who are her friends?" "Have you ever hooked up with her? Are they real? Does she have a boyfriend?" "Is she good in the sack?"

My ass had been planted in my chair for about three seconds by the time four guys lobbed these ten inquiries into my lap. I laughed in a somewhat self-deprecating manner because I knew if I was one of those four guys, I would have reacted exactly the same way, with the same foolish giddiness, and a similar list of silly questions.

I tried to answer each question, but each answer only encouraged another follow-up question, usually more humorously distasteful than the prior one. It's funny to watch how a succulent female can so easily and abruptly transform mature men into acting like juvenile schoolboys. I had to cut them some slack. Donna was extraordinarily attractive with distinctive Eastern European features. Quite frankly, she looked like a supermodel, a rare sighting in Boston.

Boston was a city that prided itself on academic achievement at distinguished institutions such as Harvard and MIT, continuously delivering world-renowned medical and technological breakthroughs. It was a place where intellect often far outweighed appearance. Beauty queens always seemed to come from southern and western states, not Massachusetts. In fact, since 1956 only two Miss USA winners out of over three-hundred entrants have come from any of the six New England states. There have been nine winners from Texas alone!

Donna's strong jaw line, her height, and her symmetrical features were a unique combination. Her beauty was radiant and whenever she walked into a place, she grabbed the room's attention. Having spent time in New York, I was accustomed to seeing women of Donna's caliber. But I wasn't immune to the frivolity, I had just learned how to mask and control it.

The best part of the night was finagling Donna's cell and work numbers. She told me she was still dating Peter, but that they were dealing with some issues, primarily because Donna wasn't ready to uproot her life in Boston and live with him in Manhattan. I encouraged her to stay in Boston, emphasizing that New York was overrated and often romanticized. I thought those viewpoints were partially true, but my move to Boston was all about proximity to the most precious thing in my life, my little girl.

My first call to Donna was to inquire about the blond babe with the nonstop legs who I had become so enamored with at her table that evening. A few weeks later Donna had arranged a "pseudo blind date" with Stacey, the statuesque model from Mistral. Having a friend like Donna in Boston was already paying juicy dividends.

Stacey and I were much more compatible than I had anticipated. She had an unpredictable sweetness about her. The evening I met her at Mistral she wore a sulking, disinterested, cold pout that shouted, "Don't even think about fucking talking to me!"

It was a look that I was infinitely familiar with since it was often plastered on every model's face in New York. In their defense New York women usually had a good reason for developing and perfecting this menacing look. The men in New York can be obnoxiously aggressive and extremely annoying. An innocent smile or a tiny hint of interest from a desirable woman could spawn a potential stalker, or some douche bag hell bent on convincing her why she should want to be his girlfriend.

Stacey was originally from Indiana, graduated from the Berklee College of Music, and was pursuing a career managing musicians. She had a small roster of clients including jazz singer Toni Bennett's daughter, Antonia Bennett. She also worked as a music coordinator booking live acts for a popular nightclub called M80. I reaped the benefits of her job one evening by being invited to a private performance by Cheap Trick. Stacey's heritage was German and she was the proud owner of incredible legs that ended thirty-six sultry inches from their origins at her petite ankles. I had never been so aroused by such a perfect set of getaway sticks.

Stacey and I dated briefly, but I will never forget the evening she cooked me dinner at her Cleveland Circle apartment near Boston College. Stacey's apartment had a living room with one wall covered by mirrors from floor to ceiling. The couch rested against the mirrored wall. After dinner and two bottles of wine Stacey was in a playful mood. She placed me in a chair across from the couch facing her as she proceeded to perform an unrehearsed strip-tease while sensual music by Deep Forest drifted from the stereo. She slowly disrobed, except for her three inch heel shoes, and proceeded to the end of the couch, placed her hands firmly on the armrest, arched her back, and shook her blond hair, making it sway like a soft towel across the curvature of her back. I looked in the mirror and was mesmerized by the sight of what was now thirty-nine inches of leg culminating at her heart-shaped ass. In a word...spectacular!

I did some back-of-the-envelope math in my head and realized that given my six-foot frame I was going to have a problem. It wasn't the first time in my life that I had wished I was six-foot-four. I scanned the room urgently searching for a solution. I saw a bookcase in the corner and grabbed two of the thickest books I could find. I could have asked Stacey to remove her shoes, but I didn't want to ruin the moment. It was an unforgettable image that remains etched in my memory. I balanced myself on the two thick books I placed on the floor behind Stacey. I began kissing the left side of her neck while I fondled her right breast. I leisurely slid my left hand across her ass and down the outside of her left leg. My hand eventually worked its way to the inside of her thigh as I carefully studied our naked bodies molding in the mirror. Two candles on the coffee table flickered softly and provided just enough light.

My calf muscles flexed as I rocked gently on my toes. Stacey strained to arch her back and instinctively thrust her ass towards me in her aroused state. I slowly leaned back, firmly grabbing both of her shoulders. Stacey's hands left the armrest of the couch and became firmly planted on the cheeks of her tear-drop ass. I glanced to my right and watched us having sex in the mirror. It was a vivid image that I would never forget. And I owed it all to my friend, Donna.

Three months later Stacey and I became victims of our conflicting work schedules. She worked five nights a week at the club and was typically there until three o'clock in the morning. My routine required lights out at midnight with an alarm clock permanently set for six in the morning. Having Stacey show up at my apartment at three o'clock in the morning, reeking of smoke, and wanting me to perform like a horse in the stud barn became too disruptive to my job requirements. I didn't even enjoy M80 on the weekends; the crowd was mostly college and graduate students, too young and unsophisticated for my taste. Stacey and I recognized our incompatibility, parted on good terms, and remain good friends.

I didn't see Donna for awhile, just an occasional phone call or a voicemail to say hello. She was exited about my relationship with Stacey, and disappointed about our breakup. Girls love to play Cupid, but get frustrated when their matches don't reach the finish line, which for them means the altar. Stacey informed me that Donna had finally dumped Peter. I was delighted by the news because it was obvious that he was verbally abusive to her. She never seemed happy around him, always on edge, worried about whatever small annoyance would ignite his childish and erratic temper tantrums.

I always felt prevailing warmth from Donna when I was around her. I wasn't sure if we could ever have a relationship since Peter was a former co-worker and because I had dated her modeling companion, Stacey. The cross-currents from those situations made me question whether or not to a physical relationship with Donna was possible. It was disappointing because she was charming, genuine, and so damn desirable.

I bumped into Donna a few times over the next twelve months. Peter left Goldman and I had lost touch with him. Stacey and I were still friendly, but our fling had been over for quite some time. I saw Donna at a holiday party in December of '98 and finally felt comfortable enough to ask her to dinner. She gleefully accepted, and I could tell from her reaction that Peter and Stacey were no longer even a remote consideration.

After another dinner, a movie night, and an art exhibit I invited Donna to a client engagement in January. I was taking a hedge fund client and his girlfriend to a concert at the Boston Garden. Donna was tipsy by the end of the evening, and after escorting my client and his gal to a town car, I invited Donna back to my apartment on Commonwealth Avenue. Her beautiful green eyes lit up.

"I have been waiting for that invitation for quite awhile."

I told her that if I had any inkling of her enthusiasm, I certainly wouldn't have waited to extend the invitation.

It was a memorable evening as I barely slept a wink. I had to work in the morning and realized I was going to be a lethargic piece of shit the next day, but I was completely unconcerned. Donna's naked body was even more magnificent than I had imagined when I first saw her lying poolside in Newport. It was perfection. The shape of her breasts, her large and succulent nipples, her tiny waist and flat tummy, the V-shape of her back and her teardrop derriere neatly packed onto her five-foot-ten-inch frame. It was surreal and somewhat intimidating. I couldn't think about anything other than her exquisite nakedness the next day at the office. She was intoxicating!

Now that we had shared intimacy, I struggled on how to approach our relationship going forward. I didn't want to seem pushy or zealous so I tried to keep things in proper perspective. Donna was unmistakably a woman with unlimited options. I had lived in Boston for two years and hadn't met anyone half as sweet or half as beautiful as her. My client talked about her for a solid week. I fielded a call from another trader asking me about Donna which left me curious as to how he had any inkling about her. Apparently my client was touting Donna's startling elegance to his hedge fund buddies. It was just a case of some horny guys living vicariously. I found it quite flattering.

I fantasized about Donna becoming my steady girlfriend, but I knew that would be tricky. There was the residue of our relationships with Peter and Stacey. Her lack of direction was also a concern. She had recently quit her job and had no clear plan for the immediate future. Donna knew I was not interested in having a roommate or a fuck buddy. She also recognized that I had too much dignity to be relegated to the role of sponsor. In my opinion, sponsorship, playing the role of a Sugar Daddy, was prostitution masquerading in a comedic moniker. And I certainly wasn't angling to be anybody's pimp. The first day I met Donna, my friend and I reasoned that she only tolerated Peter because he had played that role, even if he was oblivious to the part. She endured his abusive behavior in exchange for a lot of perks. It is a dangerous path to take because once you become addicted to the lifestyle it becomes increasingly difficult to walk away.

Donna and I had another date a few weeks later and ended up at my apartment around ten o'clock. After ravaging each other for an hour we laid on the bed staring at the ceiling. It was the perfect time for some quality pillow talk. The conversation was philosophical at first as we talked about life, love, and self-discovery, but then it turned toward a more open and honest self-inspection. I told Donna I was worried about her; she looked tired and there was a desperate sadness in her bloodshot eyes. Two of her close friends told me that she was doing a lot of cocaine. I asked her if it was true and what was happening in her life.

She admitted to 'partying' too much, the hip crowd's code word for doing blow, and was having difficulty sleeping. She confessed to being the saddest she had ever been in her life, but also claimed she was petrified. I was confused and asked why she was so frightened. I gently kissed her forehead as I soothingly combed her long, thick, brown hair with my fingers. As I tried to comfort her, I begged her to tell me what was so ominous. Donna admitted to having an affair with a married man, but not just some inconsequential guy looking for some "strange". She had been sleeping with a powerful, public figure that happened to be married to a wealthy and influential woman.

It took me two seconds to figure out who was occasionally sharing a bed with her. I recalled seeing him at Mistral on two separate nights when Donna was in the restaurant. I remembered seeing them both at a charity event. On all three occasions this gentleman was conveniently not accompanied by his doting wife. Donna categorized their romance as spotty with prolonged lapses since he lived primarily in Washington, DC. I told her she was playing with fire and asked her if she understood the magnitude of what she had become involved in. It was widely speculated that this high-profile politician was planning to make a run at the White House.

"Do you remember Donna Rice and former Senator Gary Hart sitting on that boat *Monkey Business*? Do you want to become tabloid cannon fodder or the punch line for a never-ending stream of *Late Night* jokes?" I asked her.

She shrugged off my questions and nonchalantly told me that in the beginning he was just a bored married guy looking for a little fun. I warned her that it was much more complicated and told her to end the relationship and to never talk about it. The public backlash would cause crippling shockwaves. Careers, lives, and reputations would be tarnished and supporters would be outraged. She realized some of the ugly repercussions and was demonstrably nervous about her safety.

"You're a complete knockout. Why would you take such a gamble?" I asked.

"I guess I was just bored with athletes and finance guys," she said.

A man with power and influence had become Donna's new aphrodisiac.

My advice was to walk away, but Donna was still frightened by the ramifications of what had already transpired. She claimed I didn't fully understand or appreciate the tenacity of the politician's wife. To highlight the wife's resolve, Donna shared a story about the couple's townhouse. A fire hydrant was stationed directly across the sidewalk from her front stairs. It bothered this woman that she could never park her luxury car in front of her multi-million-dollar home. After repeatedly asking the city and pleading with the mayor to resolve the issue, she allegedly spent eight-hundred grand to relocate the pesky hydrant down the block! It was a shocking example of what this woman was willing to do "to make problems go away".

Now I understood Donna's anxiety. Soon after our bedside chat, she wisely ended the monkey business, unwilling to partake in another secret rendezvous. What trail of evidence remained? That was the worrisome unknown. There were cab drivers, political cronies, and dock hands at the marina who had witnessed their tomfoolery. In the age of cell phone video, gossip mongers, paparazzi, and the internet, it is nearly impossible to keep any scandalous activity a secret.

In the summer of 2000 I moved back to New York City and my contact with Donna became infrequent over the next eighteen months. I had confirmed reports from mutual friends that she had terminated the relationship with the politician, but that she was partying to the point of becoming self-destructive.

Tuesday December 31, 2002 11:44PM

I was spending New Years in Boston with a girl I was dating named Rochelle. She and I attended a black-tie event at the prestigious Harvard Club on Commonwealth Avenue. Just before midnight I was delightfully surprised by a cameo appearance from Donna but she was with a girlfriend who had a nasty reputation as a "coke whore". As I approached I saw a glimmer of enthusiasm masked by a hint of shame in Donna's bloodshot eyes. She looked spectacular from across the room, but up close there was no hiding the destructive toll extracted by the alcohol and the drugs.

I was saddened because I sensed a faint cry for help in her glossed eyes. She recognized that she was spiraling out of control, but lacked the self-discipline to end her plight. We had a brief conversation because, as a gentleman, I didn't want to be disrespectful and ignore Rochelle. Donna's mind was in an altered state, her nose looked raw and irritated, and her speech was slightly incoherent.

Donna sensed my disappointment, but tried to remain upbeat in telling me what she had been doing since I moved back to Manhattan. She was excited about her new boyfriend and her upcoming relocation to Spain.

I was justifiably suspicious of the situation. Who was this stray Spanish guy? And who was sponsoring this move to Barcelona? It screamed "shady" like a flashing neon sign and

I became concerned for her well-being. She confirmed that her potentially explosive relationship with the politician had ended. I told her that was a wise decision; the wheels were in full motion for a run at the White House. If that announcement occurred, the magnifying glass unleashed by the competing party would intensify. I warned her that the opposition would assign a team of professional dirt-diggers to comb through every aspect of the politician's private life hoping to catch the faintest whiff of any impropriety.

Before Donna and her girlfriend left the party she invited me to visit her in Barcelona. I later heard from a mutual friend that she loved Spain and was enjoying her time there. A few years passed. The mischievous and unfaithful politician made his unsuccessful bid to land in the White House. In 2004 the red states unified again to deliver us four more years of ineptitude, misguided foreign policy, the implosion of our banking system, and insurmountable federal deficits.

Sunday December 12, 2004 7:33AM

On a cold and grey Sunday morning my phone rang painfully early, a peculiar time for an incoming call. My caller ID displayed a 617 number that I didn't recognize.

I was groggy and hesitated to answer. It was my old girlfriend Stacey whom I hadn't spoken with in awhile. She skipped the pleasantries and told me she had some somber news. Donna was dead. I was speechless.

I broke the silence and softly uttered, "How? Where?"

My immediate thoughts were of foul play and a possible conspiracy. It seemed melodramatic, but I couldn't help thinking about those diabolical possibilities. Stacey explained that Donna and her new boyfriend were driving a convertible in the hills of Los Angeles. Apparently he lost control of the car, swerved into the other lane, and Donna was hurled fatally from the front seat upon impact with an oncoming car. She wasn't wearing a seatbelt. I asked about the boyfriend. Stacey indicated he was in a coma, but would most likely survive.

I lit a candle that morning in my bedroom window and made a rare visit to a church on Park Avenue to pray for Donna's soul. I rifled through an old album and dug out some photos of Donna. My eyes welled up as I thought about the finality of it all. Our time together was brief and disconnected; that was my deepest regret. But Donna was such an adventurous, free spirit, always living her life independently and to the fullest. I don't think I was alone in hoping and wanting to share more time with her. I know others in her life felt a similar frustration. It was the first time I had ever experienced the death of a former lover. I was never entirely convinced that "too soon" was the only injustice in Donna's death. I will always have a layer of doubt when asking, "Why?" I miss my beautiful friend and still pray that her soul has found eternal peace.

6

The Golf Channel Gal

It had been an enjoyable, sunny weekend and I was determined to squeeze out every last ounce of sunshine. I had packed my small weekender bag before heading to the beach on Sunday so I could go directly to the airport and catch one of the Cape Air puddle-jumpers. I touched down at Logan Airport from the island paradise of Nantucket.

Sunday August 22, 1999 8:13PM ⏲

I arrived at my Back Bay apartment on Commonwealth Avenue exhausted and flopped onto the couch. I was emitting a strong odor that was a combination of sweat, suntan lotion, sand, and the remnants of Saturday night's excessive alcohol consumption seeping through my pores. It was a most unpleasant fragrance.

I noticed the red light on my message machine blinking brightly and discovered there were five messages awaiting my retrieval. The first one was from an old Cornell classmate and good friend, Karen. Upon relocating to Boston, Karen had become my wing woman in training. She lived around the corner on Marlborough Street and was a real sweetheart with an endearing "Cupid Complex", always trying to help me find my next wife. Although unsuccessful, I was always appreciative of her well-intended efforts.

Karen's first message was from Friday evening reminding me that her friend, Laurie, was visiting Boston over the weekend. I had completely forgotten about her friend's visit, but vaguely remembered her mentioning it earlier that week. Messages two through five were all from Sunday, the last one having been recorded about five minutes before my arrival.

"Hi, it's Karen. Laurie and I are cruising the stores on Newbury Street."

"Hey, it's Karen again. Having a drink at Sonsie. Are you back from Nantucket?"

"Hi. Me again. Sitting down to eat at Joe's. Are you meeting us?"

"Where are you? Just ordered dessert. If you aren't here in fifteen minutes you won't get to meet my friend."

Now here was the dilemma. Karen had a terrible habit of over-promising and under-delivering when it came to women, the antithesis of a well-trained sales person. She would shower a friend with superlatives prior to an introduction, to a level where the poor unsuspecting woman could only disappoint. I had experienced this phenomenon repeatedly whenever Karen set me up. Her habit became so egregious that I was forced to advise her to tone down her gushing descriptions of these young ladies. What struck me as odd was that she hadn't uttered a single word about this mystery friend, Laurie.

I glanced in the mirror to check myself and I looked like absolute hell. A few small holes were visible in my tattered shorts. A food stain decorated my white t-shirt. I hadn't showered in at least thirty-six hours, sporting a severe case of double-bed-hat-head. And I had about five minutes to hustle over to Joe's on Newbury Street. Out of respect for my dear friend Karen, I dropped my weekender bag and headed out the door. I had promised to meet her and Laurie for a drink and I wanted to honor my commitment. On the walk over I couldn't help thinking what a disaster Laurie must be. The always effervescent Karen had said nothing about her. That couldn't be good.

I was so exhausted and drained from the weekend that I almost turned around to head back home, but that would have been rude to Karen, and she had been tremendously helpful in acclimating me to Boston. Having been raised in Lexington and having lived in Back Bay for seven years, she was completely plugged in. Her skillful maneuvering had been critical in helping me make a smooth transition from Manhattan to Boston. The social scene for young professionals in Boston was dreadfully parochial and absurdly incestuous. If an outsider lacked sponsorship, it was enormously difficult to become part of the in crowd. Karen willingly provided me access, made introductions, and validated my inclusion. She was well-liked and well-connected all over the city. She worked as a fundraiser for the United Way and often rubbed elbows with many of Boston's powerbrokers. She was also once engaged to the son of an influential political family.

I arrived at Joe's and located Karen standing at the corner of the bar. There was a blond girl sitting on a barstool talking to Karen. I couldn't see her face. I gave a nod and a wave to Karen as I strolled over to where she was stationed. As she returned the wave, the blond girl curiously turned in my direction. I was mesmerized and became a deer in the headlights frozen in my tracks. A flawless smile and dazzling white teeth flashed in my direction. Her silky blond hair seemed to move in slow motion as she swung her head around, reminiscent of a fancy shampoo commercial. Laurie was drop-dead gorgeous! Then I realized my plight. I looked like death warmed over, I smelled like shit, and I was dressed like a homeless bum. I was a walking disaster! My physical state was not going to leave a memorable first impression. Karen had fooled me once again!

After being introduced to Laurie I apologized for my disgusting appearance and my slightly offensive odor. I jokingly told them I was test marketing a new cologne called A.S.S., a combination of alcohol, sun tan lotion, and sweat. I lied and told them I came straight from the beach after getting Karen's first message around five o'clock. I fabricated an elaborate explanation telling them I had used my cell phone to retrieve Karen's first message off my answering machine. Then I took the story to a whole new level by adding that my original plans included staying the night on Nantucket and flying back to Boston in the morning. I hoped Laurie would appreciate all these sacrifices I had made just to share one drink with her at Joe's on Newbury Street. I think she actually bought my entire story. I glanced at Karen as if to ask why are you tricking me like this again. I felt like Charlie Brown always being fooled by Lucy pulling away the football as he went to kick it and ending up flat on his cartoon ass.

Laurie was intelligent and athletically accomplished, having attended Baylor University on a full golf scholarship. She was also exceedingly charming, with a hint of a southern accent and a chiseled, athletic body. I was infatuated with her right from the moment our eyes met and kept reminding myself not to drool. She was everything a man could possibly want in a woman: intelligence, eloquence, beauty, athleticism, independence, and a delightful personality. Those were just a few of the qualities that I could discern in the first ten minutes. I sat on the adjacent barstool in a daze, almost fumbling for words and struggling to talk to her. I was distracted by romantic images of us frolicking on a pristine beach darting in and out of my head.

She worked in marketing for a fast growing new cable station, the Golf Channel, and was in Boston on business until Wednesday promoting a national *Drive, Chip and Putt* contest. I recognized that she was opening the door just a crack and quickly responded by asking what she was doing for dinner on Monday. Karen chimed in that they had dinner plans, but Laurie countered that I could meet them afterward for drinks. I was relieved and encouraged by her suggestion as it signaled an unmistakable level of interest on her behalf. I paid the bar tab and escorted the gals outside where we placed Laurie in a cab back to her hotel. I offered to walk Karen home to her apartment on Marlborough Street.

Once Laurie had departed I gave Karen a blank stare and asked her if she had completely lost her mind. For more than two years I had been subjected to her inflated descriptions and false advertising. I had listened to repeated stories about the perfect girl, and baseless claims that "this is the one you will bring home to meet Mom". And when she had an opportunity to introduce me to a first team All-Star, an All-American, and a future Hall of Famer, she said nothing. There was no description, no top billing, and no warning of Laurie's impending charm, wit, or beauty. I was woefully unprepared for what had transpired at Joe's and I chastised Karen for what I deemed as unacceptable behavior by a wing woman in training.

Karen then explained her apprehension about describing Laurie in advance. She knew that Laurie had been dating an older gentleman in Los Angeles. It was Saturday evening when she discovered that Laurie's relationship was on rocky ground.

"I just found out yesterday that the old boyfriend is about to get the hook. Why do you think I called you four times today?" she asked.

"I couldn't tell you how hot she was on the machine because Laurie was standing right next to me. I didn't want her to think I was pimping her out since she had just told me about her pending break-up. But I wanted you to meet her. I knew you would be all over her," laughed Karen.

I now understood her dilemma and thanked her wholeheartedly for her masterful and diplomatic efforts. Laurie was unmistakably a rock star!—a gal you would want to bring home to meet Mom.

The next night I met up with Karen and Laurie in Boston's Theater District. We enjoyed a few drinks and chatted at a restaurant bar. I was intrigued by how Karen had met such a good-looking Texas gal now residing in Los Angeles. Laurie had been dating a cable executive who lived in LA and Karen had been dating his best friend. The two friends rented a ski lodge in Colorado for New Year's Eve. So Karen and Laurie had been part of a five-couple entourage in Aspen eight months earlier. They got along fabulously and immediately became friends. Karen had only seen Laurie once since their initial introduction, so that explained why I had never heard Karen mention her.

Laurie complained that she had not had an opportunity to enjoy the numerous historical sights around Boston. I proposed a quick solution. My convertible Jaguar XJS was housed at a parking garage around the corner, so I conveniently offered to chauffeur the girls on an impromptu tour of the city. I raced to the Commons, picked up the car, dropped the top, and loaded the girls. Laurie got to see Old North Church, Paul Revere's original house, and Bunker Hill.

"You'll have to come back to see my favorite landmark, Fenway Park," I added, a subtle hint for Laurie to visit Boston soon.

Acting coy, she asked, "Is that the place with the Green Monster?"

She then revealed that she had been there in July for the MLB All-Star game. I was astonished because I was at Fenway that night as well. And when she described where she sat for the game I concluded that we were about 100 feet apart.

After our makeshift tour I dropped Karen at her apartment and drove Laurie to her hotel. I offered to walk her up to her room and she accepted my obvious ploy. As we got to her door I leaned forward and gave her a firm kiss. She responded with an even stronger intensity. After ten minutes of kissing and groping each other in the hallway, she firmly pushed me away.

"I can't do this," she gasped.

I wanted to behave like a gentleman so I respected her

wishes and digressed to bribery.

"I will leave peacefully only if you promise to go out with me tomorrow night." She readily accepted my shameless ultimatum.

The next night was perfect. We talked nonstop about everything: life, jobs, parents, relationships, and sports. It was so refreshing to be out with a lady who earned her livelihood in the world of sports. I was such a passionate sports fan, and although golf was not at the top of my list, I had tremendous respect for the difficulty and the majesty of the game.

I was an average golfer at best, mostly because I wasn't willing to dedicate the inordinate amount of time required to be above average. Laurie was a scratch golfer, good enough to earn a full scholarship to Baylor in a state where golf is worshiped. The popularity of golf in 1999 was on a tremendous upswing with the emergence of a young new master named Eldrick "Tiger" Woods. His dismantling of the record books during *The Masters* at Augusta in 1998 had spawned "Tiger-mania", and he single-handedly rejuvenated the sport. Tiger's incredible talent was a boon to Laurie's employer, and part of the reason she was in Boston that weekend.

The CEO of the Golf Channel, Joe Gibbs, had asked her to work on some national marketing campaigns to help spread the channel to more cable systems. This new job function required a move from LA to Orlando, which was music to my ears. Dating someone in the same time zone and one thousand miles south was much more appealing than three time zones and three thousand miles away. The move to Orlando was also causing her relationship with the cable executive to fade. Timing is everything in life!

As dinner ended we both agreed that it felt like we had known each other for years, not a measly forty-eight hours. I invited Laurie to come back to my apartment that evening. Although she struggled with the moral dilemma, the mutual attraction was too strong and she agreed. It was an unforgettable night and I barely slept a wink. At times I caught myself half-opening one eye just to watch her breathe. She looked so innocent and so peaceful resting gently on my pillow. Although we had just met, I was already feeling a nervous anxiety about how strongly I felt towards her. It went beyond physical lust or a sexual curiosity. I just smiled as I dreamt of happier times with Laurie that I knew awaited me.

The fall was full of weekend trips up and down the East Coast. Laurie did more of the traveling as I had promised to perform plane duty once the cold and gray winter months arrived. We attended some marquee charity events that fall in Boston, a few of which were black-tie, and Laurie always dazzled the crowd. At one fundraiser for the Boston Public Library a candid photo of us landed in *Town and Country*. We attended a Halloween Party above The Bull & Finch, the real bar replicated in the sitcom *Cheers*, dressed as Danny Zucco and Sandy from the popular Broadway musical, *Grease*.

I still remember being the envy of the financial community the night we attended a black-tie retirement party for one of the most celebrated stock traders in Boston, Paul O'Shaughnessey, affectionately known as The Coach. He got this nickname because virtually every senior equity trader in Bean Town had been tutored and mentored by Paul.

After the extravagant farewell party for the Coach, I was beginning to sense a hint of jealous admiration all around me. I was earning a reputation around Boston as a ladies man. It was flattering, but it created repercussions at a place like Goldman Sachs. The firm would never admit it, but there was a certain level of prejudice against single guys in those powerful corner offices. The firm much preferred a married guy saddled with a monstrous mortgage and lots of kids. The senior guys on the desk were constantly dropping hints encouraging me to settle down and get remarried. That meant you were far less portable, and therefore easily manipulated by the firm and the promise of a stable, lucrative career. Success in my social life was beginning to impede my professional growth opportunities. Would marriage actually improve my status internally? It was a legitimate question and the answer appeared obvious.

Since it was the end of summer when Laurie and I met, I was disappointed she never got to experience a weekend in Nantucket. Then I received an unanticipated call from Tom Donnelly, a co-worker in Goldman's Chicago office. Tom was a fellow Cornell graduate who had also been in my fraternity, but graduated two years before me. He had also played a significant advisory role in helping to steer me through the arduous interviewing process at Goldman. Tom's wife was originally from New England and they had just purchased a beach house on Nantucket. He generously offered me a weekend in October, and the price was simply to verify the workmanship on a few cottage repairs. I called Laurie without delay and set up the weekend, including some tee times on the island.

Friday October 8, 1999 9:01PM

Nantucket was even more perfect in October. It had all the same charm with colorful autumn foliage, but without the bustling summertime crowds. We were blessed with two perfect sixty-five degree days and enjoyed golfing, biking, and running on the beach. On Saturday evening we went for a leisurely stroll on Jetties Beach before dinner. The soothing sound and the crisp smell of the ocean filled our senses. We were holding hands and walking westward as the sun lazily inched its way to meet the horizon. There was a scattered cloud formation that seemed suspended in the sky as the sun snuck below the water. The orange glow against the clouds and sky created one of the most glorious sunsets I had ever experienced. Laurie and I were astonished at the natural beauty we felt so privileged to be witnessing.

It was a majestic moment and I almost instinctively took a knee on the beach that evening to ask Laurie to marry me. There was something magical in the air but the rational side of my brain assumed control of the situation. I didn't even have a ring. What was I thinking? She had only known me for two months. What would she say?

Only an idiot would ruin a romantic moment with analytical thought and rational behavior. Where was my spontaneity? As I reflect upon that cherished moment I realize that it could have been a life altering minute lost in time.

Y2K hysteria and cyber panic dominated the headlines as 1999 moved to a close. I had been invited to a lot of crazy, once-in-a-lifetime events to ring in the new Millennium. One of the most outrageous was a party hosted at Alcatraz in San Francisco Bay. There was going to be live music, dancing, fireworks, food, and if you purchased the gold ticket you even got to spend the night in your own prison cell. I loved the novelty, but it seemed a little over the top.

One of my fraternity brothers, Shane, had organized a much better outing. He rented an eight bedroom house on the water in Chatham on Cape Cod where six of my fraternity brothers along with their wives and kids congregated for the big celebration. There were no crowds, no driving, no hassles and Shane even arranged for a catered New Year's Eve lobster dinner. It provided the perfect venue for Laurie to meet my daughter. I was extremely careful of whom I would allow my daughter to meet, but after four months it was obvious that Laurie and I would be together for quite some time.

Friday December 31, 1999 2:11PM

Laurie arrived at Greene Airport in Providence where my daughter and I picked her up. The Millennium celebration on Cape Cod was Saturday night. Predictably, Laurie and my daughter got along fabulously. My little girl had the same reaction I had towards Laurie; she felt like she had known her for years. Laurie had a special quality of fostering a trust that made you feel comfortable and unguarded.

The weekend was a complete success. The celebration was perfect, the food was scrumptious, and the weather was shockingly mild. It's always nice to go for a jog on New Years day in Cape Cod wearing nothing but a t-shirt and running shorts. I guess global warming isn't all bad; we'll enjoy milder winters now and in fifty years Earth's atmosphere will be a mass of combustible gases comparable to Venus.

All of my college friends loved seeing my daughter and meeting Laurie. My little angel functioned as a built-in babysitter for all the other younger kids. Their ages ranged up to five so she played the role of the Pied Piper for the weekend and kept the children entertained. The wives all loved Laurie although there were some hints of petty jealousy over her youth, her independence, and her shapely physique. Laurie was about eight years younger than most of the crowd. I remember overhearing a comment in the kitchen by one of the wives speculating on how Laurie's body would look after delivering two children. It always makes me laugh at how competitive women are with regard to their physical appearance. I guess that's what makes the cosmetics business a multi-billion-dollar industry.

I traveled down to Orlando numerous times in January, February and March. For Easter Laurie wanted me to meet her parents so we planned a trip to Phoenix and visited them for the holiday. Laurie organized an awesome schedule: front row seats for an Arizona Diamondbacks game, climbing Camelback Mountain, and enjoying a day at the spa with sauna, steam, and full body massage. Easter Sunday included church, a round of golf with Laurie's dad, and a delicious feast prepared by her mom.

In late April Laurie suggested I bring my daughter to Orlando during school vacation, and once again proved that she was an all-star hostess. She got passes to Universal Theme Park, Sea World, Discovery Cove, and a Cirque de Soleil show. Her love for my daughter was so evident and soothing. We had a blast with each day's activities and then got to spend time with Laurie each evening. At Discovery Cove we had the unique experience of swimming in a lagoon with dolphins. I knew it was dangerous to allow my little girl to become attached to Laurie, but reflecting on that special moment on the beach in Nantucket, I had no trouble envisioning a long-term relationship. For the first time in the five years since I had been divorced, I was beginning to foresee myself married again. Whenever I would conjure up images of Laurie and me as husband and wife, it triggered a warm, comfortable, positive feeling.

The summer began and I was involved in another share house in Nantucket near the western side of the island called Madaket Beach. It was a great house with a solid group of Bostonians including my fraternity brother, Mick. The house organizer wisely arranged a house car for the summer. He finagled a used car dealer to rent us an AMC Eagle. What a piece of shit! It was easy to understand why AMC went bankrupt in the 1980's. The unsightly Eagle became affectionately dubbed "The Dirty Bird".

Laurie and I had a few memorable weekends that summer on Nantucket. We loved dining at the Summer House in Sconset, and the night always seemed to end at the Boarding House, a mainstay in downtown Nantucket. But the winds of change always seemed to blow when you least expected them.

I had become disenfranchised with Goldman Sachs. Management had inserted a new leader in the Boston office and unceremoniously uprooted my old boss. It was a game of political tag, or in this case "catch and release". My former boss had loyally served the firm for over twenty years. After the IPO, initially scheduled for 1998 and eventually completed in 1999, the firm seemed to have lost its vision. What was once a self-proclaimed "meritocracy" that was lean and nimble was transforming into a bloated political machine less focused on production, especially in the Equities Division. I decided to dip my toe in and test the waters in the spring of 2000. I immediately attracted attention from DLJ (Donaldson, Lufkin & Jenrette) and Morgan Stanley, two firms I greatly admired as competitors. Morgan Stanley offered me a lateral position requiring a move back to New York and the offer was too good to pass up. Besides, there were not too many places you could go when leaving Goldman that would be considered an up tick; Morgan Stanley may have been the only firm on the Street where one could honestly make that claim.

Monday July 17, 2000 7:15AM

I took the job and moved to the 36th floor of a high rise on West 56th Street, a building called the Symphony House, named for its proximity to Carnegie Hall. Laurie was excited and knew I was growing restless at Goldman. She loved the unlimited choices Manhattan offered, not to mention the slightly shorter plane ride from Orlando. The first weekend she came to visit she was like Julie McCoy from *The Love Boat*. She had a full schedule of restaurant reservations and chic nightclubs to visit. I had only been in Boston for three years, but it was astonishing how many new hot places had emerged on the New York scene while I was gone. I felt remorse for the old trendy places that were now labeled passé or worse, cheesy.

By fall 2000 one of the greatest scams in the history of Wall Street, the internet bubble, was about to completely deflate. Many of the technology stocks had peaked in mid-March and were struggling to trade near those peak levels through the summer, a seasonally slow earnings quarter for technology companies. The Wall Street firms who had gotten filthy rich taking these bogus internet companies public saw their stocks trading at over five times book value. Historically, three times book was considered a rich multiple. First Boston announced a takeover of DLJ in August and Goldman Sachs quickly followed by acquiring Speer Leads Kellogg, perhaps two of the most ill-timed transactions ever on Wall Street.

By September many of the "CLEC" stocks cracked. These were companies spending billions of dollars to build fiber optic broadband capacity capable of carrying the trillions of gigabytes the internet would spawn. Many of these companies had floated massive junk bond offerings to finance miles of redundant data pipelines. When it became abundantly clear that there was overcapacity and pricing limitations, the institutional holders began dumping the bonds back on the brokers who had issued them. And they kept selling, and selling, and selling. Fixed Income departments across Wall Street became swelling repositories for these soon-to-be worthless pieces of paper.

By late October there was tremendous consternation as losses mounted and people began to worry about bonuses and job cuts. I was particularly on edge because Wall Street can often be a game of musical chairs and having been hired in July, I was one of the last ones to join the party at Morgan Stanley. When it came time to make job cuts, one always worried about the LIFO (Last In First Out) method commonly used in accounting. Adding to my anxiety, the managing director who had hired me was losing some of the luster from his once shining star. He was mired in a nasty divorce and an affair which had negatively impacted his focus and his stature within the organization.

Leaving Goldman had been a difficult decision and now the markets were turning against me. I had a guaranteed contract for 2000, but I was apprehensive about the longer-term repercussions of what was transpiring in the marketplace. Laurie visited one October weekend in connection with a work-related event. A new movie was being released called *The Legend of Bagger Vance*, staring Will Smith, Matt Damon, and Charlize Theron. The Golf Channel was sponsoring some marketing tie-ins with the film given its golf backdrop. Laurie was involved on the marketing side and was in New York to participate in the press junkets and some other promotional events.

I had grown accustomed to Laurie being surrounded by celebrities. Prior to meeting me she had been romantically involved with Matt Lauer from the *Today Show* and Justin Leonard, a PGA golfer and winner of the British Open. She had shared a few anecdotes about numerous celebrities she had been paired with in Pro-Am golf outings. The Tuesday and Wednesday before a PGA golf tournament are typically filled with Pro-Am and charity events. As a scratch golfer, a Golf Channel marketing executive, and given her dazzling good looks, Laurie constantly received invitations to play in these events.

I had heard some funny stories about celebrities such as Sean Connery, Charles Barkley, and Tiger Woods. While playing a round with the former James Bond actor Laurie shared a memorable anecdote.

"I was teeing off from the men's tees on fourteen. I was playing well that day, hitting almost every green in regulation. I nailed a perfect drive about 225 yards, smack in the middle of the fairway. As I picked up my tee, 007 walks onto the tee box shaking his head. 'Laurie, your game bores me' he says in his thick Scottish accent."

I always encouraged her to join the LPGA. I often referenced the Anna Kornikova media blitz.

"You're hotter than her, you're an all-American girl, you're more personable, and you're better at golf than she is at tennis," I told Laurie hoping to nudge her.

I tried to convince her that she didn't need to win, just

to show up and compete. It amazed me how many endorsement dollars got splashed on Anna K. Sadly, I told Laurie that in women's sports it wasn't about winning, but how good you looked playing the game! It is a scathing condemnation about American values and magnifies the power of Madison Avenue, but one cannot deny it to be true. Laurie always discarded my idea by arguing that she wasn't a good enough golfer, which totally missed the point.

She stayed at my place for the weekend, but cautioned me that there was a rigorous schedule involved with the movie premier. We went out on Saturday night to a quiet dinner, but came home early as Laurie had a busy day scheduled for Sunday. We had agreed on having dinner on Sunday night at eight o'clock. The restaurant was a quaint Italian eatery close to my high-rise. I waited until 8:30 and then ordered some takeout and returned home. I called Laurie's cell phone twice, but instantly got placed into voicemail which meant her phone had been turned off, adding to my irritation. By 11:00PM I had become worried that something serious might have happened so I attempted calling two of her co-workers. Again, all I reached was voicemail. I was about to call her mother but decided against it. I didn't want her mom to panic. Laurie had always been punctual and reliable; my mind was spinning wildly, filled with some unpleasant possibilities.

I passed out on the couch while watching television and was awakened by the fumbling of keys outside my apartment door. It was 2:00AM as Laurie stumbled into the hallway intoxicated. In the fifteen months I had known her, I had never seen Laurie inebriated. She always drank in moderation.

"I've never been so disappointed at anyone in my life," I told her. "I can't believe how selfish you are. I was worried. Why didn't you return my calls?"

I told her I was glad she wasn't hurt, poured her into bed, and returned to my spot on the couch. She tried to apologize and mumbled to give me an explanation.

"I'm not interested in excuses. I'm exhausted. I have to be up at 6," I responded.

She later blamed the whole incident on work-related stuff. Her cell phone battery had died. She was dragged to an unplanned event.

"Blah. Blah. Blah. And the dog ate your homework," was my response.

Things were never the same after that Sunday night. She had dangerously compromised my trust, and that is always a difficult thing to restore. I was a zombie on Monday; I still couldn't believe the chain of events on Sunday evening. Laurie called me from Orlando that afternoon begging for forgiveness. I pretended to be overly busy at work and abruptly hung up the phone.

On Tuesday fate would again appear on my doorstep in a curious and unpredictable form. The doormen like to hand-deliver the *New York Times* and *Wall Street Journal* to each floor so that seven hundred tenants didn't have to ride the elevator to the lobby and fetch their papers. They had accidentally delivered a copy of the *New York Post* at my door. I scooped it up and tossed it on the kitchen counter.

I never read The Post; I always thought it was an absolute rag. But I knew a lot of people who loved to browse the wildly popular and infamous Page Six. So before tossing it in the trash I turned to page six where I confusingly found some local news. I finally discovered Page Six on page thirteen and I couldn't believe my eyes! The lead article was about Matt Damon, star of *The Legend of Bagger Vance*. It reported that Matt had hosted his private birthday party at the newly opened Hudson Hotel on Sunday night. I recalled Laurie telling me about a work dinner with a few people from the Golf Channel and Matt Damon about two months prior. I didn't have to be Sherlock Holmes to figure out that Laurie had cunningly attended the soiree. But why not tell me? She had willingly disclosed other dinners and meetings with celebrities. Why was this different? It just fueled my anger and my distrust. I assumed there was something to hide.

As December rolled around things were not joyous on Wall Street. The markets continued to trade lower led by the sagging weight of overvalued and overly hyped technology stocks. Stocks like Yahoo, Amazon and even Cisco had rapidly fallen from their stratospheric valuations. Laurie had invited me to Orlando for the Golf Channel Christmas party. It was an intimate gathering hosted at the Bay Hill Golf Club.

After we stacked our plates with some pasta and seafood we grabbed a table near the back. Soon after sitting down we were joined by the CEO, Joe Gibbs, and none other than the legendary Arnold Palmer. It was one of those "pinch me, I must be dreaming" moments. I couldn't help but ask myself, "How did a middle-class kid from Maine end up at a Christmas party having dinner with Arnold Palmer, arguably the most recognizable golfer on the planet?" I felt guilty enjoying this unique experience with Arnie, a true American icon. He was a blue-collar Pennsylvanian credited with spreading the game of golf from the elitists to the masses. I knew so many avid golfers that were much bigger fans than I. They would have killed to be in my seat. I wished my old wingman Steve had been with me that evening.

Laurie spent New Years in New York City. We went to a crazy party promoted as a re-creation of Studio 54 nightclub on West 54th Street. We both got foolishly hammered and spent the next two days in agony trying to recover. I journeyed down to Tampa Bay in late January to attend the Super Bowl and watch the Baltimore Ravens annihilate the NY Giants. I enjoyed the trouncing since the Giants had so rudely shellacked my Minnesota Vikings in the NFC title game, 41-0.

Monday, January 29, 2001 11:28AM

After a weekend of partying and enjoying all the hoopla surrounding the big game, I had an interesting Monday. One of my closest friends from high school had a younger brother who worked for the New York Yankees. Matt was the trainer at their Tampa facility and was in charge of rehabilitation assignments for all the players in their system. I had offered to treat him to lunch as a small token of my appreciation for taking me to Game 3 of the 2000 World Series in October.

He accepted and gave me directions to the training facility. As I waited in the reception area George Steinbrenner hurriedly walked past. Matt led me to his office through the weight room and there were only two people pumping iron that Monday. One I didn't recognize and the other was a guy named Derek Jeter, fresh off his fourth World Series title in five years. The guy was twenty-five and the toast of New York. New Yorkers, the media, and some of the hottest women in America all loved him. As a former baseball player, I was green with envy. Matt loved his job and the Yankee organization. He let me try on one of his World Series rings—an astonishing piece of jewelry! Someday I look forward to seeing him in the Yankee dugout as the team trainer.

After lunch I cruised from Tampa over to Orlando. I was going to spend the night with Laurie and fly back to New York on Tuesday. I had been thinking about our relationship a lot. She still didn't know that I had pieced together the Matt Damon incident. Her assignment in Orlando was complete and she was contemplating a move back to LA. I wasn't keen on a three thousand mile romance as Orlando to New York had been difficult enough. So that morning I decided to end our eighteen month relationship. I was miserable and depressed, but the end seemed unavoidable. The trust had been badly tarnished. I genuinely thought Laurie had cured me of my growing addiction. I had dreamed of us having a *real* honeymoon someday.

Laurie was tearful and tried to talk me out of it. I underestimated how much she cared about me and about us, but deep down she knew it was inevitable. My daughter and I visited her for a week in Los Angeles that spring. She lived on Bundy Drive in Westwood, a hundred yards from where O.J. Simpson allegedly killed his ex-wife and Ron Goldman. She played hostess and kept us busy with studio tours, San Diego zoo passes, a girls-only day at an upscale spa, and fancy dinners at Spago and Mr. Chow's.

Laurie began dating a fairly recognizable actor. I always teased her about being her only boyfriend who didn't have to sign autographs or pose for pictures when I took her out to dinner. She eventually married this gentleman, who was once a soap opera actor, but is best known for playing a recurring character on the hit show *Seinfeld*. Laurie is now a mom and remains happily married.

7

The Female Fabio

Can you imagine a worse label tagged on a woman than being referred to as the "Female Fabio"? It was a terrible moniker, but that was the media's curse placed on an unsuspecting model named Cathy.

Tuesday February 19, 2002 9:55PM

I was hanging out at a club called Moomba. It was a trendy spot in the West Village, reluctantly sharing the coveted spotlight and always vying for Page Six coverage with another exclusive lounge called Pangea. I was sporting a savage tan after returning from a raucous week of Mardi Gras partying at Carnival in Brazil. While ordering a drink at the bar, a seductive and sultry blond caught my attention. I introduced myself over the roar of the crowd and visibly sensed her interest in me. Her flirtatious eyes and the subtle forward thrust of her breasts were a dead giveaway.

I had to deliver some drinks to my friends upstairs and Cathy was about to leave. I was pressed into action, skipped the small talk, and asked for her digits. I never expected to receive thirty numbers doodled onto a napkin. She jotted down her cell number, her New York apartment number, and her Los Angeles number. I glanced at the napkin before shoving it in my pocket.

"Wow, this girl really wants me to be able to reach her," I mumbled to myself.

I figured she must be another aspiring actress if she was shuttling between New York and Los Angeles. After some phone tag and a five-day excursion to LA, I finally set up a date with Cathy. It was your typical first date in terms of the standard resume questions. She was a model, and predictably, transitioning to acting. But her real claim to fame was unique, and borderline comical. She explained to me that she had posed for the cover of over one thousand romance novels.

"You mean like Fabio?" was my knee-jerk reaction.

She shot me a cold Medusa-like stare; I felt like I was going to turn to stone. Apparently I wasn't the first person to make this Fabio comparison, but it was a reference she did not enjoy hearing. She admitted to posing on numerous covers with Fabio, but I sensed fierce resentment towards him based on the tone of her voice when speaking his name. Maybe she was pissed off that she never got offered an "I can't believe it's not butter" television ad amongst other endorsements. Somehow Fabio had managed to monetize his popularity as a romance cover boy, but Cathy evidently had not.

I politely changed the subject to focus on the actress part of the equation, but it became painfully obvious that the answer to that line of work was nonexistent. It's such a typical response from many of the models you meet in New York who are past the age of twenty-five. Sadly, the fashion industry labels them as washed up at that delicately young age, so they change their focus and convince themselves that they are actresses even though they can't act, haven't studied to be an actress, and have never earned a paycheck for acting. A few models have successfully made the transition such as Geena Davis, Kim Bassinger, and Renee Russo, but it's an arduous process with rare exceptions.

"I'm an actress" is another one of the many landmines one

must be aware of in the New York singles scene. New York has approximately 100,000 registered actors, but only enough work in the industry to support about 2,000 of them at any one time. And most of those positions are geared towards classically-trained actors working on the stage in Broadway productions. Stage producers and Broadway casting directors are generally not interested in hiring a nice-looking Amazon woman to sit on a stool, strike a pose, and look hot. The bottom line is that at any given point in time, roughly 98% of New York City's actors are unemployed including Cathy.

When our date concluded I experienced another first. Just when I thought I had seen it all, Cathy reaches into her pocketbook and hands me what looked like a business card. I didn't even glance at it as I tucked it into my inside pocket. I remembered being slightly baffled recalling the napkin incident at Moomba. I already had three phone numbers. What other contact information could I possibly need?

When I arrived at my apartment in Symphony House, I emptied my pockets on the kitchen counter and found Cathy's card. It had her name and March 1999 in gold lettering across the top and displayed a fully naked picture of Cathy's backside. Her long, flowing, golden hair was curled and hanging loosely, resting just north of the nape in her back. Her arms were perfectly straight at her sides with her hands firmly planted on each side of her thighs, while her eye-catching, glorious ass was proudly exposed. There was a little *Playboy* bunny trademark on the bottom right corner. On the flip side, Cathy was lying on a bed of multicolored rose petals tastefully nude. Her eyes were closed, her mouth and succulent lips were open slightly, her left hand was clutching her neckline, as if she were choking herself, and her right hand rested gently on her stomach.

After receiving Cathy's unique business card, my curiosity intensified, so I began a quest to acquire the March 1999 issue of *Playboy*. I found it listed on the world's greatest garage sale, eBay. Cathy had the privilege of posing for an eight-page celebrity spread in the magazine, including a Lady Godiva shot where she was sitting naked with her flowing blond locks on a big white stallion. There was also a sensuous shot of her in a bathtub full of rose petals. It was eerily reminiscent of a scene from a 2001 movie that may have stolen the idea for the film. Do you remember the dream sequence in *American Beauty* when Kevin Spacey's character was in bed fantasizing about his daughter's friend naked in a bathtub full of red rose petals? His wife awoke and caught him pleasuring himself. He didn't miss a stroke and feverishly continued his jack-hammering, a quintessential 'welcome to marriage' testimonial.

Cathy's promotional card reignited a deviant image of me as an eight-year-old and the origins of my own *Playboy* obsession. My father was helping a co-worker and softball teammate move on a Saturday afternoon. I was the bat boy for the softball team that summer so he dragged me along, and eager to help, I carried a few light items out to the moving van. During one of my treks up the ramp I noticed a box of old magazines placed on the curb alongside some trash items. I curiously sauntered over to take a peek and to my surprise discovered about twenty issues of *Playboy*. I asked my Dad's friend if I could take them as barter for my hard labor. He was dumbfounded.

"We had better ask your Dad," he wisely decided.

My father, who was only twenty-nine at the time, said, "Okay, but just promise me they'll stay in your bedroom."

About a week later I was so proud of my new magazine collection that I decided to remove the centerfolds and plaster them on my walls. I was never particularly fond of the old grungy wallpaper in my room. The next day my mother discovered my interior decorating touch and was not amused. Her response was unruffled genius. At dinner that evening she cleverly suggested that she couldn't wait for my grandmother's next visit so grandma could enjoy a private viewing of the artistic photographs that now adorned my walls. That image sparked their immediate removal. The playmates were reassigned to a box and tucked neatly under my bed. But the dream never died. During my college years a suggestive poster of Kathy Shower, Playmate of the Year in 1986, wrapped in silk red sheets, was a fixture in my bedroom.

It was anticlimactic when Cathy and I returned back to my apartment after our next date. As a kid sitting on the floor next to the Christmas tree did you ever know what a gift was even before you opened it? You had to become a stage actor, no re-takes, and feign your enthusiasm with lines like, "Just what I wanted", or "I can't believe you found the one I liked!" The mystery and the ensuing excitement were severely diminished, much like unwrapping a present you had already previewed.

I must confess I was fascinated by the novelty of Cathy's pictorial. How often do high school teenage boys (or even a demented eight-year-old) see a *Playboy* pictorial and think to themselves, "If only I could experience her nakedness?" Now I was actually touching, caressing, and tasting a woman from those fantasy-filled pages. Harking back to my teenage years in Maine, it just seemed so far-fetched to have a woman from the pages of Hef's magazine lying naked in my bed, begging me to ravage her body. Was I dreaming? Life was good!

Cathy and I spent the next few months informally dating. I couldn't offer her much more than a casual relationship because we just didn't seem to share many common interests and our conversations were monotonous. We enjoyed a few dinners, spent a few nights at some clubs, and retreated to my apartment for a few frolicsome evenings. I visited her apartment on the Upper West Side one evening and was shocked by all the romance novels proudly on display like trophies. I could accept a few covers, but it was a cartoonish and endless shrine to her work. During her travels and publicity tours she had met and partied with some interesting people. She claimed Gene

Simmons, the tongue wagging guitarist from 70's rock band Kiss, and Candice Bushnell, the author of *Sex in the City*, as among her close friends. Cathy dragged me to the Royalton Hotel in midtown one night where I actually met Candice. She was a bit intoxicated, seemed agitated, and was completely uninterested in meeting me.

It may sound harsh, but I soon became overwhelmingly bored with Cathy. We certainly did not seem to share the same cerebral curiosity and I just felt like she brought nothing interesting to the table. It's undeniable that a woman's physical beauty can initially attract any man, but ultimately it's her personality and her intellect that dictates how long that man is willing to stay. The *Playboy* novelty evaporated in a flash and after about two months of casual dating, I stopped answering her phone calls. Having been unwillingly dismissed, the "Female Fabio" had graced my covers for the last time.

8

Welcome to the Barber Shop

My college buddies were becoming tired of my relationship revolving door. They would jokingly accuse me of suffering from nymphomania, but I was far too selective to give that theory any credence. I was never interested in one-night stands or getting a blow job from some random babe in a bathroom stall willing to do anything for another line of coke. That was not my gig. Episodes like that seemed brazenly comical when you are young and foolish, but they become excruciatingly pathetic as you mature.

I was partying in the backyard of a Hampton's mansion one August when a female friend mysteriously vanished for an hour. She had lured a young, unsuspecting tennis pro into the woods and had sex with him. The act was tasteless enough, but she returned to the party and bragged about the encounter as if she had just run a marathon for charity. It was a despicable story, especially when told by a thirty-four-year-old woman who always wondered why she was still single. I lost respect for her that night and she will never regain it. Damage to one's reputation always leaves the deepest and ugliest scar.

One-night stands in a place like Manhattan can be extremely dangerous on many levels; nonetheless they happen all the time. It's a game of Russian roulette placing your personal health at risk. I recently met a girl who had just turned thirty. She had maintained her virginity until she got married at twenty-three, a difficult task in our sexually obsessed culture. She got divorced and then demanded that her next boyfriend wait eighteen months before having sex with her. Then she moved to New York City and succumbed to a one-night stand within a month. Was it the conniving persuasiveness of the City, the temptation of the Devil's lair? She deeply regretted it, but sometimes even the most unlikely candidate experiences a dim-witted indiscretion. See Bill Clinton.

Wednesday August 21, 2002

It was my favorite time of the year in New York. The end of August offers the benefits of the summer, but also signals that my favorite season is just around the corner. One of my hedge fund clients had invited me to an end-of-the-summer party at a place called Lot 61 on the West Side. I hadn't been there in quite awhile and had no idea what the party was for or who was sponsoring it. All I needed to know was that I was on the mythical, but all important list. This client was always socially reliable. He consistently attended worthwhile gigs with hot chicks, good food, and free booze—a virtual hat trick!

When I arrived it was a mob scene at the door, but my pal saw me from inside and instructed the doorman to skip the rope drama and let me in pronto. After stuffing my face with a few hors d'oeuvres I grabbed a beer and joined Jake at his table. A table in a nightclub means you get two spots on an extended couch-like bench where an 18 inch square table is placed in front of your knees holding a bucket of ice, glasses, mixers, and a bottle of hard liquor. One typically pays about $750 for all this luxury when the club is crowded and the key to entry is agreeing to table service. This is perhaps one of the biggest scams in a city full of con artists, swindlers and impostors. Three-card-Monty on the corner of 42nd Street in Times Square is less offensive.

The party was being co-hosted by two of the city's big advertising firms. By 11:00PM my friend, Jake, declared he was tired and headed for the exits. I was going to finish my last drink and leave as well since the open bar had officially ended, and I didn't really know anyone at the party besides Jake. As I was about to leave a girl sat down on the bench next to me. She introduced herself as Christina and we began having a simple conversation covering a few resume items.

My intuition and keen eye told me she was young, but I was amazed to discover that she was only twenty-one and about to begin her senior year of college after spending the summer as an intern at one of the ad agencies. She asked me how old I was and I felt compelled to conceal my age. I didn't want to scare or intimidate her with thirty-six.

"How old do you think I am?" I asked.

It was so gratifying when she responded, "Thirty?"

"So close, only off by one year," was my harmless fib.

She told me she was from Weston, Massachusetts so we shared a New England connection and a mutual love affair with the Red Sox. An old fraternity brother lived in Weston so I was familiar with that upscale enclave in the western suburbs of Boston.

Christina was a pretty girl with porcelain skin and thick auburn hair. She was wearing a thin sun dress to neutralize the brutal August humidity. She had been enjoying her internship and happily shared her summer highlights. She mentioned that next week was her last in the city and she was deeply saddened that her fun summer was drawing to a close. This comment piqued my interest. Young women are typically less reserved towards the end of an extended stay in a foreign location. I had witnessed this phenomenon throughout my dating career recalling college spring breaks. A woman's reasoning is always complex, but they are always more willing to do naughty things and shed their inhibitions when they are about to leave a place behind.

Somewhere in the middle of a babbling story about visiting the Statue of Liberty, she arbitrarily leaned over and gave me a quick, soft kiss on the lips. It caught me off guard as I was fatigued and feeling drained, barely able to listen to her touristy adventure stories. Midnight approached so with nothing to lose the kiss prompted me to invite Christina back to my apartment. At first she sensed the alluring danger and hesitated to respond. Like a veteran salesman I tossed in an enticement that clinched a decision.

"There's a million-dollar-view of Central Park from my balcony."

"Let's go!" she exclaimed.

She liked my apartment but loved the balcony, an unobstructed northerly view of the Central Park landscape. To the west you could see the reflection of the city's lights dancing off the Hudson River and the outlines of some New Jersey high rise buildings. Looking northwest you had a perfect shot of the George Washington Bridge all lit up in its majestic stature, and to the northeast you could see the Tri-Boro Bridge and the stacked planes landing at LaGuardia. It was Salesmanship 101—always be closing.

With my arms around her waist I pushed her up against the railing from behind and began to tenderly kiss her soft neck. I ran my right hand over her covered breast, down to her stomach and between her legs. She was moaning uncontrollably as we kissed. She grabbed and guided my hand back between her thighs. Christina's moans grew louder as she started moving my hand in an up and down motion. I slipped my hand to her knee and began moving slowly up her thigh underneath the thin sundress. About halfway to the Promised Land she grabbed my hand and turned around to face me saying that she was embarrassed and unprepared for what was happening.

"I can't do this. I never expected to be in this situation tonight...bad timing."

I gave her a dejected look and assumed I knew what she meant.

"Are you trying to tell me it's a bad time of the month?"

She giggled and said that was not the issue which left me temporarily confused. She re-emphasized, "Unprepared."

I had to think for a second, but then the solution to her riddle became obvious.

"Are you trying to say there's too much grass on the infield?" I asked in a coy demeanor.

"Exactly," she responded.

I assured her it was a problem we could readily solve together if she trusted me.

"Do you have a steady hand?" she asked.

"Like a surgeon! These hands set receiving records in college," I fired back.

I am not sure Christina understood the football reference, but she appeared persuaded by my alleged qualifications. We left the scenic balcony and headed straight for my bathroom where she promptly dropped her sundress on the floor. I grabbed my razor and some shaving cream and positioned myself using the closed toilet as a chair. I felt like Picasso working on a masterpiece, substituting a Gillette *Mach 2* for a brush and a pallet of white shaving cream for paint. She stood over me with her hands on her hips and staring down at me as I occasionally glanced up at her alluring breasts. So there I sat with my props, devilishly thinking that this brought new meaning to the phrase "mowing my lawn", and wishing I could be videotaping the entire escapade. Who was going to believe this story? I had just met this young vixen an hour ago!

Her eyes moved to the wall mirror mounted over the sink as I continued my artistry. She seemed quite pleased with my brush strokes and the manner in which I handled my sharp instrument, but wanted to try the bedroom for a different kind of precision performance. It was an amazing night as I thoroughly enjoyed the energy and the stamina of this lovely twenty-one-year-old college girl. She even complimented me on my endurance, "especially for a twenty-nine-year-old". It was all I could do not to confess I was thirty-six.

The next day at the office one of my co-workers noticed that I looked lethargic. On a Wall Street trading desk people are crammed so tightly together that there are seldom any secrets. I explained to my neighbor that I didn't get much sleep, and after badgering me for the details, I broke the rules and shared my deviant tale from the previous evening. It had always been my policy to never "kiss and tell", but given the comical nature of what transpired, I made an exception. It turned out to be a piss poor decision that would shortly come back and bite me in the ass!

When I returned to the trading desk from retrieving my lunch out on Broadway, Dave was buckling over in a loud belly laugh with our boss, Tim. I asked them to share the gag.

"What the hell is so outrageously funny?"

They both looked at each other as a conniving grin slowly engulfed Tim's face.

"You'll no longer be called the Hawk," declared Tim.

He performed a series of animated movements that mimicked Queen Elizabeth performing the ritual of knighthood.

"Your new title shall be.... 'The Barber'," proclaimed Tim.

The lesson learned and the rule reinforced: never kiss and tell!

9

Revisting 9/11

Monday, September 10, 2001 3:11PM

I spent the afternoon watching my daughter's soccer practice at Dyer Elementary in South Portland. I had taken Monday off from work to enjoy a three-day weekend in Maine. After practice I treated my daughter to an early dinner and then headed for the airport. My direct flight was on American Airlines back to JFK and scheduled to depart at 7:30PM.

As I arrived at the airport, I noticed canceled notations next to a few flights including mine. I was confused and headed straight for the counter. The agent said there had been terrible thunderstorms in the greater New York City area that afternoon and evening. Consequently, many flights to the three New York area airports had been either delayed or canceled. The representative told me not to worry; they had automatically booked me on their first morning departure at 6:00AM. I asked what time it arrived at JFK. She then told me that the small aircraft flew to Logan in Boston where I would be switching planes.

I was uneasy with those accommodations. It was imperative that I return to New York and be on my trading desk at Morgan Stanley by 7:00AM. I was irritated with the flight cancellation and the weather related issues since it had been such a perfect day in Maine. I went next door to the US Air counter, but their last flight to LaGuardia had also been canceled. My last hope was Continental; their last flight to Newark had been scheduled to depart at 6:45PM. The flight board screen listed it as delayed. The agent informed me there was a fifty percent chance the flight would depart that evening. I hurried back to the American counter and they made the necessary arrangements. It was the flip of a coin and luckily I called it right. The Continental flight departed at 9:00PM. I hated having to schlep into Manhattan from Newark, but at least I wouldn't miss my daily seven o'clock meeting.

I rarely flew in or out of Newark, but I vividly remember landing that evening. We approached the runway from the north and I was seated on the left hand side of the plane in a window seat. Approaching the runway I couldn't help but notice the majesty of the Twin Towers, lit up like two big Christmas trees across the Hudson River. It would be one of the last times that anyone would view those beacons of capitalism gloriously twinkling in the night.

What about that 6:00AM American flight I was originally rebooked on? That was the initial flight boarded by Mohammed Atta and the hijackers to help them circumvent the more stringent and sophisticated security checkpoints at Logan Airport. If the Continental flight had been canceled I would have shared a twenty minute ride on a puddle-jumper with those cowardly murderers. At Logan they connected with an outbound San Francisco flight and changed the course of American history. I probably would have still been airborne when all hell broke loose that morning. I can't imagine the trauma that would have caused my family.

Saturday June 21, 2003 11:44PM ♁

I was parking my car at a Southampton hotspot that seemed to get renamed every few summers. I had originally known the club as Jet East in the mid-90's, the Hampton's version of a Soho nightclub called Jet Lounge. It was now called Cain, a re-branded creation of the trendy club located on West 27th Street. As I was walking through the parking lot I noticed two pretty ladies stepping out of a black Porsche at the valet stand. The driver was blond and the other gal was a brunette. The blond was wearing a tight fitting dress that accentuated her voluptuous body. She looked like a "diced" aerobics instructor given the definition in her arms and the shapeliness of her legs and buttocks.

Inside the club I was moving to the beat of a popular club song, and as I glanced to my left, the blond from the parking lot was dancing by herself at my side. I introduced myself and attempted to have a conversation, which was futile given the deafening level of the music blaring from the high-tech sound system. We eventually fought through the crowd and chatted outside in the designated smoking area adjacent to the parking lot. I asked Kara for her number because I wanted to take her on a date back in the city. She accepted and we made tentative plans for the following Tuesday evening.

Our date was an opportunity to discuss those pesky resume questions that were denied proper coverage by the excruciatingly loud house music on Saturday night. Kara's life story was so much more interesting than mine. She told me that she had two adorable daughters, almost expecting that to spook me into a state of disinterest. She couldn't have been happier when she learned that I also had a daughter. I then made a classic mistake with a misguided assumption.

"So how long have you been divorced?" I innocently wondered aloud.

There was an awkward pause as Kara set down her drink and fumbled to find the words, "I'm not divorced."

I sensed something terrible was about to follow.

Kara firmly stated, "My husband was an executive with

Cantor Fitzgerald."

My face became pale with sorrow. I vaguely knew only one 9/11 victim, a Cantor broker who had filled out my golf foursome at Doral back in 1999. He was a salt-of-the-earth, diligent guy who left a wife whom he had met in the second grade and five children.

Kara was now the closest I had ever been to that despicable tragedy that had so deeply scarred New York City, the country, and the world. I was clueless about what to say next. I am sure my reaction of being paralyzed by the news offered no consolation for Kara. A tidal wave of guilt splashed over me and all I could do was muster four unoriginal words.

"I am so sorry."

There are just some situations where one is completely unprepared. One second I am chuckling as I readied myself to poke fun at the inadequacies of our ex-spouses, and then, as if I was struck with a two-by-four across my forehead, the laughter vanished and I was dumbfounded. My thoughts were jumbled and in complete disarray. How do you handle such a crushing revelation?

Kara was one of those thousands of people I tearfully watched for three days, staggering around Manhattan with pictures of her husband, visiting hospital after hospital, and praying for a miracle. My heart sank as I thought of her two little girls. I still didn't know their names and hadn't even seen their pictures, but with a daughter of my own, I could easily imagine their pain and their confusion. I had only known Kara for seventy-two hours, but I was amazed at her strength and her positive energy. You would never have guessed that this woman had been so violently and unjustly robbed. She was so outwardly upbeat and vivacious. I could see the strength of her soul in her eyes and heard an unrelenting resolve in the tone of her voice. It was uplifting.

After we discussed her unique circumstances and all that

she had endured, I was embarrassed to tell her about my life. My past contained almost no tragedy and some comparatively minuscule struggles. I suddenly felt like I had accomplished so little, and overcome even less, like telling someone who had climbed Mount Everest that I once ran up a really steep hill. Her courage was almost intimidating, but I also realized the fragility of the situation. It was a dilemma that required careful consideration.

Kara's husband had been an executive at Cantor who had worked hard and done well financially. Kara and the girls lived in a charming and secluded township in New Jersey. I was familiar with the place because many Goldman Sachs partners and managing directors resided there.

Kara's routine revolved around her girls and working out like a maniac at the gym. She was an exercise freak, and although she wasn't an aerobics instructor like I had originally thought, I was sure she routinely danced circles around whoever led her classes. She also spent a lot of time at the country club pool, developing a savage tan which contrasted perfectly with her deep blue, captivating eyes and long blond hair. Kara was quite simply a knockout, who literally packed a knockout punch. When she wasn't doing aerobics, she was taking kick boxing. This woman could kick my ass both emotionally and physically!

After grappling with my ability to handle Kara's tragic past, I decided I wanted to pursue a relationship. We had enjoyed a few dinners and a few nights out when I got invited to a cocktail party in a building at the corner of West 57th Street and Eighth Avenue. I asked Kara if she would accompany me to this little soirée. The apartment offered an oversized balcony overlooking Central Park. One of my hedge fund clients, Jay Applebaum, was unexpectedly in attendance when we arrived at the party.

After I introduced Jay to Kara he made a devastatingly poor

assumption. He saw her blond hair, her tan and toned body, and decided that he would flex his intellectual muscles. I just watched in complete amusement. Jay tried to challenge Kara's intelligence, but she completely outdueled him on each topic he selected. It was like watching Matt Damon's character so eloquently debate the arrogant Harvard punks during the bar scene in *Good Will Hunting*. Jay and his Ivy League degree were soundly deflated by Kara. He would later confess to me that he felt like Napoleon at Waterloo, and then humbly admitted that he thought she was a keeper. I told him he didn't even know the half of it. Jay had no clue what kind of hell she had endured in her life.

I asked Kara how difficult it was to be dating after being married for so many years and having things end so tragically. She confessed it took a year before she could even go on a date. She then scoffed at the rich, older men who mistakenly thought they could simply buy her affection. She never realized how pathetic some wealthy men could be, but figured their tactics must work on somebody.

I asked for an example and she shared a funny anecdote about a multi-millionaire software developer who had recently sold his company. She said the guy was a bit nerdy, as one might expect. But she said he was disgustingly self-absorbed and overly impressed with his newfound financial success. He had reserved a prime table at the hot night spot, Cain, and invited an entourage. Kara became completely bored with him and his lame-ass friends. Her body language and general disinterest made it clear to Mr. Softie that she was woefully unhappy.

Softie sensed her displeasure and asked Kara if anything would make her happy. She jokingly responded with the first thing that popped into her head—a double order of French fries from Pastis, a popular French bistro in the Meatpacking District. Mr. Softie whipped out his cell phone and called his driver. Twenty minutes later the driver was weaving his way through the crowded and energetic dance floor of Cain carrying a silver tray loaded with Pastis fries.

Kara laughed, "Where's the ketchup?

After munching a few fries Kara said, "Hey—I have another request."

Mr. Softie smiled a shit-eating grin as if Kara was now playing along with his tomfoolery.

"You can have your driver take me home now," she demanded.

The smile speedily ran from his face. It was such a classic story. Just another douche-bag in New York impressed with his bulging wallet. And I loved Kara for having the spunkiness to unabashedly deflate Mr. Softie's ego.

Kara and I spent a weekend together in the Hamptons. She visited my apartment a few times and whipped up some appetizing home-cooked meals, something I only got to enjoy in Maine. Then she unveiled the perfect gift to celebrate my birthday in mid-July. Kara had scored two choice seats for a Bruce Springsteen concert at the Meadowlands. I couldn't imagine seeing "The Boss" perform in front of seventy thousand of his New Jersey neighbors, the place where he was born and raised, and the state where he was most revered. I knew it would be a special experience.

Thursday July 24 2003 8:31PM

The concert could be best described as "off the hook". The music, the crowd, and the energy in the stadium were incredible. In true Springsteen fashion, The Boss played for almost four hours, giving the crowd every penny's worth of their ticket price. He played all the classics and opened with his 9/11 tribute song, *The Rising*. It seemed like more than just a concert, it felt like an historical event. I repeatedly hugged, kissed, and thanked Kara for an incredibly satisfying and memorable birthday present.

Kara had driven her Range Rover to the concert and I had arrived via a car service from afternoon drinks with a client in Greenwich, CT. The plan was for Kara and me to spend the night at her home in New Jersey. She had arranged for the girls to spend the night with friends. I was excited, yet apprehensive about visiting Kara's home. I was relieved that the girls would not be there because I wasn't ready to meet them. I fully understood the significance of introducing a new companion to one's children. It was not something that I or Kara took lightly. I had always been cautious and brutally selective when introducing a girlfriend to my daughter.

As we pulled into the driveway I was impressed with the house, the landscaping, and the neighborhood. I was exhausted so I stumbled through Kara's brief tour of the downstairs. There were pictures of the girls plastered everywhere as well as a few of her deceased husband which I had expected and could appreciate. As we climbed into bed a weird uneasiness was circling my head. And although I was extremely tired, I slept poorly that night, constantly tossing and turning. I kept waking up with the recurring thought that I shouldn't be there. It felt dangerously like I was sleeping in another man's bed. I suffered a bad case of movie recall and kept replaying Patrick Swayze's character in *Ghost*, a character who had been mistakenly murdered during a petty street theft. I know it sounded utterly ridiculous, but I kept imagining that Kara's husband was disapprovingly watching me as I lay in his bed and caressed his widowed wife.

In the morning I showered in her husband's bathroom. They had his-and-her adjoining bathrooms attached to the master bedroom. As I fumbled through the drawers under the sink searching for some toothpaste, I saw an old Cantor Fitzgerald business card. There was a men's razor and some refill blades. There was an old issue of *GQ* sitting at the bottom of another drawer. The more things I saw, the more awkward I felt, like he was there and wondering why I was in his bathroom helping myself to his toothpaste. The short time spent in that bathroom was eerily uncomfortable.

Kara was going to drop me at the train station in the morning, but then decided to drive into Manhattan to run a few errands. I was thankful for the door-to-door service, but was still feeling strange from the previous night. I realized that my silly issues were going to be a barrier in our fledgling relationship. How was I going to tell Kara that I felt haunted by her husband? Hadn't she dealt with enough grief? I certainly didn't want to contribute to her misery. Not to mention, my paranoia seemed so trivial and far-fetched. How was I going to explain unresolved ghosts and scattered thoughts of the afterlife as reasons for my uneasiness?

In the end I thought it was wise not to tell Kara how uncomfortable I felt after spending a night in her bed. Sometimes honesty can be too painful. I couldn't decide if I was being a coward or a Good Samaritan for not being forthright. After she dropped me off in lower Manhattan that morning, the intimacy began to fade and a burgeoning friendship gradually replaced it. I angled for a friendship and scaled back on time spent with Kara, hoping not to reveal my neurosis with the paranormal.

Kara was one of the most courageous women I have ever met and her daughters bask in her glow. I wish I had a fraction of her mental fortitude. Kara eventually purchased a lovely home in Bridgehampton as a summer retreat for the girls. I occasionally see her in the Hamptons and we still remain friends.

10

Hitting a Double off the Mitchell Report

As an avid baseball fan and a former competitive college athlete, it sickens me to witness how much cheating occurs in the world of sports today. It truly is the epitome of the phrase "money will make you do things you really don't want to do". I guess that is the downside to a capitalist society. People will lie, cheat, steal, and even kill for financial gain. The pursuit of money spawns some curious and irrational motivations. Today the cheating is rampant in baseball, cycling, track, football and even tennis. I am referring, of course, to steroids and human growth hormone.

It has been well documented that professional athletes such as Lyle Alzado and Ken Caminiti died at absurdly young ages, partially, if not entirely, as a result of steroid abuse. Talk about selling your soul. Is it really worth it to be dead before you're forty to hit a few more home runs or record a few more quarterback sacks? MLB once had to deal with the controversial issue of placing an asterisk next to single season records when the league expanded the regular season by eight games in 1961. Now they need an asterisk to explain two decades of Herculean performances and obliterated records.

Former Senate Majority Leader George Mitchell (D-Maine) was hired by MLB to perform a thorough investigation and publicly present his findings on the topic that had been quietly and conveniently swept under the rug for so long. He issued his extensive report on December 13, 2007, and singled out eighty-nine former and current players where he found some credible evidence of using a performance-enhancing substance. Most baseball experts agreed the number was much higher, but Mitchell had limited authority and could only muster a few key witnesses to testify. If he were granted subpoena powers the list would have been undeniably more robust. The scandalous highlight of the report was that the legendary Roger Clemens, a proverbial lock to be a first ballot Hall of Fame inductee, had cheated. The greatest pitcher of the last half century was a fraud and it was a sad day in *Mudville.*

I was more focused on two lesser known names in the report. I found it a humorous coincidence that during my travels I had relationships with two ex-wives of players included on Mitchell's list. No other sport is as consumed by statistical analysis as baseball, so one afternoon when the stock market was quiet one of my former co-workers, Finny, decided to calculate the probabilities. He shared his silly computations and statistical data with a few of the guys on the trading desk who were also baseball fanatics.

"Who else in America can put up those kinds of numbers?" asked Finny

It was a dubious distinction that generated plenty of laughter on the trading floor.

"Let's round second base and leg out a triple," Finny barked out as he began scouring the list searching for other steroid users who had ex-wives that I could possibly date.

Thursday, October 2, 2003 5:55PM ⌚

I was weaving my way through the crowded sidewalks of Times Square on my way to a charity event at the Marriot Marquis. A couple Morgan Stanley co-workers had lost a dear friend in his mid-thirties to cancer. They started a charitable foundation in his memory and hosted an event every September. I no longer worked at Morgan, but still wanted to attend, support a worthy cause, bid on items, and catch up with old colleagues.

Actor Billy Baldwin was the unofficial master of ceremonies each year and I stumbled upon a unique opportunity to chat with him that evening. He had grown up in Massapequa on Long Island, a hotbed for outstanding high school lacrosse players including one of my former housemates and fraternity brothers, Jim Lazario. Jim enjoyed a terrific career at Cornell culminating in being elected team captain his senior year and playing in back-to-back NCAA national championship games.

Jim had some insane high school buddies who used to rent a Winnebago, cruise up to Cornell, park it on our fraternity lawn, and party like rock stars all weekend. My senior year of college one of Jim's hometown pals transferred to Cornell and lived with us in a six-bedroom house. We organized the ultimate spring-break trip. He and I along with six of the Massapequa crazies jetted off to Rio de Janeiro to stay on Ipanema Beach for a week. I still remember stirring mud as a mason's assistant for five weeks during December and January in single digit temperatures to earn the money for that trip. It was the bluest of blue collar jobs, but it was well worth the sacrifice—that trip may have been the best seven days of my life! We had tossed around the idea for the boondoggle on a dreadfully cold December night during finals week while watching a movie on HBO staring Michael Caine titled *Blame it on Rio.*

As I chatted with Billy Baldwin that evening he shared a funny story about actor Chaz Palmenteri and one of Jim's buddies, a NYMEX oil trader on the floor nicknamed Nemo. The conversation triggered me to share a Rio anecdote about Nemo with the group. We were all enjoying a chuckle at Nemo's expense when someone announced the silent auction bids would be closing in two minutes. I was intensely interested in one item so I excused myself and hustled over to the display table.

My co-worker, Sandra, who was also from Massapequa, joined me as I wrote in my final bid on the clipboard. She was curious as to which item could possibly override my frugality. Sandra was asking me a work-related question, and as I turned my head I had a cosmic experience with the *Twilight Zone* theme playing in my head. Sandra kept talking, but I couldn't hear her. She tried to get my attention, but I was in a hypnotic trance. My eyes were fixated on this familiar brunette who stood a mere twenty feet away. Our eyes met with laser-beam intensity and an undeniable lust. It was the epitome of the expression "getting eye-fucked".

The real wizardry was who she was. I recognized her instantly since I had just referenced the movie that made her a big star in the mid-80's. She was the female lead in *Blame it on Rio*. It was surreal; I couldn't believe I was staring right at her. I was tempted to discuss *The Fabulous Baker Boys* to anyone within earshot, hoping Michelle Pfeiffer would miraculously appear next.

We both zigzagged our way through the crowd so we could properly introduce ourselves. It had been almost eighteen years since the release of the movie but she still looked amazing! I soon discovered that she had come to the event with a woman named Chelsea. And Chelsea had been invited by my co-worker Sandra, who was still trying in vain to get my attention. We still laugh about how rude and unresponsive I behaved; it was wholeheartedly uncharacteristic, but I guess that's what makes it so humorous.

After running through the obligatory resume questions in an effort to get quickly acquainted, I asked Mikayla if I could take her out on a date.

"Absolutely. When?" she asked.

"Tomorrow night isn't soon enough, but probably the best I can do," I said.

We exchanged numbers and I walked away feeling like I was on cloud nine. I called Mikayla at noon the next day, a Friday.

"What are you in the mood for tonight?"

She wanted to see a Broadway musical, but something non-traditional. I told her I would have to think about it, but that I would come up with something. I grabbed the *New York Times* and scoured the entertainment pages to find the perfect solution, *Blue Man Group*. I called Mikayla and told her to meet me at an old hot spot on LaFayette Street called Indochine. She asked me what we were going to see. I told her it was a surprise, but I was highly confident that she would enjoy my selection.

She arrived at Indochine fashionably late as I had expected; actresses always love a grand entrance. With her stylish outfit, her glamorous make-up, and her five-foot ten frame, she achieved her goal—she looked absolutely stunning! I told her we were going to see *Blue Man Group* and she was euphoric since it had been on her list of things to see. We skipped next door to the theater and settled into our seats. The show was every bit as good as I had remembered from when I took my daughter to see it. The music was captivating and I always enjoyed the Jefferson Airplane classic, *White Rabbit*.

Mikayla was in New York for two months checking out real estate and contemplating a move from LA to Manhattan for a change of scenery. She had been staying at the Thompson Hotel in Soho, close to the theater on Lafayette Street. After the show ended, Mikayla locked our arms together and we leisurely walked down Broadway towards Soho. We were chatting, laughing, and sharing stories. She insisted we take a detour at McDonald's for some French fries.

Upon admitting her addiction to McDonald's fries, I shared a story documenting the origin of the French fry and how it was created accidentally by Napoleon's head chef. She was amazed at my plethora of useless knowledge and asked where I learned all this crap. I told her it was either two degrees from Cornell University, or late night *Trivial Pursuit* board game battles with my Dad, digging up obscure answers such as Mitch Ryder & the Detroit Wheels or Oscar Wilde to insanely haphazard questions. I confessed to an insatiable intellectual curiosity.

Mikayla told me about her divorce so I reciprocated by sharing my marriage failure with her. She had been married to a member of the Arizona Diamondbacks, the team that beat the dreaded New York Yankees in the 2001 World Series. As a lifelong Red Sox fan I explained to her how intensely I was cheering for Arizona; my two favorite baseball teams were the Red Sox and whoever was playing the Yankees. I did admit feeling remorse for the first time ever following a Yankees' loss because of the overwhelming effects of 9-11. A Yankee win would have been spiritually uplifting for a 376-year-old city in the wake of the most somber moment in its celebrated history. Even the most avid Red Sox fan would permit that indulgence.

I told Mikayla there was one player on the Arizona squad who I hoped was not her husband. She flashed a puzzled look and asked who. I professed that no man would want to date a woman formerly married to a guy nicknamed "The Big Unit". The implication would be intimidating for any guy who wasn't a porn star. We both laughed as she said that flamethrower Randy Johnson was a friend and that his wife was a doll.

We arrived back at the Thompson Hotel and proceeded to the second floor bar. Mikayla was unimpressed with the crowd and the loud music, so she suggested we go upstairs. Who was I to argue? The room was spacious, offering a bedroom, a living room, a balcony, and an oversized bathroom with a tub and separate shower. The bathtub had become a temporary holding bin for her laundry, filled to the brim with clothes.

It was getting late and I suggested it was time for me to go home. I didn't want to leave, but it was the gentlemanly thing to do. She backed me up against the door and twisted the door lock. I leaned out and gave her a prolonged, deliberate kiss.

"Call me first thing in the morning. I want to have breakfast on you."

She used the preposition "on", not "with". This could have meant she wanted me to pay for breakfast, "it's on me", but we both knew that was not what she inferred. It was a playful twist on words that conjured all sorts of sexual imagery.

I slept like a baby that night, but I had forgotten to turn off my cell phone. At 8:30AM my phone was ringing. It was Mikayla telling me she couldn't stop thinking about me and was having trouble sleeping. She asked me if I wanted to come join her for breakfast so I told her I would be there in about an hour.

I arrived around 10:30AM, a bit groggy from my unexpected wakeup call, and knocked on the door.

"It's open, come on in," she yelled.

There she stood with her hands on her hips, ten feet from the door, and wearing only a white terrycloth bathrobe. The robe was opened slightly at the waist, barely covering her bodacious breasts. I had to hesitate for a second and let her sensuous image soak in. When I came to my senses I covered those ten feet in a nanosecond like an Olympic sprinter bursting out of the blocks.

The next time I saw the light of day was about forty-eight hours later on Monday morning as I woozily drifted to my office at 40 Wall Street. The only time we left the room was on Saturday night to grab a quick bite at Ciprianis and to swing by a Soho loft party. Chelsea was at the party and was happy to see us together, but surprised it had happened so fast. Mikayla allowed me a ten-minute furlough on Sunday evening to grab some sandwiches at a nearby deli, but that was it. I was thrilled to act the role of sex slave for the weekend.

During one of my rest and recovery phases I was watching my beloved Red Sox mount a comeback in their playoff series with the Oakland A's. Having been married to a ball player for five years, Mikayla had seen enough baseball and was annoyed with my dedication as a member of Red Sox Nation. She just didn't understand how rabid eighty-five years of futility can make a fan. Not to mention the five grand I had bet back in April at seven to one odds on the Red Sox winning the World Series. Trot Nixon was the hero in winning Game Three and David Ortiz delivered the clutch hit late in Game Four, tying the series at two games apiece. What a weekend I was having!

At one point, to distract my attention away from the baseball game, Mikayla sauntered out of the bathroom in a naughty schoolgirl outfit. She was wearing the plaid skirt, the white blouse, and sporting the pig tails. I felt like Halloween had come a little early that October. Her ploy worked and I had no choice but to take a three inning break. How did a guy from Maine end up in a boutique hotel in Soho watching a pin-up starlet dance around in a sexy role-playing outfit? The best analogy I could think of was "Mr. LL Bean, please say hello to Mr. LL Cool J". Where was a video camera when I needed one?

As I departed the hotel on Monday morning heading downtown for work I felt sadness. Like most Americans, I began each work week looking forward to the freedom and the adventure of the coming weekend. My dilemma was how could next weekend possibly compare to the last forty-eight hours? Could I deliver a worthy encore performance? The weekend with Mikayla was certainly a tough act to follow.

Mikayla and I had a relaxing dinner the following Tuesday. For some reason we decided to divulge our shortcomings as a husband and as a wife. We also revealed why our former partners were far from perfect. It was cheap therapy to use each other as a sounding board. I complained about myopic stuff but her complaints were much more serious. She shared stories of mental and physical abuse often dictated by her ex-husband's performance on the field that day. She mentioned violent mood swings, which was a screaming red flag and begged the question.

"Was your husband on the juice?" I asked.

Mikayla's husband was a better than average third baseman. He was voted to the National League All-Star team five times and was the runner-up for the National League MVP in 1994. But baseball is a sport that can be cruel and unforgiving. One play at a critical moment can immortalize or discredit an entire career. I watched Carlton Fisk's fame and career skyrocket after his legendary Game Six home run in the 1975 World Series, and conversely, the devaluation of Bill Buckner's solid resume after an ill-timed error in Game Six of the 1986 World Series. Baseball is a game built on statistics. It is littered with excellent players who either failed only to achieve longevity or fell short of some superfluous benchmark and retired in relative obscurity.

Mikayla's husband had a chance at immortality, but it evaporated because of events entirely beyond his control. In 1994 he was on a torrid home-run pace that was in line with Roger Maris' 61 in 1961. He had clubbed 43 homers in 112 games and still had 50 games remaining to hit 19 more for the record. "I would rather be lucky than good" is an old Wall Street adage; Mikayla's husband was good, but not lucky. The players union went on strike and what remained of the 1994 season was canceled. It was a devastating blow for an above average third baseman on pace to become a baseball God.

Mikayla said that season haunted him like an angry ghost. Great artists and world class athletes often struggle to replicate a masterpiece or a storybook season. It simultaneously becomes a curse and an obsession. Imagine a great golfer shooting a 61 on a challenging course at a young age, playing that same course for the next forty years, and never shooting better than a respectable 67. It can be maddening. At some point Mikayla's husband decided he would cheat in hoping to reproduce the "lightning in a bottle" that magically graced his bat in 1994.

He joined a fraternity of frauds and shamefully ended up as a member of the Mitchell report.

It is so fitting that Jose Canseco has become the front man for this band of steroid junkies. Jose played for the Oakland A's, a team that originated in Philadelphia and was once owned by P.T. Barnum. The A's still wear a commemorative patch, an elephant holding a bat with his trunk while balancing on a beach ball, on the sleeve of their uniforms. Canseco has been anointed the ring leader of the circus that has transformed two decades of baseball into the Steroid Era. I'm sure P.T. is laughing in his grave at all the suckers who paid to watch Bonds, Clemens, McGwire, Sosa, and Alex Rodriguez.

The ramifications of steroids for Mikayla went far beyond cheating the game and the fans. Mikayla and her husband's young children were left to deal with the mood swings, the verbal abuse, the tirades, and the paranoia that often accompanies drug usage and substance abuse. And now those children must confront the shame and humiliation that there father bought and injected illegal drugs while cheating at a child's game.

Mikayla and I arranged another date a week later. She had been invited to a dinner party hosted by a high profile Manhattan nightclub owner. I was skeptical about attending as I could easily guess the composition of the crowd. I had concocted an image of washed up models, club promoters, VIP waitresses, and an assortment of other shady individuals—the vampires of Manhattan. I labeled them vampires because they worked at partying all night and slept all day, as if they were allergic to sunlight.

When we arrived my predilections were accurate so I asked Mikayla if we could make this a short visit. She quickly introduced me to a sexy brunette named Terri claiming that she was a close friend. I don't know why, but it is commonplace to claim someone as a close friend in New York, even if you have only known the person for about a week. I guess it creates a false sense of importance, a common theme with New Yorkers. I easily recognized that my introduction to Terri was to create a distraction.

At one point I ventured to the bathroom down the narrow hallway. The door was locked but thirty seconds later a guy and three girls came strolling out of the bathroom. It was an obvious cocaine rendezvous, and most likely arranged behind closed doors not to be discreet, but because the scruffy dude probably didn't want to share his stash.

The bathroom incident pushed me over edge. I immediately found Mikayla and told her I wanted to leave pronto. She looked stoned.

"Relax. Chill out. Enjoy the party," she said nonchalantly.

Having no patience for the all the happy horseshit that was happening, I told her I was leaving either with or without her. She looked at me as if to say, "You can't do that. Do you know who I am?" I knew exactly what she was thinking.

"Don't even think about trying to big-time me. I'm leaving. Watch it happen."

I went into one of the bedrooms and rifled through the heap of coats, found my leather jacket, thanked the host, and headed for the elevator. As I was waiting for the lift to arrive, Terri emerged into the hallway. At first she tried to persuade me into staying and then she told me she had a lot of respect for my decision to leave. I wasn't sure what that meant, but then she pulled me close and tried to kiss me. Mikayla's friend was trying to jam her tongue down my throat less than ten minutes after meeting me. How classy? It all seemed so desperate and pathetic.

I didn't speak with Mikayla for quite some time after that incident. She returned to her comfort zone in the Hollywood Hills and abandoned the idea of moving to New York. More than a year had passed when she randomly decided to call my cell phone at eight o'clock on Christmas morning. I was sound asleep at my parent's house in Maine, but my mother, who owned the exact same Motorola phone, mistakenly answered the call thinking it was her cell phone vibrating across the glass kitchen table.

Mikayla and my mother chatted for an hour. I came downstairs for our traditional family Christmas breakfast.

"Who is Mikayla?" asked my mother.

I had not heard her name in quite some time and was perplexed by my mother's question. She then explained what had happened and shared pieces of their extensive conversation. I called Mikayla back and invited her to Maine for Christmas weekend, knowing that she was just spontaneous enough to hop on a plane. I guess you could say we kissed and made up that Christmas day. We occasionally call each other to chat about life, love and relationships. She has become my Oprah, so I guess that makes me her Dr. Phil.

Sunday February 12, 2006 12:58PM

The title of this chapter is "hitting a double" for a reason. I lived on 60th Street near the corner of Park Avenue and my block was a shopper's paradise. I was only a hundred yards from Barney's or Bloomingdales and within three blocks of Donna Karan, Calvin Klein, Hermes, Dooney Burke, Magaschoni, Diesel, and Roberto Cavalli to name a few. These stores are like houses of worship to beautiful, wealthy women. Shopping is like an Olympic sport, and women approach it with the same intensity as a finely tuned athlete. It is only natural that they get hungry after exerting so much energy. One of their favorite spots to recharge their batteries was a tiny eatery called Le Bilboquet. I used to go there frequently for Saturday or Sunday brunch. It was a quaint spot with a seating capacity of about thirty and one of the best Cajun chicken dishes in the city.

I was enjoying some eggs benedict with my good friend

Carl, another divorced, successful guy trying to find emotional happiness in this crazy city. To my right was a table of four women with a mountain of shopping bags. All four ladies were good-looking, but one had caught my attention. Two were sporting some large hardware, but the one I found most interesting had a naked ring finger.

The women had just asked for their check and I was trying to figure out how to make a tactful approach. The nice-looking blond headed for the ladies room while her three friends huddled outside. I was sitting with my back facing the restrooms across the tiny dining area. I asked Carl about a full court press as she emerged from the bathroom. Carl peered over my shoulder.

"Too late, she's walking this way," he said.

The next thing I knew there was a tap on my shoulder and this gorgeous woman is telling me how much she admired my black velvet blazer. I complimented her on the snazzy cashmere sweater she was wearing. She introduced herself as Margaux and asked if I ever visited Florida. I told her my sister lived near West Palm Beach.

"Great. I live in Orlando. Next time you visit, give me a call," she said.

She joined her friends outside as they huddled on the sidewalk like a small platoon discussing their next target store. I turned back to Carl with her business card in my hand.

He shook his head in disgust while uttering, "The magnetism is unbelievable." We both laughed as I happily stared at her card.

I called Margaux later that week. The longer I spoke with her the more I wanted to see her. She seemed like such a sweet, sincere, and genuine person, a welcomed divergence from some of the tainted and disgruntled New York women I had been meeting. She was from San Francisco and had attended the University of Southern California. I confessed that as a child growing up in the 70's, USC was my favorite college football team. The Trojans dominated the decade, and inevitably, whoever earned the starting tailback job at USC was an automatic Heisman Trophy candidate.

I planned to visit my sister over President's Day weekend and we arranged to meet for dinner at a restaurant called Chez Carlos in West Palm Beach on Thursday. I couldn't believe she was going to drive two hours just to have dinner with me, but I certainly wasn't complaining. Chez Carlos was romantic as the piano player sang soft melodies to an empty dining room. Margaux and I hit it off fabulously. She had been a competitive skier, loved sports, and her ex-husband had been a major league baseball player.

I remembered her last name from her business card.

"Is your ex-husband Matt, Jack or Hal?" rolled off my tongue.

My brain was like an encyclopedia of useless baseball knowledge. When she answered I rattled off an extensive list of her ex-husband's baseball career. She was amazed, almost frightened, at my robust and accurate scouting report.

We shared stories about our kids and complained about our ex-partners. We had consumed quite a lot of wine at dinner and Margaux was a little tipsy. I suggested we leave my rent-a-car in the parking garage and I would drive her car back to my sister's house where she could spend the night in the extra guest bedroom.

I couldn't wait to see her again so I arranged to fly to Orlando two weeks later. Her mother was visiting which made things awkward, but she explained that I would have my own wing in the house. I was curious what my own wing meant; it sounded so stately. She picked me up at the airport and as we drove to her gated community called Isleworth, she explained to me the alibi for her mother. She fibbed about me being a friend from New York and just wanting a relaxing, sunny weekend away from the commotion of the city. I told Margaux there was no way her mother could be that naïve. I understood a mother's intuition and was sure that she would see right through this flimsy fabrication.

We arrived at the house and the kids were all in bed. I met Margaux's mom and then she led me up the back stairwell to my wing. It was quite a space: a workout room, full bathroom, and an oversized loft that sat above the three-car garage. The loft area had a bed, a wet bar, and a movie screen unit with an overhead projector. It was three times the size of a normal studio apartment in Manhattan. I was tempted to ask if I could move in; it was much more spacious than my three-grand-a-month digs back in Manhattan.

She told me she could fall asleep with me that night but had to sneak back to her bedroom before the kids woke up. I understood her reasoning and was more concerned about keeping up appearances for her mother's sake. I was convinced that she wasn't going to buy the "just friends" story.

The weekend was incredibly relaxing. I went jogging through the tree-lined streets of Margaux's lavish gated community. The neighbors included many PGA golfers such as Tiger Woods, John Daly, and Mark O'Meara. Other top athletes lived there as well such as Ken Griffey Jr. and Shaquille O'Neil most likely for tax reasons since Floridians enjoyed no state income tax.

Margaux had arranged for us to have dinner with some friends at the country club dining room that evening. When we returned home, Margaux and I escaped back to my wing where she decided she needed a relaxing shower. I loved "water sports" so how could I say no when she asked if I wanted to join her? According to the single-guy's handbook, water sports would be defined as any situation where you are in the presence of a naked woman and cascading water is in the vicinity.

The shower scene marked the conclusion of a marvelous weekend where I felt like I had been the "boy toy" stashed away in the attic. It was a role I was more than happy to play. Margaux was an exquisite, voluptuous woman who had a multitude of options. I was thankful she had chosen me. The weekend proved to be an opportunity to observe Margaux in a wide variety of roles: a mother, a daughter, a business woman, and a lover. And she played all those parts magnificently.

Thursday April 20, 2006 6:22PM ⌽

I was scheduled to return to Florida in three weeks for a reunion of sorts in Tampa. My closest friend and best man at my wedding, Jay D'Amato, and his wife Trish, had organized an impromptu "we're all turning 40" party. Jay and Trish invited all of Jay's best friends from high school and college along with wives, fiancés, and girlfriends. What better way to cope with the impending mid-life crisis than a bash celebrating the milestone. It was an opportunity for a bunch of middle-aged men to congregate and convince themselves that life begins at forty.

Nine couples participated in the festivities including me and Margaux. The weekend included a golf outing, a chartered sailboat ride around St. Petersburg harbor, a party bus, and two elaborate dinners. It was a great weekend as I got to reconnect with Jay's buddies from Boston College, many of whom I hadn't seen since his wedding. Margaux had a wonderful time meeting all the characters in this distinguished group.

On Monday morning Margaux called me in a panic. Her ex-husband had called and asked her what she was doing in Tampa all weekend. Who was watching the kids? Why was she acting so irresponsible? I told her he probably hired a private investigator. I was concerned about safety issues and asked Margaux if her ex-husband was unstable or suffered from paranoia. Given the profile she described and some of his behavior, I became more nervous. I never inquired about the possibility of her ex-husband taking steroids. Based on his meager home run totals, I was shocked when his name was revealed on the Mitchell Report, but there were some players who took these drugs to overcome injury and prolong their careers in battling the natural aging process.

As an avid baseball card collector it's comical to compare a rookie card of Bonds, McGwire, Giambi, or Sosa to their bloated physiques years later. They transformed from svelte young men into miniature versions of the Incredible Hulk. Even a casual observer could easily see what was happening in baseball. It wasn't a secret that offensive numbers were escalating almost as fast as their biceps. It finally took one guilty whistle blower to expose what we already knew. The irony is that the ESPN bobble heads and other experts berated Canseco as just a bitter ex-player who was fabricating stories to sell books. Although he accused dozens of taking steroids, there was not one single libel lawsuit. Maybe it's because every accusation turned out one-hundred percent accurate.

Margaux joined me a few months later for a long weekend in the Hamptons and then she came to New York for the Video Music Awards in late August. As usual we thoroughly enjoyed each other's company, but those would be our last two romantically involved weekends. I will never forget the sexy dress she wore to the VMA's and dancing with her that night at hotspot, Pink Elephant. It was low cut and formfitting, accentuating her outrageously curvaceous body. The dress remains vividly etched in my mind because of the Walk of Shame we performed on Friday morning. From my perspective, our little saunter was more like a Stride of Pride.

Margaux had spent the night entangled in my bed while performing some sexual acrobatics. Friday morning we attracted quite a bit of attention from the rush-hour crowd as we strolled down Park Avenue trying to hail a cab. Margaux was wrapped in this outrageous dress, her bodacious breasts barely concealed and wearing three-inch heels. I wish I had

had a camera to capture the drooling expressions on some of the men's faces. It was quite an eyeful for eight o'clock in the morning. One stunned passerby was so awestruck that I would bet he bypassed his cubicle at the office and headed straight for the bathroom stall to pleasure himself.

Margaux was indisputably the sexiest mother of three I have ever had the pleasure of knowing. Her husband is certifiably insane for ever leaving her and their precious children. Maybe the steroids made him do it!

11

Sunday August 29, 2004 2:42PM

I was cruising south on the Taconic Parkway after spending the weekend in the picturesque enclave of Saratoga, New York soaking up its Norman Rockwell charm. I am always excited to attend a big party, but it's even sweeter when attached to a major sporting event. The Travers Cup has always been considered the mythical fourth leg of the Triple Crown in horseracing. Saratoga Racetrack is nicknamed the Graveyard of the Favorites, a moniker earned from infamously poor showings by champion racehorses. Even the legendary Secretariat lost in the Travers Cup less than three months after his blistering thirty-one length victory in the 1973 Belmont Stakes, a performance forever etched in the minds of sports fans, and a win that earned him the coveted Triple Crown.

The Travers had been delightful, but my friend, Sandra, and I were feeling the effects of drinking all day at the track in the hot August sun and celebrating all night downtown. Riding shotgun, Sandra was pumping Diet Cokes into me almost intravenously. I was speeding, partially because my head was pounding from a hangover and partly because I was meeting a friend for dinner. One of my old Cornell teammates, a devout horse lover originally from Louisville, had flown from Kansas City to partake in the annual Saratoga bash. He had conveniently arranged business meetings in Manhattan on Monday. We had reservations on the patio at Dos Caminos, a Mexican joint located on West Broadway in the trendy Soho neighborhood.

I had to drop Sandra off in the West Village, find parking, and meet him at the restaurant. Somehow I managed to arrive early and he had yet to post. While sipping on another Diet Coke and waiting at the bar, I noticed a statuesque brunette to my right. She turned towards me and our eyes met.

"Hello," she blurted in a friendly and hearty voice.

Her enchanting smile and inviting demeanor were infectious. But there was a catch, and I recognized it immediately. My trained eye detected the hardware; she was a married woman.

"How are you doing?" she asked in her cute and unfamiliar accent.

"I'm in tremendous pain, but I have no one to blame but myself and Anheuser Busch," I shot back. Her puzzled face indicated that she had no idea what I meant.

"I'm hung over from drinking a lot of cheap beer from a can."

We both laughed and she pulled up a stool next to me.

"My name is Banu."

She was a twenty-eight-year-old Turkish woman from Istanbul who had attended the University of New Hampshire. It was definitely an unusual path, but there was nothing ordinary about Banu. She stood five foot eleven, exceptionally tall for a Turkish woman. She was strikingly attractive with olive skin and soft brown eyes. She seemed to have a magnetism that demanded a man's attention. We shared tiny pieces of our life stories as I waited for my friend to arrive. By the time Marcus made his entrance, I didn't want my conversation with Banu to end so I invited her to join us at our table. She was also waiting for a friend and was delighted to accept my invitation.

Marcus had invited another Louisville friend to tag along

so we enjoyed a shaded patio table for four. Marcus and Stuart were enamored with Banu's exotic Turkish features. As two married guys living in Kansas City and Louisville, they seldom had the opportunity to meet many Turks, and certainly none as glamorous as Banu.

Banu eventually asked, "Are you single?"

"Yeah, I'm available," I shot back.

"Excellent. I want to set you up with my friend, Jasmine."

She described Jasmine as a tall, attractive Indian model who had just moved to New York.

"And if you want to see what she looks like, take a cab ride through Times Square. She's plastered all over some silly Bank of America billboard."

It was an intriguing proposition and I felt compelled to accept this blind date, a practice I typically shunned. Curiously, I trusted Banu and my intuition told me I would be rewarded for that trust. It marked the beginning of a fruitful and platonic relationship.

As our appetizers arrived so did Banu's friend. Before she departed we exchanged cell phone numbers and she promised to call me Monday to arrange my date. Marcus and Steve looked at me with playful disgust as they shook their heads in unison.

"Can you believe that shit?" Marcus said to Stuart. "I mean seriously, we're five minutes late to dinner and now glamour boy negotiates a blind date with some billboard babe."

I just smirked and arrogantly uttered, "Happens all the time."

Stuart was confused. He didn't understand my lack of interest in Banu.

"What's wrong with Banu? She's hotter than a tic on a camel's ass!" raved Stuart.

"You're such a rookie. No appetizer for you as your punishment," I chastised Stuart while shaking my head in disappointment.

He still looked baffled so I belittled him further.

"Didn't you notice the hardware?"

Once again he was still clueless. I explained to Stuart that Banu was married and sporting a rather noticeable rock on her ring finger.

"No appetizer for me, thanks," Stuart told the waiter as he buried his head on his chest in shame.

The date with Banu's friend Jasmine went well, but there was a lack of chemistry so I walked her home and we decided to just be friends. Banu had not disappointed me. Jasmine was every bit as good-looking as she described, but sometimes the spark just isn't there. I called Banu to thank her for her valiant effort to play Cupid and asked if she had any other friends I could entertain. Like a successful salesman—Always Be Closing. She said she would give it some consideration, but invited me to a party later that week.

I arrived at the intimate gathering and found Banu sipping wine by the eight-foot windows of this luxurious and spacious Tribeca loft.

"Where's your husband?" I curiously asked.

"He's working late and might join us later," she responded in a nonchalant and uninterested tone.

It was clear that she could care less if her husband came or not. I was slightly disappointed because I had been looking forward to meeting him.

Banu and I rendez-voused six more times that fall for drinks at various restaurants and hotel bars, but I still hadn't met her mysterious husband. I was beginning to wonder if he truly existed and was confused by Banu's behavior. What married woman meandered around Manhattan until midnight, hanging out at hotel bars and random restaurants? I wasn't sure how to interpret it and chalked it up to her strong European, carefree attitude. She was a fiercely independent woman, which I found fascinating and desirable. I certainly wasn't complaining because I always enjoyed her company, and a selfish motive was budding. I was contemplating the idea of training Banu for the coveted role of being my wing woman.

A talented wing woman in Manhattan can be worth her weight in gold while trying to navigate the single scene. She can be asked to play multiple roles: scout, friend, recruiter, deflector, or the competition. Scouting involved pre-qualifying a potential target so as to avoid wasting time on someone who was ineligible. At times she may be required to play the role of friend by providing a glowing endorsement. Who is a woman more likely to trust?—some male stranger who tells her how wonderful he is or a fellow female who cunningly highlights your most positive qualities.

The wing woman can also effectively recruit other females for a party, a table at a club, or even a boat ride. Single women always feel more comfortable joining a gathering if they know in advance that a gorgeous, classy woman like Banu is attending. It offers validation. The wing woman can assume the role of deflector when you are approached or cornered by a female that you find completely annoying or uninteresting. She can even pretend to be your girlfriend, or fiancé in extreme circumstances to ward off an aggressive "cougar", a starving "puma", or some other wild animal.

Some women just love the challenge of competition. When they see a guy accompanied by a beautiful, statuesque woman, their competitive juices start to flow. Banu has ignited that burning desire on more than one occasion. And when that woman discovers that you have a purely platonic relationship with a woman as sexy as Banu, they are even more intrigued. It signals that you exhibit restraint and that you are not just a typical man-dog trying to dive into every girl's pants.

Often times a guy is interested in a girl, but is unsure of her relationship situation. Are the guys she is with just friends? Is one her boyfriend? Is she involved with someone else? Does she even like men? This is a valid question in Manhattan. The wing woman can get some or all of these questions answered before you invest the time to engage your target.

I had an Irish buddy in New York who had befriended and cultivated the ultimate wing woman. He rarely ever went out for a night on the town without her. She was a priceless asset who became his confidant and best friend. This woman was so valuable and precious to him that when he finally got married, he asked her to be his best man. How cool is that? She reciprocated years later and asked him to be her maid of honor. I witnessed her skills in action on a few occasions and she had truly mastered the art of being the wing woman. If there was a PhD program in this discipline she would have certainly been a candidate to be the Dean.

Banu was intrigued by my all-American, boy next door persona. She genuinely wanted to better understand American men; it was obvious that she had struggled with that pursuit. I thought that perhaps she was trying to crawl inside my head so she would better understand her husband. One of the reasons I wanted to meet him was to test my theory. All I needed was a brief conversation with her husband and I would be able to discern if I was right about Banu's motivation. I tried to explain to Banu that single men in Manhattan were a terrible benchmark for the average American male; New York was far from normal on so many different levels.

After the holidays passed Banu organized a surprise birthday party in January for her husband and invited me to join in the celebration. I was excited to finally meet Daniel. It was a nice gig hosted at a stylish bar on the Lower East Side. I chatted with Daniel and readily understood Banu's dilemma. She wasn't trying to sneak inside my head. She had become bored and uninspired by her husband. He was a handsome, intelligent guy, but not very dynamic or gregarious. He clearly could not compete with Banu's "*je ne sais quoi*" quality.

I prayed Banu wasn't growing romantically interested in

me because a married woman was emphatically off limits in my rulebook, no exceptions. With regard to infidelity, nothing is to be gained and all could be lost. There are mentally unstable husbands lurking out there who have spiraled into an uncontrollable rage, injuring or even fatally wounding their wives' lovers. Besides, there was a plethora of unattached, gorgeous women in Manhattan. Why waste time with a married one? I was still comfortable thinking that Banu was only interested in me for friendship.

For the next seven months I saw Banu usually three or four times each month. I eventually met her Mom, who lived in Manhattan, and I also met her Dad and her best friend, who both lived in Istanbul. Banu eventually met the most joyful part of my life, my adorable daughter. Our friendship grew stronger with each passing month. We began spending more time together and even haphazardly discovered we shared a close personal friend in Boston.

This chance encounter redefined a few degrees of separation. Banu and I were having dinner at one of my favorite Soho spots, Raouls, when in walked my old girlfriend, Stacey, from Boston. I hadn't seen Stacey in almost five years. Banu and I both looked up from the table and shouted, "Stacey" at precisely the same moment. We then turned to each other in amazement.

"How do you know Stacey?" we wondered aloud in perfect unison.

It turned out Banu and Stacey had hung out together when Banu was in her final year of college and spent her weekends entrenched in the Boston nightlife scene.

Friday July 1, 2005 6:06PM

I received a frantic call from Banu that I had been expecting for a few months. Her marriage with Daniel had been slipping; it wasn't a secret. But he blindsided her by serving her with a divorce motion at work just before the July 4th holiday weekend. She was filled with many emotions: sadness, anger, embarrassment, shock, and anxiety. I was the first person she thought to call. She knew I had been through a divorce, understood the process, and most importantly, empathized with the emotional havoc she was experiencing. I had become her closest friend over the past eleven months.

I promptly invited her to spend the weekend in the Hamptons. I knew it would relieve her mind of all the issues created by the divorce. She hesitated because she was in such a whirlwind, but then accepted and searched the internet for the Hampton Jitney bus schedule. I scooped her up at the East Hampton bus stop on Saturday afternoon and entertained her for the long weekend. She appreciated the distraction and certainly enjoyed all the attention she received from the men at Cain nightclub on Saturday night.

I even discreetly auditioned for the role of Banu's wingman. I never would have condoned such activity when she was married, but the divorce decree had changed the game. While in line waiting for the men's room I bumped into a guy that I had met earlier in the summer. He was popular with the ladies and appeared to have his shit together, so I requested a small favor, a pleasantry amongst gentlemen.

I briefly explained Banu's situation and asked this guy to swing by our table and show her some attention, some light flirtation, a little something to make her feel desirable. It worked like a charm. After he spent fifteen minutes chatting with Banu, he politely asked for her number. A permanent glow was plastered on her face for the remainder of the weekend. Sometimes a tiny confidence boost can perform wonders. This is what a good friend does and these are the duties that a professional wing person performs. Look around when you've been kicked to the curb and remember who is there to help you get back up. It's easy to be a good friend when all is well.

It didn't take Banu long to reassert herself on the dating scene. She was ten years younger than me and had only been married for three years so the transition was relatively seamless. She and I made a great team and I was thoroughly enjoying the role of playing wingman to a female. It was unfamiliar territory, but the concepts were identical.

Banu was humorous, but could be annoying at times. She was so maniacally picky when it came to men. It was hysterical to listen to her criticize some of the guys she met. One guy was too short, another too tall, too skinny, too unfashionable, too frugal, and too much of a meathead. One guy was discarded because of his cheap footwear. That's when I took Banu to the woodshed.

"Banu, you are becoming way too high maintenance," I told her.

"Are you serious? Am I really high maintenance?" she asked with an air of innocence.

A look of complete fear overtook her face as I chuckled at her genuine concern. Banu wasn't even entirely sure what it meant, but she knew it wasn't a positive attribute.

I told her it was okay, but that she needed to recognize who she was. There were plenty of chumps in Manhattan who sought a high-maintenance woman. I wasn't one of them, but there was a subset of metro-sexual men that couldn't wait for a female to walk all over them with uncompromising demands and outrageous requests.

I never understood what motivated these "tools" as we liked to call them. Do some men actually enjoy being treated like an inconvenient ATM machine? Yes, and there were plenty of them strolling Fifth Avenue, dining at top eateries, and just waiting for a sultry and seductive woman like Banu to blatantly take advantage of them. She dated a few and enjoyed being the cat in that game of cat and mouse, but always recognized that she wanted a real man, a guy with some backbone. Banu desired a man who wasn't going to always kowtow to her brazen demands and outrageous expectations.

Her circular arguments with herself concerning the men in her life were hysterical. She was always analyzing the positive and the negative features of each guy she met or dated. I told her she often sounded like she was reading *Consumers Report* before purchasing a kitchen appliance. I tried to reinforce to Banu that choosing someone to date on a serious level had to come from the heart. It couldn't be predicated on whoever owned the longest list of positive attributes doodled on a martini napkin. She accepted this truism, but still got occasionally seduced by the material sweepstakes that consumed so many Manhattan women on the prowl.

Wednesday December 21, 2005 7:12PM

I was leaving the next morning to drive up to Maine with one pit stop in Providence to drop off a close friend who was from Rhode Island. Banu called me that evening to invite me to a loft party on Mercer Street in Soho. I always enjoyed the randomness of those types of parties so I was thrilled by her invitation. She hedged herself by saying she didn't know how good the crowd would be, but that it was being hosted by a fashion designer who had a lot of rock-n-roll friends. It sounded eclectic, which was fine. Banu called as I was heading to the gig and complained that the crowd personified an 80's rock scene, and that we should meet downstairs to crash another party. I told her that was nonsense. I prided myself on being able to blend in anywhere and with anyone, so I insisted on coming upstairs for at least one drink.

The moment I arrived I was thrilled that I had deflected Banu's suggestion. In the kitchen I instantly spotted David Lee Roth, former lead singer of the rock group Van Halen. I had been a huge fan of their music in the early 80's, but there was a personal twist. I had a close connection to David Lee Roth and now my challenge was to create a scenario to effectively exploit it. I had a football teammate in college who was David's first cousin and I knew they were fairly close. Diamond Dave was in the kitchen laying his rap on a hot babe who was undoubtedly a model.

When Dave finished his conversation and was exiting the kitchen, I grabbed him by the arm.

"Hey, don't I know you?" I asked in an inquisitive tone.

He flashed a slightly disgusted look as if I were some psycho fan. There was an awkward pause by all those around us. New Yorkers pride themselves on never, ever being star-struck. Then I broke the strained silence.

"Correct me if I'm wrong, but aren't you Brandon Roth's cousin?"

Sheer joy overtook his face and he nodded his head in a telling sign of pleasant surprise.

"Why yes…yes I am. Dave Roth. Nice to meet you!"

He extended his hand for a hearty handshake. He anxiously wanted to know how the hell I knew his cousin, Brandon. We chatted for the next thirty minutes and our conversation was the highlight of Christmas dinner in Maine that year.

After I finished sharing comical anecdotes with Mr. Roth, Banu pulled me into the hallway with a bottle of Bacardi in her hand.

"Let's do a Christmas shot. C'mon. It's the holidays! Shot time!"

I had never witnessed Banu acting like a crazy college sophomore. It was cute to see the usually reserved Banu letting loose. I was never a big fan of the hard liquor shot so at first I resisted. She took a swig and then grabbed me, placed her mouth on mine, and let the alcohol pour into my mouth followed by her tongue for a kiss. We both took a step back and gazed at each other in a spooky, sort of eerie manner. I didn't feel right and we both knew it. It felt like I had just kissed my sister; it was beyond awkward. We fumbled for a conversation topic to squelch the weirdness before heading back inside and acting as if nothing had happened. We still laugh about that accidental incident.

I can't tell you how easy it is to meet gorgeous women when you are hanging out with a gorgeous woman. An eye-catching wing woman is an invaluable asset. And it works in the other direction as well. Banu guaranteed a level of credibility with the other women in the room. There was a sense of validation that emanated from our friendship. An outlandishly hot woman can smell intimidation dripping off the brow of an anxious guy, the same way a well-trained Doberman can smell fear. And when they smell it, you don't stand a chance. Banu always contributed to my confidence level. It was funny to watch a female approach me with tepid uneasiness, not knowing the nature of my relationship with Banu, but being just curious enough to inquire. The one danger with a wing woman as appealing as Banu was it could be intimidating to a prospective date. I had to subtly make it apparent that Banu and I were not together as a couple so not to discourage anyone.

Banu and I continue to prowl the war zone, also known as the singles scene in Manhattan, protecting each other's wing. We have been to the Hamptons, Miami, and numerous charity events together, always watching each other's back. We have introduced each other to many prospective partners. She has been a great friend and a good listener over the past five years. Hopefully I have returned the favor. I think we have honored the tradition of Maverick and Iceman from *Top Gun* proudly. We remain close friends and I still intend to exercise her open-ended offer to play the role of my wing woman in historic Istanbul.

12

Tailor Made for Sex

Saturday September 2, 1995 10:07AM

When I opened the front door she looked perfectly angelic, perched innocently on the stoop while the Pacific's waves crashed soothingly on the beach over her shoulder. It was one of those rare moments where I was so overwhelmed by a woman's natural beauty that I actually gasped for a breath. What a fucking rookie! I felt like a grown man who had just uncontrollably pissed his pants like a toddler on Santa Claus' lap.

"Is Len here?" she asked in a soft, demure voice.

My senses were so overloaded that my auditory skills had temporarily jammed. It was embarrassing, but all I could do was gawk in amazement.

"Is Len here?" she asked again.

I was dumbfounded by her question. What in the hell could this heavenly creature want with my devilish friend, Len?

She introduced herself as Taylor. She had just turned nineteen and was a statuesque 5'11" with soft green eyes and long silky blond hair that fell to the middle of her bronzed back. Her image was that of the quintessential California beach girl. I felt like I was witnessing a girl from a college dormitory poster brought to life. She was wearing roller blades which only accentuated her magnificently shaped, endless, sexy legs. She wore tight fitting shorts and a sports bra, exposing her toned and tanned tummy, and accentuating her perfectly heart-shaped ass. I was in a trance as I searched the apartment for my pal, Len.

Len stepped onto the veranda and had a quick conversation with Taylor before returning inside. He looked at me with a mischievous shit-eating grin.

"Y'all liked that didn't ya?" he teased me in his authentic Southern drawl.

I begged him to tell me they were just friends. He admitted it had begun that way when they met at the gym, but now they were sort of dating. He explained that she had been dating John Stamos, a popular television actor, when they first met. I inquisitively asked for some clarification on "sort of dating". He gave a vague and cavalier response that hinged on their busy travel schedules trying to downplay the relationship, but the smirk said it all. I was green with envy and baffled by their connection.

Len nonchalantly boasted that girls like Taylor were standing on every street corner in Los Angeles.

"No fucking way!" I exclaimed in protest to his crazy generalization.

Every guy has their own image of the perfect female specimen; Taylor matched mine. Even a catty and competitive woman would wave the white flag and acknowledge her insane beauty. I thought she was physically flawless. If Bo Derek was a *10*, then Taylor was an 11. I lived in Manhattan and I spotted stunning women every day, but none of them had ever made me forget how to breathe.

Len just chuckled in amusement at my aroused reaction. Maybe he wasn't lying—this was my first visit to Los Angeles. Maybe girls like Taylor did hang out on every street corner. I kept thinking to myself it just wasn't possible.

It became a breakthrough weekend for me in many ways. Over the previous few years most of my college buddies had journeyed west to visit Len, the self-proclaimed Mayor of Manhattan Beach, and the star of a kid's show called American Gladiators. That's right—my former Cornell teammate, who had graduated with a 3.3 GPA, who had earned his MBA from the prestigious UCLA Anderson School, and who had briefly been a Miami Dolphin, now donned red, white and blue tights looking like Captain America while wielding an oversized Q-tip, and trying to knock contestants off a small platform in a silly event called Joust. He had acted like a cartoon character all through college, and now he was getting paid handsomely for his cartoon-like behavior.

Len had been living on The Strand in Manhattan Beach for three years, but my ex-wife, having met Len on a few isolated occasions, told me if I ever traveled to visit him in LA that she would change the locks. Len was the only one of my friends whom she could not tolerate. She thought he was the quintessential male chauvinist pig. I had to concede that sometimes his actions were a tad reckless and offensive, but I always told her it was just an act by a good 'ole Kentucky boy. She never accepted my flimsy rationalization. Her opinion was solidified by the cadre of nicknames for his former lovers: Mud Ring, Jackpot, and my all-time favorite—a striking, olive-skinned Mexican gal he dubbed "Rebecca the Pecka Wrecka".

Len knew I was going through the final stages of a divorce so he had invited me for Labor Day weekend to ease my mind. He tossed in tickets to the Miami/UCLA home opener football game at the Rose Bowl, as if I needed any more enticement. If he had sent a picture of Taylor in a bathing suit before the flight, I might have driven to LA with all my belongings in a moving van.

One revelation from the weekend was a renewed appreciation for physical fitness. It was an epiphany of sorts, and Len's apartment was the perfect location. Just outside the front door there was a small porch. One step down and you were on a smooth cement walkway called The Strand. Across the fifteen foot wide walkway was sand and the beach. Another thirty yards and you were dipping your toe in the Pacific Ocean. It was a phenomenal setup, and once again, I was green with envy.

I sat on Len's porch each morning, injecting caffeine and carbohydrates to soak up the previous night's alcohol intake, and curiously watched svelte Californians whiz by me. They were young and old, skinny and muscular, athletic and uncoordinated. But they all shared one thing in common; they were obsessed with fitness. They all dressed in fashionable gear. There were bikers, rollerbladers, runners, speed-walkers, and shadow-boxers. There were grandmothers pushing their young grandchildren in strollers. There was an eighty-year-old man in a tank top and a headband speed walking with weights in each hand. I had never witnessed such a diverse and dedicated crowd of exercise enthusiasts.

By noon I was resting my third can of beer on my portly belly sitting shirtless on the veranda and watching all this physical activity. I glanced down at what had once been the sculpted body of a college athlete and I was disgusted by what I saw. Marriage had lulled me into complacency and turned my body soft. I felt embarrassed by all these exercise freaks who I am sure were laughing at me as they zipped by. Was there a city ordinance in Manhattan Beach that prohibited its citizenry from being unfit? The fitness lifestyle is deeply entrenched in the minds of southern Californians.

I vowed to join a gym back in Manhattan and get my sorry ass back into shape. I figured that since I was about to become officially single, I might as well attempt to reconstruct some of the muscular tone I once possessed. After that weekend I began religiously attending the gym four times per week. I began jogging, which I used to abhor, and now I experience withdrawal if a go more than three days without it. Exercise has become a mini-addiction and given the exorbitant cost of a decent gym in

Manhattan, if I don't hit the gym fifteen times per month, I am being fiscally irresponsible.

I tried to casually sneak in a few innocent questions about Taylor throughout the long weekend. Len would just laugh and brush off my inquiries. He could see right through my flagrant obsession. He remembered both of my two serious girlfriends in college and was acutely aware of my weakness for a blond who oozed sexiness. I thought Taylor was the most beautiful woman I had ever met and became exasperated with Len's carefree attitude towards her. It was a lesson in moderation. Even when a girl was exceptionally good-looking it was wise to act mildly unimpressed and to squelch your effervescent enthusiasm. It reminded me of my old college football coach, Maxie Baughan.

"When you score a touchdown and you're standing in the end zone, act like you've been there before," was one of his many pearls of wisdom.

I never imagined that some of his wise sayings would be applicable when it came to dating.

On Saturday night Taylor was meeting us out. We had amassed quite a motley crew in Len's living room. The line-up consisted of his three roommates, two dudes from next door, a stray sword who had wandered in from The Strand, and one obnoxious, unattractive girl. Len announced we were hitting the hottest new club on the Sunset strip as we headed for the cars in the alley. I told him he was nuts. Our crowd consisted of eight unfashionable dudes, a chick best described as a plain Jane with attitude, and it was Saturday night on a bustling Labor Day weekend. We weren't even stylishly dressed.

"We don't have a snowball's chance in hell of getting into some hot club," I told Len and even joked, "With this squad we'd be lucky to get a table next to the restroom at Applebee's."

We arrived at the club and the crowd was six bodies deep all around the infamous velvet rope. Len calmly told me to relax, assuring me that it was all arranged. I kept harping on what a complete waste of time it was for us to even attempt to gain admittance. I expected the doorman to laugh hysterically when he saw our wretched crew. And then out of thin air, a tall, golden-haired Goddess in high heels appeared in an outrageously sexy outfit. Taylor turned, faced the doorman, made a quirky hand gesture, and the crowd created a lane almost on cue. It was a re-enactment of Charlton Heston parting the Red Sea in *The Ten Commandments.* We strolled past the rope like celebrities, no cover charge and no wait. We had to be the most sorry-ass-looking-group of swords to ever crash that nightclub.

I did get a chance to chat with Taylor that night. I was shocked at how humble she was despite her devastatingly good looks. She had graduated near the top of her high-school class and was an accomplished volleyball player. And she had grown up in Redondo Beach, a few miles south of Manhattan Beach in a section of LA called South Bay. Len had mentioned that she was being considered for the *Sports Illustrated* Swimsuit edition, and if selected, it would catapult her fledgling modeling career. I was excited to have made her acquaintance. I envisioned myself snatching the *SI Swimsuit* issue in February from a Manhattan news stand.

"Oh yeah, I know that babe. Hung out with her for a weekend in Tinseltown," I would brag as I flipped through the scantily-clad pages.

Nine months prior I had been styling in my flannel LL Bean shirt, horned-rimmed glasses and khaki pants while spending my weekends pushing a stroller around a nondescript mall. To say that my weekend in LA was an eye-opening experience would be a massive understatement. I now knew why they called it The Land of Make Believe. I had met the Wizard and I was ready to "follow the yellow brick road".

Taylor left shortly after that weekend for an extended stay in Europe as her modeling career unsurprisingly flourished. Len started traveling to Orlando and other second-tier cities to perform Gladiator related appearances, so the two of them didn't see each other much after that fall. Unfortunately, she didn't make the cut for the SI edition. I think I was probably more disappointed than Taylor. Over the next seven years I would periodically inquire about Taylor's whereabouts.

"Whatever happened to that gorgeous blond babe?" I would ask Len.

Sometimes he would brush off my query with a blunt answer, but most of the time he had no idea where she was or what she was doing.

In 2003 Len emailed me a website link. Taylor had shot a twelve-page bathing suit layout in an Australian magazine called *Sport*. It looked like the Aussie's version of *Sports Illustrated*. She looked sexier than ever! In one of the pictures she was on her knees in shallow water, sporting a thong, and peering over her left shoulder while her thumb rested gently on her bottom lip. Her ass was complete perfection and the titillating pose was deliciously naughty! There was a link to her private website so I wrote her a brief note and attached a recent picture of myself hoping she might remember meeting me eight years ago.

She had a vague recollection of me, but said I looked different; she remembered me being a little heavier. I proudly told her I had been exercising religiously to shed some of my chubbiness. We began an email dialogue that lasted for about nine months and I was thrilled with my new pen pal. She had visited Australia in early 2003 on a scuba-diving trip to the Great Barrier Reef and fell in love with the country. She was living in Sydney, doing some modeling, and enjoying everything the city had to offer. By the spring of 2004 she returned to LA and we finally agreed on a weekend and a place that fit our busy schedules. We decided to rendezvous at the Delano Hotel in Miami over Labor Day weekend, exactly nine years from the day we first met in Manhattan Beach.

One of my fraternity brothers had graduated from the prestigious Hotel School at Cornell and was the General Manager of the Delano. I always tried to stay there; it is the premier property on South Beach, another success story chalked up by Ian Schrager, co-founder of the legendary Studio 54. After buying a decrepit, shit-hole hotel on the corner of Collins and 17th in the early 1990's, Schrager, the "King of Cool" as I like to call him, had a vision of what South Beach could become and was determined to return it to its former glory. He single-handedly initiated the sweeping revitalization of the SoBe neighborhood. After Delano's success, the developers and boutique hoteliers spread across Miami like a raging forest fire feasting on cheap credit and wealthy South Americans searching for second homes and condos.

Mike always hooked me up at Delano whenever I came to Miami. I called ahead and told him I was entertaining a special female guest that weekend so he upgraded me to Bungalow Five next to the sleek and sultry infinity pool. The eight poolside bungalows are top-shelf. They are outfitted with a living room, a wet bar, and a full entertainment center on the first floor. Up the spiral staircase is the bathroom, the master bedroom, and a furnished balcony area that overlooks the pool, the beach, and the ocean.

Taylor had made a few changes over nine years including her name. Her heritage was Slavic so her real last name was agonizingly difficult to pronounce or spell. Like many performers she had assumed a new name to benefit her modeling career. Would Tom Cruise be a big box office star if he remained Tom Nepother? Would Americans be foaming at the mouth to buy shirts and linens designed by Ralph Lifshitz instead of the stylish Ralph Lauren label?

Friday September 3, 2004 6:44PM

Taylor arrived at the Delano before me on Friday night.

She called to alert me there was a problem; there was only one king-sized bed in the bungalow. I told her not to worry and that housekeeping was bringing a roll-away bed for downstairs. I blamed the mix-up on the upgrade as I had originally booked a room with two beds in the main building. Although perturbed at the inference of one bed, my explanation seemed to alleviate her concerns.

Fifteen minutes later I pulled up to the Delano. The sight of the extra long white curtains gently blowing in the wind, the oversized porch furniture, and the manicured hedges always gave me the sensation of sexy chic. An aura of excitement overwhelmed me as I strolled past the cherry wood walls of the lobby, the pool table, the Rose Bar, onto the veranda, and down the stone steps to the pool.

I arrived at Bungalow Five, took a deep breath, and knocked on the door. The door slowly opened and there stood Taylor in a white terrycloth robe, her hair still damp from having just taken a bath. It had been nine years since that first introduction, but she still looked every bit as gorgeous as I had remembered. The robe was positioned to reveal the shadowy outline of her enticing breasts. We both smiled as if to acknowledge the awkwardness and the excitement of the moment. After a clumsy hug I headed upstairs to shower and shave before heading to dinner.

We had a superb meal at a place called The Pearl. While eating we tried to retrace the past nine years of our lives. My friend Rob was in Miami for the weekend so I invited him to join us at the Shore Club for an after-dinner cocktail. Rob arrived and was unabashedly overwhelmed by Taylor's striking appearance. He had always been appreciative of a beautiful woman and was never shy in expressing his opinion. Taylor excused herself to go to the ladies' room.

"Wow!" said Rob as he turned to face me.

Nothing additional needed to be said; wow accurately

summed it up.

I knew exactly what Rob meant. I experienced the same thing before we left for dinner. I was dressed and ready downstairs while Taylor was applying the finishing touches to her make-up. I told her I was going to visit the pool bar to grab a frosty beer and asked her to come gather me when she was ready. While I was enjoying my Amstel Light on a bar stool, two nice-looking women approached me. I was watching a college football game on the flat screen suspended from the canopy beam. The ladies became annoyed at my complete lack of interest in their blatant advances. They became more aggressive and determined as I stretched my neck to see the television over their shoulders. My reaction caused them more consternation as nothing pisses off an attractive woman more than a disinterested straight man. Their expressions screamed, "What's wrong with this guy? Why isn't he interested in us?" Taylor suddenly appeared placing her arm around my shoulder.

"Ready to go honey?" she asked.

I wish I had a camera to snap a shot of the stunned look on their shell-shocked faces. It was a rare moment that all men would enjoy. Those two women looked like they had been struck by a Taser gun and were electrified by Taylor's boundless beauty. They now grasped my complete lack of interest. I'm sure both of these women have ignored the advances of many eager men. I call it "getting Heisman-ed"—the act of getting shunned by a woman that pays homage to the iconic pose of the bronze statue awarded each year to college football's top player. It may sound arrogant, but I always feel like I am notching a rare victory for the men's team when I am able to act so cavalier towards a desirable woman. No one enjoys rejection and some women can be downright vicious in doling it out.

Taylor, Rob and I walked over to Washington Avenue where one of my local friends was promoting the opening of a new lounge. It was a small, dimly lit place with a decent crowd.

My friend Andrew had a table in the back. Rob found a new companion and quickly disappeared. Andrew was busy working the crowd and making sure everyone was enjoying themselves. Taylor and I found ourselves comfortably alone at a table tucked away near the back. And then it just happened. I leaned over with the trepidation of a nervous twelve-year-old boy preparing for his first kiss. It was a purposeful and passionate kiss. Our faces slowly separated as we both flashed smiles of comfort and satisfaction. To commemorate the moment I whispered in Taylor's ear.

"I've been waiting nine years for that kiss. But it was well worth the wait."

We returned to the Delano and sat on the balcony holding hands and enjoying the serenity of the moon, the pool, and the ocean. We eventually drifted into the bedroom where I gave Taylor a good-night kiss and retired to my cot downstairs. As I fell asleep that evening I felt that my life was about to embark on some major changes. Forty was a milestone visible on the horizon, but I felt completely rejuvenated!

On Sunday night we visited the Raleigh Hotel for the evening. They had a well-attended party every Sunday by the pool, complete with curtained cabanas, couch beds, and a big bonfire. We sat on a couch with big comfortable cushions feeling the warmth and the flickering light of the fire as we talked deep into the night. There were legions of Miami hipsters circling us, but they were like inanimate props as we were consumed by our conversation. I'm not sure how I wasn't distracted given the hullabaloo occurring all around us, but there was a subtle message in that observation. I was shocked how close I felt to Taylor after being a fleeting weekend acquaintance, then a stranger for seven years, and a cyber-buddy for about twelve months.

We returned to the Delano for our third and final night. I had to fly back to New York on Monday afternoon. Taylor planned to stay in Miami for at least a month as she had lined up some modeling gigs through her old agency, Michelle Pomier Modeling. We both felt some sadness that I was leaving, but I vowed to return the following Friday. For our final evening Taylor upgraded me from the downstairs cot to the king-sized bed and the sexy oversized mirrors of the master bedroom.

It was a night I will never forget and the kind you can never erase. I had never experienced a more intense sexual encounter. Taylor was the classic definition of insatiable, and I couldn't have been happier attempting to satisfy her appetite. It was a hot and humid September evening. At one point I was kneeling over her while holding her legs at the ankles in the chopper position and watching the small beads of sweat dripping slowly off my chin and collecting neatly in her belly button. It was enormously erotic as we resembled two wild and ravenous animals mating in a sauna. I have never been so aroused by the smell of sweat and the saltiness of its taste. Taylor experienced multiple orgasms, her body shaking intensely as her eyes rolled to the back of her head.

We assumed so many different positions: missionary, doggy style, the catcher, the reverse cowgirl, the reverse catcher, sixty-nine, and the pile driver. When she assumed the catcher position I was almost frightened by the intensity in her face. Her deep concentration reminded me of an Olympic power lifter about to attempt a world record. But seeing the rippling of her abdominal muscles and feeling her vaginal contractions redefined erotica. Her perfectly tanned body glistened with the moisture of her own perspiration from head to toe. My years of jogging four miles a day, 180 days a year, were all in preparation for that night, a marathon that I so willingly initiated. It was undeniably the most physically demanding sexual encounter of my life.

After about two hours of uninterrupted sexual aerobics and acrobatics, I finally keeled over like a redwood falling in the forest and laid face down on the bed. I was physically and literally drained, and still in complete shock from her stamina. As a well-conditioned athlete in my youth and now as a decade-long committed runner, I had never encountered a woman who could exceed my endurance. This twenty-eight-year-old sexpot was still shouting "its go time" after two intense hours. The fact that she still had gas in the tank was quite impressive, but also intimidating and terrifying. I had lost count of how many orgasms Taylor had moaned, shaken, and screamed through, but their intensity never waned. I was accustomed to dating younger women, but I could always outlast them between the sheets. I had finally met my match and was crying "uncle".

I was in a daze all week back in New York. All I could think about was the sexual highlight reel playing over and over in my head from Sunday night. I couldn't wait for Friday to arrive and the chance to see Taylor again. She had checked into a boutique hotel on Ocean Drive. When I arrived that night, the weather was the big story. South Florida was battening down the hatches for a hurricane spinning up from the Caribbean. It was raining hard when the cab dropped me off, which just gave us an automatic excuse not to leave the room. It was a repeat of Sunday night, but with a new twist. Taylor decided to share her unrelenting craving for sex toys.

It usually takes a lot to shock me, but that evening was an eye-opener. After ninety minutes of another intense encounter, I excused myself to the bathroom. I needed a quick shower to rinse off the pungent aroma of sex and sweat that permeated my pores. When I emerged from the bathroom I could not believe what I witnessed. Taylor had experienced so many orgasms that I had lost count. Now she was on the bed screaming in ecstasy while applying a vibrator to her clitoris. I realized that I was in big trouble; four-mile runs weren't going to be sufficient and the term insatiable had been redefined!

The weather outside was frightful as the hurricane hit the

Florida coastline just north of Fort Lauderdale, but the rain and wind drenched and pounded SoBe all weekend. Everything was closed and boarded up with the exception of News Café on Ocean Drive; it became our cafeteria for the weekend. Given the treacherous weather, what else could we do other than have sex? And the more sex we had, the more I learned about her body, which meant it just kept getting better. It was a vicious cycle of improving ecstasy; the more we did it, the better it got, and the more we wanted it. I was beginning to grasp the theory of how the Roman orgy contributed mightily to the fall of Rome.

Taylor and I could not get enough of each other both in and out of the bedroom. Most weekends I flew down to Miami. On the first weekend Taylor came to New York, one of the highlights was breaking my bed. I slept in a one-hundred-year-old family heirloom—a cherry wood, full-sized sleigh bed. The bottom of the bed had six one-by-four wooden slats that supported the box spring. In the heat of passion, Taylor and I managed to snap one in half. When it happened we stopped momentarily, laughed for a second, and quickly went back to work.

"There are still five left. Do you think we can break another one?"

"I'll be disappointed if we don't," she responded

During an October weekend visit we had an interesting experience. I flew to Fort Lauderdale on a Thursday afternoon so we could attend Miami University hosting Louisville in a marquee college football game. I wanted Taylor to meet my sister's family so I arranged dinner at their house before heading to the stadium. We arrived around 5:30PM and my brother-in-law fired up the grill for some steaks.

My nephew had just turned three, but he stole the spotlight that evening. He was obsessed with Taylor and it was hysterical. He followed Taylor around the house from room to room. He kept looking at her with a goofy smile as he giggled uncontrollably. He kept taking Taylor by the hand and trying to lead her into his bedroom. He kept crawling up on the couch and trying to sit in Taylor's lap while stroking her long golden hair. My sister begged him to stop and was apologizing repeatedly to Taylor for his uncharacteristic behavior. My brother-in-law and I laughed.

"I guess I don't have to worry about my son's sexual orientation," he joked.

I congratulated Taylor; it was obvious that her sex appeal even expanded to the three-year-old demographic.

We decided to spend Thanksgiving in Maine with my family. Taylor didn't want to fly six thousand miles roundtrip for the big meal. She had never visited the great state of Maine, "God's country" as I liked to call it. My parents loved to entertain guests so in typical fashion they rolled out the red carpet for her visit. We dined on fresh Maine lobster and some of the finest seafood on the East Coast. Mom cooked a lavish, five-course, traditional Turkey Day dinner that placed us all in a food coma. I took Taylor on a brief tour of historic Portland, chartered in 1632. We posed for pictures at Portland Head Light, allegedly the most photographed lighthouse in the world.

On Friday night my high-school class had organized its twentieth reunion. To celebrate the event I had invited my closest seven friends and their wives over for a pre-party. We were having such a good time that no one wanted to leave. I told Taylor I didn't have to go, but she insisted that I attend the reunion. I promised her it would be a brief cameo appearance. Then I gave her the option to join us, expecting her to say no thanks. Surprisingly, she said she would love to come.

I had to guide her expectations for the party. The party was scraped together on a shoe-string budget and wasn't going to be elaborate. Maine is a simple place full of hard working, down-to-earth people. LL Bean was a major employer and their clothing was considered fashion forward. It was a galaxy away from the glamorous world of vogue. Portland was not quite on par with Milan, New York, and Paris. It was great to see old classmates whom I hadn't seen in ten years. Of course there were a few old girlfriends in the crowd as well. One named Julie sought me out aggressively and I knew trouble was brewing.

Julie and I had experienced a forbidden romance and it was probably my most embarrassing high school memory. She was the best friend of my teenage sweetheart and I was just a horny sixteen-year-old kid who surrendered to temptation. The fling lasted a few weeks before we got caught. After dumping my sorry ass, my old girlfriend eventually took me back, but I never recovered from how guilty and ashamed I felt and her trust was never fully restored. I fucked up, and it certainly wouldn't be the last time!

When I first said hello to Julie, she couldn't tell me fast enough that she was going through a divorce. I promptly motioned for Taylor and introduced her as my girlfriend as a momentary look of disappointment spread across Julie's face. But she suddenly became infatuated with Taylor, pulling her aside and settling down at a table in the corner for a conversation. I kept peeking at Taylor, making sure she didn't need to be rescued from the inquisition. I could only imagine what Julie wanted to discuss.

"Most of her questions were about Milan," Taylor later shared with me.

"Then she asked a lot of questions about how and where we met," she added.

Sunday arrived and we packed for the five hour ride back to New York. Our first stop was a half-hour south of Portland to watch my daughter's AAU basketball game.

Halfway back to the city Taylor announced, "I'm fucking horny!"

I was not shocked. I asked how I could help with a steering wheel in my hand cruising west on I-90 at seventy miles per hour.

"Do you want me to find a place where we can go parking?" as if we were a couple of high-school kids. "We'll be back in New York in two hours baby."

"I can wait but there's no reason why you should have to..."

She unexpectedly leaned across the front seat, unbuckled my pants, and sent me into orbit.

I do not recommend this maneuver while in a moving vehicle, especially at a speed of seventy miles per hour in heavy traffic and in the darkness of night. But my half-hearted attempts to convince Taylor to stop were fruitless. We did manage to get a round of horn whistles from a guy in an eighteen wheeler. The shadowy image from the dashboard lights enabled him to figure out what was happening. I kept thinking about a famous scene from *The World According to Garp*, which made it painfully difficult to concentrate. If you've seen the movie, you know exactly what I am talking about.

We arrived at my midtown apartment and Taylor was like a wild animal in heat. Celibacy wasn't part of the weekend, but given the proximity of my parents' room to the guest bedroom, it wasn't our usual floor-shaking, door-rattling, reckless-abandon type sessions. And now I was going to pay for the shortfall. She had the eye of the tiger that night, her jaw wide open and looking to extract a few pounds of flesh.

New Year's Eve was going to be our final weekend in Miami as Taylor's modeling assignments were complete. She was relocating to her four-bedroom house in Redondo Beach, a place she had barely visited for the past eighteen months. We had a fantastic New Year's Eve in Miami, hanging out and partying with Jamie Foxx and director Michael Mann at the Delano. They were in town preparing to shoot *Miami Vice*. I finagled the role of an extra in two scenes. After New Year's we headed to Key West for a few days of rest and relaxation. I had never visited Hemingway's house or Duval Street, the place of worship for all of Jimmy Buffet's cult-like Parrot Heads.

Taylor and I had been together for four months and "the honeymoon effect" was starting to fade. There was one thing about Taylor that I loved and feared—her ferocious sexual appetite. Taylor used to have her own personal competition as to how many times she could get me to climax in a twenty-four hour period. I peered ten years into the future and worried about how I was going to satisfy her. Would I have to start running marathons, or could the miracle of Viagra be my solution? Was this just another example of my creative rationalizing? It was such a silly excuse. Seriously, what jackass contemplates dumping a bathing-suit model because he's worried how horny she might be ten years from now?

I spent a lot of time visiting Taylor in California during January and February. She owned a meticulously landscaped home complete with an enclosure in the back yard for her pet Peking duck, Petey. The master bedroom was gigantic with a walk in closet the size of a New York City studio apartment. There were two double-decker rows of clothing on each side, everything from thong bathing suits to expensive fur coats. There were piles of shoes and sexy boots as well as a mountain of purses from top designers.

I know women are obsessed with clothing and accessories, but this was unlike anything I had ever witnessed. Her closet had three hundred square feet of space with ten foot ceilings, slightly bigger than my old studio apartment on East 78th Street. She also had a Magnum-357 and an AK-47 in the closet. I didn't even ask for an explanation on those two unique items; I was much too fearful of what the answer might be.

The frustration of being separated by 3000 miles was starting to take its toll on our relationship. We traveled to her parents' condo in Laguna Beach for Valentines Day. During an evening of pillow talk it become abundantly clear that Taylor was never going to sever her connection to the West Coast, and because of my daughter, I had no intention of leaving the East

Coast anytime soon. I already felt guilty enough about being three hundred miles away from her, so three thousand miles was not even a consideration.

I also devised a new rule for the dating etiquette handbook while dating Taylor. Through my experiences I had determined a six month rule should be in effect for any woman who was over thirty. It was an unselfish rule designed to protect the women in my ongoing saga of honeymoon romances and crashing failures. The self-imposed regulation stated that when dating a woman who was thirty or older, I had a six month timeframe to determine whether the relationship had any chance of progressing to a more serious level. If it was unclear, I owed it to the woman not to waste her time.

A thirty-year old woman who wants to get married and have kids doesn't have the luxury of spending a few years in a dead end relationship. Let's assume a thirty-year-old woman meets a desirable partner. If it takes a year for the courtship to play out, a year to plan and execute a decent wedding, and a year to get pregnant, that woman is almost thirty-four before she is married with child. Women do have a biological clock and men have to be sensitive to the sound of it ticking.

Sunday February 27, 2005 7:50AM

Taylor and I flew to the Dominican Republic on a whim hoping to reinvigorate our passion. As I reflected upon the six months since we first reunited on Labor Day weekend, I remembered how fantastic everything had been during the first two months. It dawned on me that I had fallen prey to a new, unfamiliar addiction. I was a certifiable "honeymoon junkie", constantly searching for the newness and lusting for the high of personal exploration and discovery with each woman I fancied. Like a married couple on their honeymoon, the first two weeks of becoming acquainted and enjoying intimacy in a dreamy, tropical destination were always Nirvana-like, followed by a painfully slow period of unintentional withdrawal.

"The honeymoon is over" is a common cliché to indicate things are getting tougher. It seemed that I was extending the honeymoons without getting emotionally attached. I began to question my own shortcomings. When and how would my addiction end?

Taylor and I had such a strong bond at the outset; our honeymoon high was powerful and unwavering. At first we sunbathed on the sands of South Beach like newlyweds and convinced ourselves that we were living the fairytale. It seemed peculiar that we were fading because of geographic incompatibility.

Sadly, by the ides of March the relationship was over, but we maintain a strong friendship. Taylor has visited me for extended stays in New York on three occasions since we split. I still thoroughly enjoy her company, her perspective, and her low-maintenance attitude. She gives me great hope. I find her so refreshing compared to the obnoxious shenanigans I often experience when dealing with some of the overly pampered, game-playing, manipulative women cruising the pot-holed streets of Manhattan.

13

Kiwi Surprise

Tuesday December 31, 2005 10:44PM

I was partying like a rock star at the Delano in Miami. The private party featured some interesting musical acts including Ludicris, Snoop Dogg, Jamie Foxx, and Billy Joel. The bash raged on as we headed toward the midnight countdown to ring in 2006. Just after midnight I received a text message from my good friend, Tess. She was trying to find me at the Delano and we finally rendezvoused by the pool table in the lobby. She was accompanied by her close friends, Carolyn and Andrew. Tess was excited to see me as I had not been in Miami since the previous March. After we said our hellos and got reacquainted, Tess received a text message from one of her girlfriends raving about how good the party was over at Setai. She bragged about sitting at a table next to Leo DiCaprio and Vin Diesel, so the four of us headed north on Collins Avenue.

Setai was a new high-end beachfront property only three blocks from the Delano. It was a multi-use facility with condominiums, a hotel, a restaurant, and a night club. When we arrived we were greeted at the door by Tess's girlfriend and whisked away to a side entrance to avoid the mob scene and the paparazzi surrounding the main door.

I didn't recognize any of Tess's friends, and quite frankly, wasn't interested in meeting them. They looked like a mindless pack of Miami hipsters who spent all of their time hanging out in trendy clubs waiting for I-don't-know-what to happen. There was always a dangerously seedy element lurking in the shadows at any Miami nightclub. The drug culture was rampant and the value placed on education and career seemed limited. I would not label Miami as America's most industrious city.

I grabbed a drink and decided to take an obligatory lap around the party and convinced Carolyn and Tess to join me. I took about five steps before randomly bumping into one of my fraternity brothers. We both looked at each other in a puzzled manner.

"What the hell are you doing here?" I yelled.

Jim was married and had two lovely daughters back in Connecticut. He was with one of his former Cornell lacrosse teammates so I assumed that his wife and kids hadn't made the trip.

"The family is in Italy visiting with my wife's parents," he roared over the music.

We shuffled another ten feet and Tess bumped into two girls that she knew. She introduced me and I became immediately interested in Rachael. She was soft spoken, but I detected an accent. It was miraculous that I could hear anything; the music was loud enough to make my ears bleed. My two biggest issues with night clubs were dark lighting and excruciatingly loud music. It was never conducive to meeting people.

Rachael told me she was originally from New Zealand. After I shared the sheep joke which every New Zealander has heard a hundred times, I reminisced about a crazy business school classmate who was from Auckland. I quipped that every male I had ever met from New Zealand was an exact replica of my classmate, exhibiting a devout passion for two things: rugby and beer. She pretended to laugh as we struggled to hold a conversation above the ridiculous decibel level, so we exchanged cell numbers and I promised to call her. Based on her facial expression, she appeared receptive to the idea.

The next afternoon I called Rachael from my comfortable spot planted on a deck chair next to Spike Lee and Jay Z, while the tempting Delano pool lay at my feet. I invited Rachael to come join me and soak up some rays. She arrived an hour later and we sipped some tropical drinks at the pool bar before returning to the lounge chairs for some sunbathing. She looked fabulous in her bathing suit, sporting a nicely toned body achieved through years of ballet training. She had soft porcelain skin and thick light brown hair. She was tall so I figured she must have done some modeling, but I asked anyway. Girls are always flattered by that question whether they admit it or not.

She grinned and said, "In my twenties I focused on acting, but I did a few modeling gigs to pay the bills."

She was embarrassed to admit landing on a few billboards, and about touting beer while wearing a dental floss bikini when she lived in Sydney. She had television ads and a soap opera stint amongst her acting credits. We recapped our life stories including places we had lived. I claimed Chicago, Boston and Washington, DC, but her list was much worldlier. Rachael's roll call included Sydney, Tokyo, Dubai, London, and Milan.

As she progressed through her timeline, I detected a two year gap that was unaccounted for in her late twenties. She brushed over it and seemed agitated, so I could sense it was something she didn't want to discuss. She asked a lot of poignant questions about decisions I had made in my life and was keenly interested in my daughter. Displaying a genuine interest in my child was always an easy way for a woman to endear herself to me. Rachael was an intellectual conversationalist, a fascinating world traveler, and I thoroughly enjoyed our lengthy afternoon chat.

The good news was that Rachael currently lived in the Murray Hill section of Manhattan. I was scheduled to depart Miami the next day, but I was being heavily pressured by some new Penn State friends to stay an extra night. Johnny and Bobby wanted me to attend the Orange Bowl and watch Joe Paterno's Penn State team square off against Bobby Bowden's Florida State squad. These were the two winningest coaches in the history of college football, so the game had historical appeal. I asked Rachael if we could meet for lunch if I stayed an extra night. She readily accepted and although I love college football, I was more excited to spend time with her.

Deciding to stay the extra night proved to be a prudent decision. The Orange Bowl was decided in triple overtime and ended with Penn State victorious. On the ride back to South Beach one of the guys said he was from Pittsburgh.

"I know one guy in Pitt, an old baseball coach. He's the older brother of a guy who was in my wedding and GM of the Pirates…"

"You know Dave?" he excitedly blurted. "I play hoops with him on Sundays."

It was another surreal example of six degrees of separation. But the best part of staying was having lunch with Rachael. We met at News Café on Ocean Drive and then went for an afternoon stroll on the beach. We covered many topics including the unexplained gap in her life's story from the conversation at the pool. I guess Rachael trusted me enough to share her nightmare.

She was home in New Zealand on holiday from Tokyo and was car-jacked while idling at a traffic light. Rachael was kidnapped at gunpoint, raped, and beaten within an inch of her life by the perpetrator who then left her for dead in a remote wooded area. After the ordeal she required reconstructive surgery and cosmetic procedures to repair the horrific damage inflicted by this vicious madman. She then had to attend the trial and testify for the prosecution, which fortunately ended in a conviction.

It was the darkest chapter in her life and I could feel every ounce of her emotional pain as she retold the story. I was shocked by her terrifying ordeal, and surprised that she felt comfortable enough to share it with me. It was one of those rare moments where I felt like I could penetrate someone's eyes and see their soul. And what I saw was a sweet and compassionate woman who held no bitterness or vengeance in her heart.

I had never felt so intimate with a woman whom I'd never even touched or kissed. Our blossoming friendship was moving at mach three. A lot of people have dark secrets buried deep in their souls because they are much too painful for public consumption. Rachael had mysteriously placed enormous trust in me after seventy-two hours. I think she found me to be genuine and trustworthy, but there was a second part of the equation that probably weighed more on her decision.

My instincts told me that it had been awhile since she had shared her pain with anyone. I think she assumed I would have a deeper level of sensitivity since I was the father of a teenage daughter. She was right. I firmly believe that no man with a daughter could ever comprehend or commit such a heinous crime. I understood her vulnerability and I cherished her trust. I reciprocated by sharing some of my dirty laundry with her, but it was not nearly the magnitude of her nightmare. She appreciated the gesture.

It was late afternoon and I had to get back to the Delano to get ready for the big game. I walked Rachael back to her hotel and gave her a kiss on the cheek.

"Can we go on a real date back in New York?" I asked.

"That would be quite nice," she answered in her sexy Kiwi accent.

I held both her hands and told her that I was glad I had gone to Setai and had the privilege of meeting her.

She smiled happily, "I look forward to our time in New York."

I returned to the Big Apple exhausted from the five days of

drinking and partying. South Beach can be unbelievably entertaining, but the fun can be exhausting. I had no time to rest and jumped back on a plane bound for Maine to watch my daughter play in a high school basketball game. Over the weekend I spoke with Rachael a couple of times and we planned dinner for Wednesday. I made reservations at a new Chinese restaurant called *Philippe*, which was conveniently located twenty yards from my front door. This stylish spot was managed by the son of the founder of the legendary *Mr. Chow* on East 57th.

Wednesday arrived and we enjoyed a delicious dinner. We shared every scrumptious dish, feeding each other playfully. If you were a stranger seated at the table next to us you would have thought we had been dating for years. We frolicked at our table and exchanged stories from our past including some less than memorable first dates.

I shared a great yarn about a gal my parents set me up with shortly after my divorce. My folks had taken a second honeymoon to Hawaii and flew first class on the outbound segment. My father befriended a flight attendant during the six-hour haul from Logan to LAX. Mom proudly flashed some pictures of me and this young lady was impressed. My mother jotted down her contact information and arranged a date. She was Memphis-based, but worked some routes to JFK on American Airlines each month.

It was a rainy Friday in the spring of 1996 when I met the stewardess at the exact same restaurant where Rachael and I were sitting. Back then it was ironically called *Match*. The dinner with this gal from Tennessee wasn't going well; there was no chemistry. Midway through what was becoming an agonizing meal we began talking about exercise, gym amenities, and training routines. She bragged about how strong she was given her diminutive size. I nodded my head in agreement, but apparently I didn't look convinced.

In the middle of dinner in a crowded Midtown restaurant

on a Friday night, this girl rose from her seat, and used the booth bench to perform dips, an exercise designed to work the triceps muscles. As I glanced around the room I begged her to stop and repeated that I believed her. She ignored me and dropped to the floor to perform a set of pushups. At this point I was begging for the check as I practically crawled underneath the table. Half the patrons were looking curiously in our direction and wondering what the hell was going on?

Like a gentleman I walked her back to her hotel, said goodbye, and sprinted down the block frantically searching for a cab. Rachael was laughing hysterically as I pointed across the room to the table that had hosted the scene.

After dessert Rachael asked if I had any pictures of my daughter with me. I told her I had at least a dozen proudly on display in my apartment.

"Let's go! You live close, right?" Rachael eagerly responded.

Given how close my front door was I tried not to laugh. Rachael loved my apartment and commended my decorating taste, and then lavishly complimented my daughter's pictures.

"She is so beautiful. You are so lucky," said Rachael while picking up a walnut frame with one of my favorite pictures of my daughter and me at Fenway Park.

"Believe me, I'm well aware. She's a great kid, a parent's dream. She does well in school, is a good athlete, has great friends, and stays out of trouble."

I unselfishly bestowed much of the credit upon my ex-wife.

Rachael settled onto my couch and I offered her a drink. I poured each of us a glass of wine and joined her on the couch. She giggled and apologized, but could not stop thinking about the image of some random girl doing pushups in the middle of a crowded restaurant. I could laugh now, but it certainly wasn't comical at the time. We both set our wine glasses on the coffee table and awkwardly stared at each other. We were both thinking the same thing. Where did we want this to go?

We simultaneously leaned towards the center of the couch and embraced for a nice leisurely kiss. We both knew that this would change everything. Although our friendship was not in jeopardy, physical interaction always increases the complexity of the relationship. We were crossing that boundary and quickly heading towards intimacy. Temptation prevailed as I scooped her up off the couch like Prince Charming, carrying the Kiwi princess over the threshold to my bedroom. It was the beginning of a magical evening and the next morning we both awoke with a calming smile.

Over the next few weeks we enjoyed more time together. I traveled to Maine every weekend that January to watch my daughter excel on her varsity basketball team. On the last weekend of the month I flew to Maine on Friday afternoon to watch two games and planned to drive back to Manhattan on Saturday night. Rachael badly wanted to see me since we had yet to spend a weekend night together. But she understood my need to watch my little girl kick ass on the basketball court.

After the game ended I hopped on the highway and headed south. As I reached the Merritt Parkway Rachael called.

"It's snowing pretty hard in the city," Rachael warned me.

"I'm about ninety minutes away," I told her.

"Meet me at a bar on 73rd and 1st. I'm here with some friends."

It was a place I had once known as Yorktown Brewery, the venue for my first ever date in Manhattan, but had been renamed Session 73.

I arrived on the Upper East Side at 1:00AM and found a parking spot on 73rd Street. Rachael was in the back pounding shots. She had spent the early part of the evening bar hopping with three girlfriends and was a little tipsy. By the time we left at 3:00AM nine inches were on the ground and the streets had become treacherous.

Given the weather and the time, a cab wasn't even an option. I loaded Rachael and one of her friends into the rental car and became their late night chauffeur. After dropping off her girlfriend we drove to Rachael's place on 30th Street. She asked me to spend the night so I parked and we headed inside. The thing I remember most about that evening was the oversized full length mirror on the wall adjacent to the bed.

The next morning I awoke and stared at the sliding glass door that led out to a small balcony. A pile of snow was pushed up against the slider which I assumed was just a snow drift. When I peeked outside I couldn't believe what I saw. It had snowed all night and there was three feet on the ground. Parked cars were barely visible.

It was going to be a lazy snowbound Sunday so we decided to spend it lounging in bed. The only thing I had to do all day was return the car by 5:00PM. Rachael and I were also attending a concert that evening at Lincoln Center. We were both fans of the rock band INXS. Their lead singer had died in a bizarre accident which was labeled a suicide, but the rumor was that he had asphyxiated himself while performing a deviant sexual act.

The band had decided to partake in the reality television revolution by staging a contest to find a new lead singer. Once the victor was announced the band embarked on a world tour to promote their new front man. Rachael had scored some choice seats to the performance that evening. We ordered food and lazed in bed all day, watching television and ravaging each other repeatedly.

That evening we decided to walk through Central Park en route to Lincoln Center. The park was so picturesque with all the fresh snow dangling from the tree branches; a slow-moving horse drawn carriage created a soothing and romantic backdrop, reminiscent of simpler times in a bygone era. The streets were empty as the city was still in lock-down mode from the paralyzing snowfall.

We reached the venue and to our collective dismay the

concert had been canceled. INXS never arrived in New York because of airport closures. Although disappointed we hailed a cab back to my apartment where we climbed into bed and snuggled tightly to share each other's warmth.

"I have something very important to tell you," said Rachael as she pulled away.

Her voice and her body language carried an alarming urgency that frightened me.

She began her heartfelt confession with a stark sadness in her eyes.

"I've wanted to tell you this for quite awhile, I'm just not sure you're going to be able to handle it."

I paused and thought about what it could possibly be for a moment.

"Just don't tell that you're married or that you're dying. Anything else I can handle," was my response as she laughed a sigh of relief.

I couldn't imagine what was going to come next, but I could tell from her tone it was going to be something earth-shattering. She flashed back to her haunting past and talked about her situation after the painful ordeal in New Zealand. She returned to Tokyo in dire straights. The medical bills that had accumulated were astronomical and her insurance coverage was capped. She was on the hook for a large sum and her forty-five-thousand-dollar-a-year job was not going to be sufficient to cover her mountain of debt. Her best option was to become a burlesque dancer at night and on weekends or face bankruptcy. I was relieved.

"That's no big deal. I have a college friend who married a French burlesque dancer. It's no different than lying topless at the beach."

"Wait, there's more," she added.

She told me that once she had conquered the awkwardness of exposing her breasts to a room full of strangers, she took things to another level. I knew what she meant, but I had to hear it to be sure. She explained that the money from the burlesque show was a nice supplement to her salary, but she needed more cash.

Then she dropped an atomic bomb in my lap. Rachael had wandered into the world of high-end call girls. I wasn't sure what to think or how to react. I understood her motivation but I was strangely intrigued by her confession. I wasn't sure how to pursue my curiosity about her experiences while remaining sensitive to her difficult decision.

I had never experienced a money-for-sex encounter, not even a "happy ending" at a massage parlor. I was probably the only thirty-nine-year-old on Wall Street who could make that claim. But I always thought that paying for sex was similar to admitting "game over". If a man didn't have the ability to find a willing partner in New York, which is loaded with horny single women, then that guy should hang up his spikes.

My naivety piqued my interest in this undercover world of sex for money. And in Manhattan it wasn't exactly undercover. I knew where to go if I ever decided to take the plunge. I was plugged in to the massage parlors, the strip clubs, and the websites where you could get anything and everything for a price. All of Wall Street was familiar with these shady hideaways.

Spending the money on any of those options was like cheating. Males have an evolutionary instinct to hunt, not only for food, but for a mate. Paying for sex is to completely abandon the chase, no different than fishing in a barrel with dynamite. Where is the challenge in that? Not only is soliciting sex illegal, and many would argue morally reprehensible, but in my opinion it is an admission of failure.

We spend so much of our lives trying to gain the affection of the opposite sex. Think about all the things we are conditioned to do from an early age; they are all related to finding a mate. The cars, the clothing, and the cosmetics we ferociously consume are three easy examples of industries that are driven more by sex and imagery than by functionality. We are bombarded by sexual advertising as it penetrates our daily lives on television, radio, billboards, buses, and even elevators. Americans are obsessed with personal image, and Madison Avenue is happy to exploit our narcissistic obsession. Volumes have been written about the motto "sex sells", Madison Avenue's mantra.

As an example of the insanity, women in New York routinely pay five-hundred dollars for a pair of shoes that contain ten dollars worth of material and labor. But I've yet to be attracted to or disinterested in any woman because of her shoes. Call me crazy, but as long as she isn't wearing Bozo-the-Clown footwear, I barely ever notice what a woman has on her feet.

I wasn't sure how Rachael would react to my inquisitiveness. I understood her predicament. I promised I would never judge her and admired her courage. Then I admitted I was insanely curious about this black market for sex that I realized existed, but knew so little about. She appreciated my honesty and was amenable to educating me on the intricacies of her secret past. I was thankful for her willingness to openly discuss her private experiences.

She began by telling me the golden rule, "The whole business is based entirely on discretion."

In the world of high-priced call girls the clients are men of wealth and power. Some of the ladies were former stars in the world of modeling. What are the options for a twenty-five-year-old girl who used to get paid a few thousand dollars per day when she becomes washed up at such a young age? That same girl typically skipped college, if that was even an option, to pursue her short modeling career. Modeling is similar to professional sports. The media's adulation and exposure constantly remind us of the ones who have made it, the heralded supermodels recognized by their first names, but never reveals the fate of the thousands who fade into obscurity.

The average man on the street could not afford Rachel, which led to my first question. What are the rates and how are they determined?

"That depends on many factors such as whether a girl works for an agency or decides to become an independent contractor," she said.

Independent operators controlled all aspects of pricing and scheduling, and their only overhead was renting space on a website such as Eros. If you contracted with an agency, they set pricing, provided some security and screening functions, and handled the transactions, but there was a significant cost to performing those functions, upwards of fifty percent. And those fees certainly didn't include a healthcare plan or a 401k option.

Rachael was an independent contractor and controlled all aspects of the process. She would negotiate scheduling and travel expenses. She often performed her own background verification, but occasionally subcontracted that task. She required deposits and money transfers with balances due in cash upon arrival.

The business was remarkably efficient, and by leveraging technology and the internet, it had become productive and transparent. There were offshore bank accounts, Western Union transfers, and cancellation fees just as in any mature business. There was a marketing component. Rachel created a stage name, Camille, and built an entire brand around this character. Her webpage had images of Camille dancing ballet in a professional studio and reading philosophy in a mahogany-drenched Victorian library. There were elegant photos from black-tie events with her outfitted in extravagant gowns. Rachael was adept at creating an image to differentiate her sophisticated luxury-brand.

Her assignments were sometimes simple one evening affairs where the client just needed an elegant date. This might require a few hours and no physical contact. Other packages were more elaborate, involving international travel, four-day weekends, and lots of physical interaction. The other part of the pricing equation was appearance, which was entirely objective. The more spectacular the woman, the more she could charge, no different from any other product-based business. To simplify it she used an analogy.

"A Ferrari and a Porsche are both sexy cars, right? But the Ferrari costs more."

I still wanted to know what kind of money was involved.

"One night might cost a few thousand, but a four-day weekend could be a twenty-thousand-dollar tab," she said nonchalantly.

She smirked and added, "The funny thing about these expensive trips is they include exotic locations with first class accommodations, the kind of weekends most girls would kill for, let alone get paid thousands of dollars to enjoy. And I get to choose when, where, and with whom."

She admitted there was a moral sacrifice with repercussions, but everyone has to make difficult choices sometimes based on circumstances beyond their control.

"What about the health risks?" I asked.

She said that access to certain parts of a client's medical information was a requirement of the screening process, and condoms were mandatory. She shared a story to highlight the efficiency of the process. There are lab services where you can prick your finger, place a blood sample on a swatch, and send it FedEx. HIV and other STD test results are available the next day by using a tracking number and a PIN code.

"What about the money trail?"

Once again she highlighted the ease of setting up offshore accounts to handle wire transfers, confirm deposits, perform currency conversions, and spread funds across multiple accounts to avoid detection. She reiterated that the clients understood these processes and accepted them as part of the business.

I was beginning to understand that this was a sophisticated, multi-billion dollar, global business, and I was becoming increasingly intrigued by the model. Prostitution was illegal in the U.S. except for Nevada, but either legal or rarely prosecuted in many other corners of the globe.

"So how would you categorize the client?" was my next question.

Rachael explained that they were wealthy, sophisticated, intelligent men who were powerful politicians, titans of business, celebrities, or entrepreneurs who typically battled for the most precious of commodities, time. They didn't have the time nor did they want to make the effort to be involved in a relationship. They simply wanted to buy companionship off the shelf. Some were bored or unhappy husbands. Some were highly intelligent, bordering on being socially retarded, and struggled with female interaction. Many of her clients were simply looking for a short-term spark to make them feel alive.

She also mentioned that one of the perks of the job were the gifts. The client might take her shopping for a special dress or dazzling jewelry that was appropriate for the event they would be attending. Sometimes there was a full-fledged rehearsal because Camille had to create the illusion of a legitimate girlfriend or a full-time mistress.

I was still struggling to understand how any man, no matter how wealthy, could waste all that money on something I viewed as cheating. I am not talking about the ones cheating on their wife; that is an immoral choice complete with its own set of ugly consequences—just ask disgraced former New York Governor, Eliot Spitzer. I am talking about cheating the process. When I explained my reasoning Rachael redirected my attention to her first comment and the foundation of the business; it's all about discretion.

These men weren't just paying for sex, or company, or companionship. They were paying to not get caught. Whether they were concerned about business risk, career path, political fallout, marital backlash, negative publicity or reputation, the common denominator was that no one could know that they had cheated the hunt. Sometimes these women bolstered their image and they did not want to be exposed as a fraud, someone incapable of wooing these pretty ladies.

After discussing this fascinating dark side to Rachael's past, I had to confront the inevitable questions of how I felt about her shocking revelation. I was so enthralled in my quest for knowledge about the business that I had overlooked my short relationship with a former call girl. It brought back memories of the talk-show discussions fueled by the Robert Redford movie, *Indecent Proposal*, posing the question: Would you have sex with someone for one million dollars? Who was I to judge Rachael? She could have done something much more reprehensible, such as dealing drugs or robbing a bank.

My second reaction was a health concern. We had always used protection, but I was justifiably nervous and wanted to schedule a blood work evaluation by my physician. She understood my reaction. I told her it was all in the past and that I appreciated her honesty after six weeks instead of postponing the truth. She asked my opinion about that and I said being honest early is mandatory. Any man would feel severely betrayed if that kind of information went untold and was discovered accidentally.

As for us, I thought we should just let our relationship follow its natural course. Then she dropped the biggest bomb of all! She was contemplating a Camille sequel. Now I was really Johnny-on-the-spot. She explained that she had spent the last five years in legitimate jobs, leading a normal life. She had burned through the excess cash she made during Camille's first tour and now her financial position had again become precarious. This presented a much more difficult question.

I interpreted Rachael's plan to return to her sordid past as a roundabout plea for help. She either wanted me to step up to the plate and angle for a relationship, or to offer some financial assistance. It was a tactical suggestion as she was cleverly forcing me to decide where I wanted our relationship to go. Rachael's undoubtedly knew that the return of Camille would immediately end our relationship. I prided myself on being open-minded and understanding, but one has to draw the line somewhere, and this was way beyond the realm of acceptable. Acting as a Sugar Daddy was also not part of my repertoire.

I was content to just resume my close friendship with Rachael and let her pursue her unconventional career opportunities. She wasn't surprised by my reaction, but probably hoped I would demand Camille's retirement. As our friendship blossomed I enjoyed many anecdotes chronicling the adventures of Camille. There are some strange, rich, powerful men out there running the planet and leading the masses!

14

Who's Your Daddy?

Amagansett is an eclectic and earthy seaside town wedged into one of the most upscale corners of the universe known as the Hamptons, the summer destination for everybody who is anybody in Manhattan. South, Bridge, and East Hampton are the big oceanfront towns where a cluster of celebrity compounds hug the pristine coastline. And then there are the low-rent districts such as Sag Harbor and Montauk. But don't be fooled—low rent meant a crappy three-bedroom house with no land and no view that starts at about $1.25M. The Hamptons is a surreal place, immune to the trials and tribulations of the real world, and loaded with extravagant mansions that are often only inhabited for about a dozen weekends each year.

Saturday August 5, 2006 4:44PM

A mysterious brunette sat on a bar stool at the legendary Cyril's overlooking the dunes of Amagansett. I was hosting a former business school friend for a sun-filled weekend in East Hampton. He was going to reciprocate and entertain me in Spring Lake on the Jersey Shore the following weekend. Always with a sharp eye for talent, Dan was an extraordinarily gifted wingman, a real pro's pro.

Cyril's was an odd establishment for the Hamptons. Where else could you be surrounded by multi-million dollar homes, one-hundred-thousand dollar cars, and drive ten miles out of your way to drink from a plastic cup in a gravel-covered parking lot, and then relieve yourself in a Port-a-Potty? But in a peculiar way, that was part of the appeal.

A lot of successful people in New York City come from humble backgrounds, and Cyril's clam shack was a perfect reminder of those simple beginnings. Every Saturday from Memorial Day to Labor Day, a subset of the Hamptons crowd religiously arrived at Cyril's from two o'clock until sundown for happy hour. Many of the patrons come straight from the beach or the pool and are in dress-down mode. Many are still drenched in a rancid combination of suntan lotion, salty seawater, and sweat. If you are dressed to impress, you risked looking like an idiot who was trying too hard.

I pointed out the lady on the bar stool to Dan, which effectively meant I had the right of first refusal. There are many unwritten rules in the single-guys handbook, but Dan knew and understood them better than anyone. He was a legendary wingman during his heyday in Hoboken and on the Jersey shore, and now he was bringing his polished skill-set to the Hamptons. I was thrilled to be flying with him.

The first collaborative observation we had to make was her involvement. Was she there with another guy? The initial qualifier is the hardware, a classic rookie mistake that is extremely embarrassing if missed. It's like getting picked off first base in a baseball game because you are too busy scratching your balls. Checking for the hardware meant looking for either an engagement or a wedding ring. If one adorned the ring finger, "on to the next one" was the battle cry.

She had thick brown hair and dazzling facial features with succulent lips, a regal nose, a dark tan, and a welcoming smile. She was having a conversation with the guy to her right and the girl on her left. Two determinations had to be made. Was the girl her wing woman? And was the guy her boyfriend, a date, or just a friend with no benefits? Only a moron would take a girl to Cyril's on a date, so that option canceled itself out.

After Dan and I analyzed the situation, we concluded that the girl was her wing woman and the guy was either a casual friend or some poor schlep fighting to keep her attention. I strategically positioned myself in her sightline from where I stood in the parking area. After a few seconds she looked up, caught me eye, and stared long enough to airmail a definite invitation.

"I have confirmation, she just eye-fucked me. We're going in. Take the friend out of play," I whispered in Dan's ear.

And like a navy SEAL, Dan responded, "Check."

We approached the girls with bright smiles, and introductions were made with a welcoming enthusiasm. The brunette was named Darien and her friend was Linda. The poor guy who had been talking Darien's ear off for the prior twenty minutes finally realized the futility of his efforts. He also understood the rules of engagement in the single-guys handbook. He recognized that his time was up and now I was on the clock. I allowed him to graciously say goodbye before I stepped into the batter's box. He and I looked at each other, as if to acknowledge a proper transition had been executed. In the Manhattan mating game, it's all about etiquette.

Darien and I shared the typical resume questions.

"Where are you from? What do you do? Where do you live in the city?"

These three mundane questions are the foundation of every relationship that occurs in Manhattan. They were so commonplace I often felt like I should carry a business card with answers for all three. Single word answers will usually suffice, but there are instances where clarification or an explanation is required. As an example, every neighborhood in Manhattan has its own identity and people are inclined to make assumptions about your personality based on your 'hood. As a single guy you need to know those connotations, and if necessary, explain why they may or may not fit.

Darien was born and lived in Brooklyn until she was eight, but was raised in Dallas. That required an immediate explanation. Nobody willingly wakes up one morning and decides to leave Brooklyn and become a cowgirl. She described why without me even lifting an inquisitive eyebrow. She explained that her parents got divorced and her mother wanted to relocate far away from the ex-husband.

Darien lived on the Upper West Side which inferred a mundane, kind-of-boring label. And she worked at CBS. This clarified the Upper West Side decision as a choice of convenience because the CBS headquarters are located on West 57th Street. I cut her some slack for being a humdrum Upper West Sider.

Now I had some easy hooks, bits of information a salesman uses to connect with people. When strangers meet, they typically search for common ground. Is there something about this person that I can connect to? When you boil it down to the core that is what this whole dating and mating game is all about—salesmanship. The woman and the man are continuously engaged in selling themselves in the early stages of any relationship. And in New York City, the home of Madison Avenue and the advertising business, a first date can be a field study in Marketing 101. It's a job interview where the parties are looking for romance, not a means to pay the bills, except for the gold-digging crowd. And there are plenty of buxom, gold prospectors rummaging through the wealthy mines of Manhattan. The tough part about New York City is whether you are searching for a job or a romantic partner, the competition is fierce and the rapid stream of candidates is talented and endless.

I tossed out three easy hooks. I had spent time in Dallas, most recently to attend the Breeders Cup at Lone Star Racetrack. I had lived on West 56th Street which was close to her apartment. I also had a friend who worked for CBS in the news department.

"What department do you work in?" I inquired.

"Sports," she answered.

How perfect? I was an admitted sports junkie, one of those obsessed and well-informed fans who could walk onto the set of ESPN and be on par with the anchors given my wide array of sports knowledge.

After some more small talk, we noticed that Dan and Linda had been making some progress of their own. They had drifted about ten feet away from us and were enthralled in deep conversation. Darien and I joked about how well they were getting along. Linda and Darien were former co-workers at CBS Sports. Dan, the consummate professional, was flawlessly performing his obligatory duty as my wingman.

The crowd was thinning out as the sun rested on the horizon across the railroad tracks signaling it was time to exit Cyril's and move on to phase two of our Saturday evening. Out of the corner of my eye, I saw Dan and Linda embrace for a fiery kiss. I was somewhat shocked, but Dan always did work fast and efficiently. Darien and I both looked at each other with an expression of surprise.

"Wow, and I thought we were getting along," I said to lighten the moment.

Darien responded, "I think I'm jealous. Where's mine?"

That was an open invitation that could not be missed. I instinctively grabbed my red NASCAR number 8 hat, spun it around backwards to take the visor out of play, and went in for the kill.

It was a deep, passionate kiss. She pulled me tight as if she hadn't been kissed properly in quite some time. Women confess to me often that kissing is a lost art. I think it has a lot to do with a lack of patience. After parting lips Darien slowly opened her eyes and looked up at me.

"Wow!"

She paused and then reoffered, "I mean really...Wow!"

I confidently enjoyed the strong endorsement.

"When do I get to see you again? And the answer better be tonight," I boldly stated.

We arranged to meet at a restaurant called Saracen in Wainscot. Dan and I grabbed their cell numbers and told the girls we would be there around eleven o'clock. Getting the digits was critical. Why? We could be running late and may want to call so they don't think we blew them off, or we could meet Mick Jagger at dinner and get invited to a crazy party. Now we had the option of sending a text message if we had no choice but to blow them off, a clear-cut example of pursuing the BBD, the Bigger and Better Deal. Unfortunately the BBD drives the decision-making process in Manhattan and its' endless pursuit generates megawatts of frustration for all market participants. The key point is that with a cell number there's always a chance to reunite at a later date.

We went back to the house to clean up and headed to dinner at Nick & Toni's, one of the Hamptons' most prominent dining establishments. If Mick Jagger was in the Hamptons, there was a high probability this joint would be his restaurant choice. At dinner Dan met another girl at the table next to us whom he found interesting. She was a movie producer who had been involved with a few recognizable films. He schmoozed with her throughout dinner and got her cell number. Always hustling, he was fun to watch when he put on his hard hat, grabbed his lunch pail, and went to work. Dan was the embodiment of Alec Baldwin's character in *Glengarry, Glenross* whose famous line, "ABC-Always Be Closing", is well covered in the single-guys guide.

Dan and I strolled into Saracen fashionably late at 11:45PM. The dining room had emptied and they had set up the DJ booth and a makeshift dance floor near the entrance. We met the ladies at the bar. Darien flashed a big smile and I could tell she was excited to see me. She was wearing a sexy, form-fitting red dress and I was stunned by her curvaceous body. Her clothes at Cyril's had been loose-fitting, so her *Jessica Rabbit* figure packed onto her tiny frame was a delightful surprise.

We embraced with a short soft kiss and ordered some cocktails. We drank, danced, and sang along to some great 80's tunes. I led Darien off the dance floor into the empty dining room so we could share a private moment. She sat in my lap and said she couldn't believe how nice I cleaned up, rubbing my soft, clean-shaven face. My stepping-out look was a gigantic upgrade from the three-day stubble and the NASCAR hat I had been sporting at Cyril's.

By 2:30AM we decided it was time to leave. Darien invited us back to her house where Linda was staying with her. Dan and I followed the girls into the north woods of East Hampton. We compared notes and decided that Dan had the best shot at carnal knowledge so my job became to keep Darien occupied, an easy assignment. I really liked her; she was intelligent, charming, and worked for CBS sports. What's not to like?

When we arrived I led Darien outside by the pool and we sat on the deck chairs. This gave Dan free reign in the house and all the privacy he would need to seal the deal. I would be rewarded with a John Stockton-like assist if he was successful. This is what a good wingman does; he sets the table and dishes the ball so his teammate can slam-dunk it for a score. It's all about sacrificing yourself for the glory of the team.

Darien shared with me that she had been married and divorced.

"Ditto," I responded.

We spent the next twenty minutes commiserating about our failed marriages. I told Darien what a nice share house she had and thanked her for inviting us back. She corrected me and said it wasn't a share house but *her* rental.

"How many bedrooms?" I inquired.

"It has four downstairs with an upstairs master," she brashly replied.

Having spent numerous summers in the Hamptons, I knew the average price of a bedroom in a house of this quality was at least ten-thousand dollars per room so the red lights were flashing in my head. How could a gal working for CBS Sports afford to throw away fifty grand on a summer rental? None of what she was telling made any sense.

"Did you win a Powerball jackpot?" was my sarcastic response.

She knew I was intelligent enough to figure things out and sensed the wheels churning in my head. I am a cerebral guy who is always evaluating the situation and analyzing the information. It's a required skill in Manhattan because the city is loaded with imposters who operate on nothing other than smoke and mirrors. These are the scam artists, self-promoters, and wannabes who are constantly trying to sell their phony image of wealth or importance to anyone willing to buy it.

"I need to share something with you. I have a one-year-old daughter named Zoë," Darien offered, clearly expecting me to be spooked by this revelation.

"Just one more thing we have in common because I also have a daughter."

She was shocked and thrilled to hear it and asked all about my precious little girl. After bragging about how great my kid was, I was still unclear about her situation. She had told me that she had been divorced for over five years.

"I assume your ex-husband is not your daughter's father," I said with some reservation.

I had once proposed a second child to my ex-wife almost eighteen months after we split up because I didn't want our daughter to grow up an only child. She and I both had siblings and understood the benefits. I explained that we didn't even have to have sex, that she could be artificially impregnated. The look on her face that day made it abundantly clear that my proposal was not gaining any traction.

"You've officially lost your *effing* mind!" shouted my ex-wife and that was the end of that brilliant idea.

Darien responded that her ex-husband was not the dad, and that her daughter's biological father lived in Florida. I asked if her daughter was in Florida with her Dad for the weekend.

"No," motioning toward the house, "she's asleep upstairs."

"Who's watching her?" I curiously asked.

"The nanny," she answered.

Now I was factoring in another whopping expense to go along with this fifty-thousand-dollar rental. What the hell was going on? None of this was making sense.

She said it was complicated, and that she was taking a sabbatical from CBS. Darien hadn't worked since a few months before the baby was born. Now I was even more baffled. How could she account for all these expenses coupled with no tangible income? Who was paying the bills?

"Is Zoë's dad a gangster?" I asked half jokingly.

It was a sarcastic poke to mask my nervousness because I was beginning to think that perhaps illegal activities were funding this lavish lifestyle. She just laughed and told me not to worry about mobsters and violence.

She explained that she had dated Zoë's dad, but that they had broken up after she became pregnant. She was in her mid-thirties and wanted children. Although she was being vague and unresponsive, I kept asking questions about her ex-boyfriend, the father of her child. In order to stifle my curiosity she told me that Zoë's father was a famous actor, that she couldn't discuss it, and that she sincerely hoped I could handle it.

"Handle it? I can handle anything," I said in a boastful tone.

I could now reconcile the spiraling expenses, but my curiosity about the father's identity was spinning out of control. We kissed and held each other by the pool while making plans for Tuesday night in the city. We headed back inside to check on

Dan and Linda. I stopped on the deck and purposely made some noise. I didn't want Dan to get caught with his pants down so I was stalling for a minute to give him advance warning that we were coming inside. We found Dan and Linda snuggling on the couch in the den. Dan and I said our goodbyes, jumped into my Mercedes SL 500, and cruised back to my share house.

We discussed the girls all the way back. Dan had not sealed the deal, but not because Linda wasn't wholeheartedly in favor of the idea. He blamed Darien for making Linda pitch a shutout. Apparently Darien had established some non-negotiable house rules at the start of the summer. She allowed Linda to come and stay any weekend, but no sex in the house. Darien didn't want any strange men in the house with the nanny and the baby there, which as a parent I could appreciate. If Linda wanted to get laid she would have to put on the travel uniform and play an away game.

I shared Darien's intriguing story with Dan and his curiosity surpassed mine by a wide margin. He immediately began dissecting the clues: actor, Florida, New York, CBS. He was like a homicide detective studying the evidence board. In the coming weeks he became obsessed with determining the identity of Zoë's father, even suggesting a stakeout of Darien's lobby or hiring a private investigator. The scary part was that he was dead serious.

I laughed and told him that visitation with the baby always occurred in an undisclosed hotel room somewhere in Manhattan. Darien would get a call from one of his handlers with a time and a location so he could spend some quality time with his daughter.

I told Darien that spending an hour in some nondescript hotel room wasn't going to enhance or solidify the father-and-daughter bonding process. But Darien insisted that it was the best they could do given the complexities of the situation. It caused me to think about a laundry list of issues. When would

Zoë be old enough to know the real story? How long was Darien going to maintain this charade? Would little Zoë ever have a real relationship with her celebrity Dad? Was that even possible if the world could never know who her father was? As the doting father of a wonderful little girl I felt deeply saddened when I pondered the answers to my hypothetical questions.

Apparently this mystery guy was too recognizable to be strolling around Manhattan with a baby carriage. He had an image to protect. I envisioned a PR moron advising him about how his Q rating would be negatively affected by having a child out of wedlock. In the entertainment world, a celebrity's Q factor is equivalent to a Nielson rating in television. The higher the rating, the more money he can command for roles, endorsements, appearances, etc. The Q factor measures two components of a celebrity's appeal: how recognizable he is and how likable he is perceived to be. It seemed like complete bullshit to me. I guess one has to be a celebrity to understand and appreciate it.

Dan and I spent the next weekend on the Jersey shore. It was the first time I had been there since visiting a friend in Avalon, which was where the Philadelphia crowd went to soak up the rays and frolic on the beach in the summertime. Dan's house was in Seagirt, a short walk from the beach, and more importantly, an even shorter walk from the Parker House. The Parker House was part restaurant, part bar, and part inn. But it was the epicenter of the social scene around Seagirt. Dan had the all-important VIP membership card. It was essential in terms of avoiding lengthy lines and shoddy service.

The entire weekend Dan played this silly game of blurting out daddy possibilities at unsuspecting moments, and I would respond with a reason to disqualify each prospect.

"George Clooney."

"I think he lives in Italy," I shot back.

"Sylvester Stallone."

"He used to live in Miami," was my answer to that guess.

"Colin Farrell."

"Not sure where he lives but I think it is well-known that he has a child out of wedlock. So why keep a second one secret?" I rationalized.

"Tom Cruise."

"He's already married. And Darien is not converting to Scientology anytime soon," I joked.

Then Dan came up with another plausible possibility. Maybe Darien provided some misinformation to confuse the search. Maybe the answer wasn't in Miami. Perhaps Zoë's dad lived somewhere else, or maybe he was currently in Miami for a movie project. Besides, why would a famous actor live in Miami? Actors tended to live in either Los Angeles or New York. And if they were publicity-shy they lived on a ranch in Montana, not a crowded scene like Miami. Maybe this celebrity wasn't an actor, but perhaps a singer or a politician. And maybe this dude was married with a family and that was the key reason for the veil of secrecy. An illegitimate love-child could have been damaging to his precious Q rating if he was a married man.

I thought about Dan's line of reasoning and flashed back to the conversation with Darien that first night by the pool. As I scratched my memory banks I remembered the "Miami" response being without hesitation, but there had been a slight delay when I asked what he did and she had responded "actor". The more I replayed that moment in my head, the more I was convinced that Dan was right. She had cleverly used some half-truths to throw me off the trail. Dan continued with his litany of names.

"Nicolas Cage."

"I think he is into Asian women," I said.

"Ben Affleck," blurted Dan, laughing at his own desperation.

"Dating Jennifer Garner for awhile," I responded.

"Leonardo Dicaprio."

"Why would he fool around with Darien when he has that Brazilian babe, Gisele waiting at home? Darien is hot, but c'mon man, we're talking *Gisele*," I countered.

"What does the kid look like?" as Dan switched gears.

"Cute. Curly, light-colored hair. Tall for her age. Pretty blue eyes."

"I got it, I got it," Dan blurted out. "Brad Pitt!"

I chuckled and told him to stop reaching. Dan laughed a sinister laugh and admitted he just wanted the mystery dad to be someone outrageous. He was enjoying the speculation, and the more he joked about it, the more I was enjoying it as well. I speculated that Zoë's dad was most likely a B-list celebrity and Dan was going to be woefully disappointed. But that didn't curtail his inquiries as he kept rattling off random names all weekend.

Darien invited me out to the East Hampton house for the last three weekends in August and Labor Day weekend, but requested that I sleep in one of the downstairs bedrooms. She didn't want Zoë to witness me in bed with her in the morning. I was a little annoyed, but I understood her reasoning. Like most babies, Zoë was an early riser, and I wasn't too keen on being awakened at 5:30AM. By the second weekend she was begging me to sleep with her in the master bedroom. Our relationship was moving into overdrive and I wasn't doing anything to apply the brakes. She was smart, outgoing and beautiful, with an insatiable appetite for sex. Why would I slow anything down?

The weekend before Labor Day we decided to attend an early church service in East Hampton at a church on Route 114. I was feeling the need for some spirituality since my beloved grandmother had passed away a month earlier. It was another case of good intentions gone awry. Darien selected a pew near the rear of the church and I sat on the aisle. Two minutes later a family of four sat across the aisle one row in front of us. They looked like a preppy, affluent East Hampton family with a teenage boy and an older daughter. The daughter was in her early twenties and was seated closest to me. And she was agonizingly gorgeous! I was laughing at myself for trying so hard not to stare. During the sermon my mind wandered uncontrollably to some erotic places with this charming, unsuspecting young lady. I couldn't believe the disturbing images I was envisioning in the House of God! If there was ever a day when I thought I might need some psychoanalysis, that Sunday was it. But I'm part Irish and didn't Freud suggest that the Irish were impervious to psychotherapy?

Darien and I did have our first real fight that weekend. Darien was reminiscing about Zoë's one-year birthday party earlier in the summer, before we had met. Her sad expression indicated how badly she wished I could have shared in the celebration.

"I wish I had known you then. I'll bet it was fun," I answered in a regrettable tone.

She then described how elaborate the party had been with farm animals, juggling clowns, and a magician. She purchased round-trip plane tickets and accommodations for family members. It sounded like quite a festive gathering.

Darien abruptly changed the subject to boast about her commitment to a project building a hospital in a poverty-stricken area in Africa. I couldn't help but point out to her the irony of the two unrelated topics. She gave me a puzzled look.

"What was the tab for Zoë's party?" I politely asked.

"About fifty grand," she proudly responded as if the monstrous sum was a badge of honor.

I almost spit up my drink. I was appalled at the staggering price tag.

"How much of the party do you think Zoë will remember?" I asked.

I reprimanded her for wasting the cost of a college education on a birthday party that Zoë will never recall. I then tried to explain the concept of opportunity cost and the benefit that the fifty thousand might have provided to her alleged philanthropic interests. She became irate so I told her to calm down and think rationally. I asked her to consider what that sum of money could have provided to her African cause. Deep down Darien understood my point and realized the selfishness of the extravagant birthday party. In the end the party wasn't about Zoë, it was all about her and misguided revenge aimed at Zoë's dad.

Early September brings a day called Super Saturday at the U.S. Tennis Open. It offers the women's title match and the men's two semifinal matches; three incredible matches all at center court and all in one day. Since CBS owned the contract for the event Darien was able to secure some nice seats through Linda; Darien's relationship with CBS was tenuous at best. We had a fabulous day in Flushing. The matches were marvelous and the weather was perfect. I even grabbed a memorable souvenir.

Roger Federer had just won his semifinal match to earn a spot in the Men's Final on Sunday. A woman from the US Open committee came onto the court with three new tennis balls and Federer autographed each one. After smashing the first two into the upper deck, he turned and faced our section whacking the last ball with his racquet. It came straight toward me on a rope. I reached up and snagged it out of mid-air like the gold glove centerfielder I had always dreamed I would be. It was a surreal experience, almost as if my hand was a homing device and the fuzzy yellow ball had no other possible destination.

As Darien and I began to celebrate my good fortune, a mother and her chubby daughter looked up at me from the seats one row down. They both had a dejected look on their faces.

"Almost sweetheart, we almost had it," the mother said to her plump daughter.

I thought about it for a second. On a personal note I was an avid collector of sports memorabilia. But most of the items I owned were related to baseball and football, the two sports which I am most passionate about. I wasn't a devoted tennis fan and my ass never would have been in those seats if not for Darien's CBS connection. I figured this eleven-year-old girl must be a serious tennis fan to be there on Super Saturday, so I asked the little girl if she wanted the ball. Her eyes lit up like it was Christmas morning and a Grinch-like smile curled up from ear to ear.

"Really?" she blurted out in gleeful amazement.

I reached in my pocket and gave her the ball. Her mother looked at me as if I was a fireman who had just carried her daughter out of a burning building. Her look of euphoria was worth the whole gesture. I imagined being at Fenway Park with my daughter and missing a foul ball by inches off the bat of Manny Ramirez, her favorite player. If that ever happened I just hoped the expression "whatever goes around comes around" would ring true. After gifting the ball I turned to Darien. She gazed at me with the look of a fairy-tale princess who had just been saved by Prince Charming. Sometimes the greatest rewards in life are found in the simplest of gestures.

Thirty seconds later my cell phone was vibrating in my pocket. I answered it and it was my former hedge-fund client, Jay Applebaum. He was an avid tennis player and fan having played tennis at the University of Pennsylvania.

"Are you at the U.S. Open and are you wearing a light blue shirt?" he hastily asked.

"Yes. Are you here somewhere?" I asked as I turned to search for him.

"No. I just saw you catch the Federer ball on TV."

We laughed and Jeff added, "Hold on to that ball, it will be worth a lot someday. Federer is a Hall of Famer."

It was so typical of Jay to think of the financial angle. I just smiled and gave Darien a big kiss and informed her that my catch had made it onto the CBS broadcast. It was a *Ferris Bueller* moment.

The next morning I awoke alone at Darien's apartment. I sauntered into the living room but there was no sign of her, or the baby, or the nanny. It was the first time that I had been all alone at her place. I decided to take a shower in the master bathroom. As I opened the closet next to the bathroom to grab a fresh towel, temptation was staring me in the face. A big filing cabinet with three drawers was tucked against the back wall.

At this point Darien had confessed to me that there was a substantial monetary settlement involved in keeping the identity of Zoë's father a secret. She even insinuated that CBS had been involved in the negotiation and the settlement. Moving back to Dallas had been part of the deal but she had somehow renegotiated a return to New York.

I told her that I didn't have to be Sherlock Holmes to have already figured out there was money involved. The East Hampton rental, the charming two-bedroom Upper West Side apartment one block off the park, the Range Rover, the full-time Nanny, and the fifty-thousand-dollar birthday party presented some rock-solid clues. I threw in the fact that Darien had been on sabbatical since Zoë was born to summarize that foregone conclusion.

My assumption at that moment was that a copy of any legal documents would most likely be concealed in that file cabinet. What should I do? I remembered Dan in his unrelenting quest had once suggested there must be some documentation somewhere in Darien's apartment that would reveal the answer to the mystery. His theory was a birth certificate, a contract, or a picture of Zoë and her Dad stashed away somewhere.

It was deviously tempting, but morality prevailed and I just grabbed a towel and headed for the shower. About twenty minutes later Darien, Zoë, and the nanny returned from their stroll to the Central Park playground. Darien pulled me into the bedroom to tell me that one of the handlers had called and she had to rendezvous with Zoë's father. She was expecting a call back shortly with a time and a location.

We had planned something for that afternoon, so she apologized repeatedly. This wasn't the first time this had happened and I knew it wasn't going to be the last. But I trusted her and she was appreciative of my understanding. She had warned me at the outset that another guy she had dated found her unique situation too taxing. It takes a special individual to let his non-chaperoned girlfriend spontaneously meet a former lover in a random hotel room. Not many guys would be secure enough to tolerate her situation. Maybe I was being naïve, but somehow I didn't feel threatened.

It was the end of September and we had been seeing each other for two months. My daughter was coming to New York for the weekend and Darien was especially looking forward to meeting her. I was spending four nights a week at Darien's apartment and she was getting incredibly comfortable with me in her life.

In the mornings she would bring Zoë into bed with us. It rekindled great memories of my daughter at that cute age where everything was new and exploratory. I enjoyed making Zoë laugh and would do anything goofy to illicit a giggle. Darien marveled at how well I interacted with Zoë, and I reminded her that I had more experience with a baby than she did. At one point that weekend Darien dropped a bomb by suggesting that I move in with them. The oxygen masks dropped from the overhead compartment and there was a sudden loss in cabin pressure! The red lights and exit signs were flashing brightly.

I knew Darien was growing comfortable with our relationship, but I was blindsided by her proposal. It seemed a bit desperate on her behalf since we had only known each other for two months and neither of us had a legitimate job. I was day-trading on a small scale, mostly to stay fresh on the markets and to prevent my licenses from expiring. She was still "on sabbatical" as she liked to call it. And although I had boastfully asserted that "I could handle it", the mystery-father situation was becoming bothersome. Curiosity and suspicion were gradually eroding my tolerance.

I had been gathering small clues for two months and had a strong idea about the answer to the mystery. I never asked Darien directly because I knew that would bug the shit out of her. One Saturday morning Zoë was fixated on Pablo, a blue penguin from her favorite cartoon *The Backyardigans*. She and I were rolling plastic balls back and forth across the living room carpet.

"Who's your Daddy?" I candidly asked her.

She just gave me a blank stare and pointed impatiently at the red ball in my hand.

The most obvious clue hinged on CBS. Having worked at Goldman Sachs for six years I had witnessed numerous office affairs. It always amazed me that really smart guys making million-dollar decisions and being paid millions to do it could be so stupid. They risked their careers, lost their wives, and destroyed their families, all in the pursuit of getting laid.

When I worked in the software industry directly out of college, I had a wise boss who liked to preach the general rules of business. Rule # 5 was: Don't shit where you eat! Translated it meant never have sex with anyone in the office because nothing good ever comes from that pursuit, professionally speaking.

When I gave the riddle some more thought it was a no-brainer. Let's review what I knew: Miami, celebrity, actor, CBS. It was really easy. I had landed on this guy as a likely candidate within the first week of meeting Darien, but I kept it quiet. I was concerned that if I revealed to Darien that I had solved the riddle, she might panic and not want me around anymore.

The major question became, did she purposefully trap him and was he stupid enough to get trapped? I figured the answer was yes and yes. If someone with these credentials—Rhodes Scholar, Yale degree, and President of the United States—can get caught playing a game of Hide the Cigar in the Oval Office, then I guess anyone is capable of having a complete lapse in judgment.

The real irony of it all is there are so many intersections in life. Places where secrecies and fortuitous vectors cross paths. My freshman year in college I had dated a girl from Delray Beach, Florida. Tamara was an All-American cheerleader and a state diving champion. I spent many nights in her dorm room and awoke each morning facing two large posters on the wall. One was of a former water-skiing champion, Wayne Grimditch, and the other was an oversized poster of Zoë's dad.

My senior year at Cornell there was three outstanding players on my team including my friend Len. A few scouts came to conduct tests and meet with us, but unfortunately, none of us got drafted by the NFL. Len, a two-hundred-and-eighty-five pound offensive lineman, got invited to a summer mini-camp. He got cut and returned home to Louisville with fond memories and some funny stories. One of the funniest was an anecdote about a tobacco-chewing player who arrived disgustingly out of shape, was untouchable in practice, and was pampered like a demi-God all around town. It was Zoë's dad. He joked about the first time he heard his voice in the huddle barking out a play. Len was dripping with sweat and more tired than a sled dog at the finish line of the Iditarod, but had a fleeting thought of unbuckling his helmet and extending his hand.

"Hello Mr. so and so. I'm Len from Cornell University."

Figured it out yet? It was ironic that I met Darien on the only weekend my record-breaking wingman, Dan, visited the

Hamptons.

Whenever Zoë and I were throwing the plastic balls around the living room, I often mentioned her quick release, a well-documented trait exhibited by her legendary father. Darien never quite grasped my witty innuendo.

One rainy Friday night in late October Darien and I returned from dinner. Darien sent the nanny home. We enjoyed a bottle of wine in the living room as Darien guzzled down many more glasses than usual. Darien soon fell into a reflective mood and began to reminisce. She shared an intimate story of how Zoë's dad used to rise in the middle of the night and place socks on her cold feet while she slept. I could tell from her demeanor that she still had strong feelings for Zoë's dad and silently hoped he would someday leave his wife and kids to return to her. It was a moment of clarity.

Zoë was fast asleep and it was tranquil in the apartment. The city outside seemed to have stopped, if only for a moment, as the traffic below on Broadway was unusually light. The bedroom window was cracked open and the smell and sound of the soft rain filled our senses. We made passionate love that night, sprawling on the pillows afterwards, our naked bodies entangled and interlocked. I gently kissed her cheek and divulged that her secret was palpable. I knew Zoë's dad was Dan Marino. Her eyes briskly gazed up at me. She then closed her eyes, pulled me tighter and whispered softly in my ear.

"I guess that hamster running on the treadmill in your head has been working overtime. I knew from the moment I met you—you were way too damn smart. I just wish you weren't so God damn intoxicating!"

15

A Decent Proposal

In the fall of 2006 I decided it was time to reconnect with the Church. My relationship with God had suffered an embarrassingly prolonged sabbatical. I wanted to pray for my recently departed grandmother and to ask God for His help in finding *the one*. As a young boy I often attended church to appease my devout Irish Catholic grandmother. Boredom typically led me to gape at the majestic architecture and the intricate details of the stained-glass windows or daydream about my athletic endeavors.

As a teenager, I remember constantly praying for two things: my grandfather's health and that my football or baseball team would win our next game. My prayers were answered as my grandfather lived to be eighty-nine and my teams won many more games than we lost. Now I was feeling desperate in my ten-year search for a wife and begged God for help after a twenty year hiatus. Can you believe my hubris?

Sunday October 22, 2006 7:31PM 🕒

I had spent a rare fall weekend in Bridgehampton attending The Hamptons Film Festival. I arrived back in the city and decided to unwind at a place I had not visited in many months. It was an old strip joint on Broadway called *Flashdancers* located near the Ed Sullivan Theatre, the famous home of the *David Letterman Show*.

I had occasionally frequented the gentleman's club when I lived on West 56th Street. Anytime I entertained clients who enjoyed the foolishness of lap dances, I would escort them there because of its proximity to my apartment. But upon moving I hardly ever frequented the place. There was a Russian dancer, Eliza, from St. Petersburg, who loved to glide past the tables as proud as a peacock. She had one of the most flawless bodies I had ever seen. Eliza was the club patriarch and no one was more adept at prancing around like a diva.

My routine was always the same; I sat near the back, ordered a beer, and tried to become anonymous as I molded into the cheap furniture. I only allowed the incredibly buff and erotic Eliza to dance for me. If she wasn't there on a particular night, I was content to enjoy my beer, watch some stage dancing, and leave.

When Eliza was there she was never immediately available because she was in such high demand. I laughed watching these middle-aged men peel off twenty after twenty so a half-naked woman could grind on their crotch, get them aroused, take their cash, and leave them with a severe case of blue balls. I never understood the benefit. I guess there was a fantasy component, but there were much cheaper methods of dreamy fulfillment. Occasionally some schlep would pay five-hundred bucks for an hour-long package of private dances from the same girl. Once again, I just didn't get it.

When I first arrived that Sunday I assumed my usual spot and scanned the room for Eliza, but she was nowhere to be found. Many of the dancers sashayed over to my table hoping to reach their hand into my wallet for a dance. I politely and graciously declined them all. I finished my beer and was about to leave when a curvaceous Latina woman approached and sat down. She introduced herself using a fictitious stage name and we began a normal conversation. It wasn't the typical hit-and-run tactics employed by most of the gals. They would approach in a sultry waltz, introduce themselves in their sexiest voice, and then go for the money shot.

"Can I give you a special dance?" they would ask.

The second you uttered "no thanks" it was all over. The walk, the talk, and the persona vanished as they moved on to the next potential sucker sporting a wad of twenties.

This sexy Latina had me baffled. She was asking topical questions and had abandoned the role-playing crap. Suddenly I was involved in a real conversation about family, politics, and Hugo Chavez, the President of Venezuela. She had a pleasant demeanor and seemed content to just sit and talk. I didn't want to prevent her from making money or mislead her, so at one point I casually mentioned that I preferred to sit in the back because I didn't enjoy lap dances. She said she understood and admitted that she had observed me decline all of the other dancers.

"Can I give cell number?" she humbly inquired.

"Is that a trick question?" I joked.

"I give da' *numero* for you if promise use it," she said in broken English.

I cheerfully responded, "I promise."

It felt like a set up so I glanced around the club to make sure no one was playing a gag on me. As I exited the club, I wasn't sure what to think about the encounter with my new Venezuelan friend, Rosa. I had been hit on by dancers before, but not quite as aggressively so I was justifiably suspicious. It wouldn't be the first time someone caught a buddy in a strip joint and offered one of the girls some dough to trick a pal into an embarrassing situation. The unwary friend would be derailed by the illusion and betrayed by his own gullibility.

I hit the street on Broadway searching for a cab and feeling a little cocky. I dialed Rosa's number to verify it wasn't a fake, assuming that her cell phone was in the dressing room and would go unanswered. I recognized the voice and the accent as belonging to Rosa. I was now gushing with confidence. It's quite an ego boost when you are in a room full of men patiently waiting to pay twenty bucks for a three minute dance with a sultry babe who just gave you her phone number.

I didn't call Rosa for almost two weeks. I got sidetracked by some market volatility and a few rounds of phone tag, an annoying game of exchanging voicemails like a volley in a tennis match. The same monotonous messages are repeatedly lobbed back and forth. Many New Yorkers invoke this tactic to create the mirage of a hectic schedule. It is taboo in New York City for anyone to appear as if they are ever idle. There is a strange myth in Manhattan that unavailability, even if fabricated, meant you were important and desirable. It is an infuriating game that gets replayed constantly, and is just one more of the simple joys of dating in New York.

We finally connected on the phone and I made sure to earn credit for fulfilling my promise. She said the club had been unusually busy and she was working as many nights as she could get scheduled. Rosa admitted being tired from logging so many hours and encouraged me to call her the following week. She hinted at the idea of needing a night off and hoped I would provide her with a sensible excuse to make it happen.

I took her cue and called her the following Monday with a dinner invitation to a steak joint. I hadn't been to the Post House in ten years and I was in the mood for some quality beef. I gave Rosa directions and we agreed on an eight o'clock sitting.

The highlight from our dinner conversation involved naming conventions for exotic dancers and porn stars. She confirmed the rumor: street names and pet names provided a plethora of options when picking a stage name. I was familiar with the joke about combining the name of your first pet with the street you grew up on. If I ever opt for a career in the porn industry, my alias will be Cotton Deblois (pronounced deb-lo-wah). We were both laughing hysterically as I conjured up an image of some Cajun stud cruising the New Orleans French Quarter like a gigolo in a Panama Jack outfit.

There was a monsoon brewing outside and my apartment was close, but it was raining sideways in sheets. Rosa had driven to the restaurant and her Lexus was conveniently parked adjacent to the restaurant's canopy so she offered me a ride home. I joked that if I accepted she would know where I lived and that could be dangerous. She flashed a piercing look. I just assumed something must have been lost in the translation. When we pulled up to my building I invited Rosa upstairs for a night cap. At first she was reluctant, playing hard to get, but then gleefully accepted my invitation.

She wanted a vodka drink so I poured her a Ketel One and cranberry. I sat on the couch as her curiosity led her on a trip around the apartment asking questions about family pictures, artwork, books and other items that adorned my shelves and walls. She was like a CIA agent building a dossier and became infatuated with a photo of me shaking hands with President Clinton. I couldn't help but seize the opportunity to fabricate a story about how close I was to the President. Her eyes mushroomed in amazement as I kept spinning a larger tale, until I finally just giggled and conceded that I was joking. I confessed that the picture was snapped at a fundraiser.

I rose from my comfortable perch on the couch while she continued surveying the premises. My back felt tight so I began to stretch by bending down and touching my toes. My movements distracted her and she asked if there was something wrong. I told Rosa that I jogged often in the park and sometimes my lower back stiffened from running on hard pavement. I always tried to run around the reservoir in Central Park because it offered a softer gravel surface, but when pressed for time I ran the loop, an all tar course.

"Would you like a massage?" Rosa offered.

My face lit up like the Vegas strip; she would not have to

ask me twice. I promptly flopped on the floor with a throw-pillow comfortably tucked under my head. She laughed at how speedily I had assumed the spread eagle position.

"Do you have any body oil?"

Now I was keyed up; this body rub was going to be the full treatment. I directed her to the massage oil in the bathroom as she instructed me to remove my shirt. When she returned she kneeled down and straddled my legs, poured some of the oil on my back, and began to feverishly work it into my pores. I could tell from the first stroke of her firm hands that she was an experienced masseuse. It was a phenomenal feeling of tension release as her hands powerfully glided down my back. It was almost as good as sex.

Rosa continued to penetrate deep into my trapezoid muscles at the top of my shoulders, my neck, and the rest of my back. She was exceptionally strong, and knew how to use her body weight as leverage to intensify the effect. I exhaled with a soothing moan each time she ran her hands down my back, enjoying every minute of Rosa's magic touch. I asked her if she had ever studied the art of massage because she was superb; she was a workhorse and I didn't want it to end. At one point she asked if I wanted her to rub my legs. Why not? Rosa was better than professionals that had charged me ninety bucks an hour. With soft music playing on the stereo, I laid on my floor in complete ecstasy. I finally asked her to stop as I was becoming paralyzed and dizzy with satisfaction.

I just rolled over and looked up at her with a big smile on my face and jokingly asked her if she would marry me—it was that good! I think she wanted to have sex, but I felt like I had just experienced a triple orgasm. We polished off our drinks and I walked her downstairs to her car. The torrential downpour had ended, but the street was oddly empty of traffic or pedestrians. We enjoyed a long kiss as she leaned up against her car. She straddled one of my legs and was grinding herself into my thigh. I wanted to invite her back upstairs, but I had no energy and didn't want to deliver a lackluster performance.

There is nothing worse than a lousy sexual performance the first time you are with someone. There is so much truth in the old cliché, "You only get one chance to make a first impression". I can still vividly remember a bad sexual experience with a girl during my senior year of high school. And the worse part is it's hard to even know the difference when you are a naïve eighteen-year-old schoolboy.

Sometimes a lackluster outing can be useful if you are trying to discourage the other person from wanting a second round in the sack. Not everyone understands that. Sometimes it is intentional to be unimpressive between the sheets. If you are in a situation where you want a short-term sexual encounter, the one-night stand, then it is not a good idea to bring your "A game". Your partner will only desire you more. If you want to impress your new partner, "bring the heat" as they say in baseball. It all sounds logical, but some people have only a "B game" available for all occasions.

If a guy is gentle, patient, and unselfish during that first encounter, the woman won't forget it—and she is taking notes. Unless she is a virgin, there have been guys there before you, and if you are lucky, most of them have been lousy. It's not their fault. It began when they were improperly trained as horny, rambunctious teenagers, failing to understand that every woman is different. Each woman has various levels of sensitivity within her erogenous zones. This is why patience and exploration are required. One has to experiment gingerly to discover her hot spots. Some women will tell you exactly what they want and some won't. Most women are careful not to be too specific; no man wants an instruction manual read aloud during sex.

There is anxiety and adrenaline when you are on the doorstep of intercourse. We have all experienced it, but take a deep breath, relax, and approach things delicately. Men often expedite the foreplay, and then mount a woman like a horse in the stud barn. I feel bad for those poor fillies. Another issue rattling through the brain is performance anxiety. Did I last long enough? Am I big enough? Think about the question of size in this frame of reference. Most women can masturbate and pleasure themselves using their middle finger up to the second knuckle so view that as your fiercest competitor.

After being practically sedated by her incredible massage, I didn't want to disappoint Rosa so I conveniently hid behind the "I'm a gentleman" excuse. This tactical ploy also made me more desirable in her eyes. Nothing drives a beautiful woman more insane than a man who can resist her overt sexual advances. Scarcity value is a good thing and any man who shows sexual restraint is a rare commodity, thus raising his desirability. Rosa drove away quite aroused and even more determined.

We agreed to rendezvous a few days later, but this time she wanted to introduce me to some Venezuelan fare. Rosa wanted to order some takeout from her native country and bring the feast to my apartment. As I hung up the phone I realized Rosa was skipping a busy night at the club, picking up dinner, and driving to my apartment to feed me. It dawned on me that tonight I better bring my A game.

Rosa arrived and organized everything in the kitchen preparing a full plate for me to sample. I sat there on a bar stool next to the kitchen counter as she spoon-fed me all the different dishes she had selected. I felt like she was trying to fatten up the Christmas goose before the kill. And she had that savage look in her piercing bedroom eyes. Sex was on the menu tonight whether I was hungry or not.

After we finished eating she began to rub my shoulders just to loosen me up a bit. Now I felt like a prize-fighter getting that last rub down before being summoned by the referee for final instructions at center ring. She stopped rubbing, rose from the couch, grabbed my hand and led me into my bedroom. She stepped back towards my bed, and while maintaining eye contact, began to slowly disrobe. This was it. Game time. Go time. Post time. Tip off, or maybe tip in—whatever you wanted to call it.

She stood there naked massaging her breasts and let me take in her voluptuous body. She smoothly slid her left hand down her stomach and tickled her clitoris, sliding passed her freshly waxed hardwood floors, an exotica dancer trademark. She crawled onto my red silk sheets as I undressed for her. The night was magical. Sometimes two bodies just fit one another so perfectly, like two pieces in a complex puzzle or a key in a lock.

Rosa's body shook with an intense orgasm within the first few minutes, and the slower I grinded my hips, the deeper her sharp nails would sink into my back and buttocks. She climaxed so quickly I assumed she hadn't had sex in awhile. Two minutes later she trembled again while shouting Spanish phrases I could not understand. I recognized only two words, "Ay, Papi!" I knew that *Papi* was short for *Papacito*, which meant boyfriend. I stopped during her moment of release and could feel her vaginal muscles slowly contracting. Five minutes later she screamed in ecstasy as she ripped off a third orgasm.

"Oh my God, Papi!" she yelled.

Her body was quivering uncontrollably and I thought I might be wading into uncharted territory. I continued to slowly grind my hips as a fourth and a fifth exploded from her core. Her eyes rolled back in her head as if she were going to faint. She started gasping and panting.

"No mas, Papi, no mas."

She confessed that she had never experienced five orgasms in one encounter and based on the reaction of her body I had no trouble believing her. I had brought my A-game, but I also knew that by delivering it, I would face the consequences. Rosa was addicted and I was now her drug dealer. She was hooked on a chemical compound that is released by the pituitary gland during intense exercise causing the runner's high, and during sex. Rosa had experienced an endorphin rush which some equate to morphine.

"Sex addiction is a real disease, with real doctors and medicine," said Will Farrell's character in *Blades of Glory*.

It is more commonly called nymphomania. A drug's potency varies depending on crop origin, growing conditions, harvesting, and the processing. Sex is also subject to many different variables. A partner's smell, their taste, and even their moan all play an important and underrated role during sex. Rosa had experienced a sensory overload.

I knew I was in big trouble the next day when Rosa called and asked if she could visit me after work, which meant a 4:30AM arrival, also commonly known as the booty call. There aren't many things that can excite me enough to wake up that early, but a gorgeous Venezuelan stripper would earn a spot on most men's lists. What choice did I have? I am only mortal. I did negotiate one stipulation—a massage after sex.

There is nothing like a good rub down after an athletic performance and good sex can require imitating an Olympic gymnast. It demands balance, body control, hip rotation, strength, and cardiovascular training. Sex is a contact sport and the more physical it is, the more enjoyable it becomes. The best sex I ever experienced was with athletic women who had a strong core: defined abdominal muscles, flexible hips, and a firm ass.

I sensed Rosa's addiction and angled for a full body rub down. She was amenable to my terms, so I set the alarm for four-thirty. She buzzed my door at 4:31. I knew I was setting a bad precedent, but I didn't care. Rosa's energy was impressive. I don't think that after eight hours of dancing in outlandishly high, high-heels I would have the energy for sex or a massage. She was eight years younger than me so youth was on her side.

It was a repeat performance as she experienced multiple

orgasms. I joked about how hard she was making me work and that my lower back was stiffening. Sarcasm can be easily lost in translation and she reacted by working more intensely on my lower back muscles. Once again her massage was orgasmic, such a soothing way to fall asleep. I told Rosa if I won the lottery I would forego the driver, the maid, the chef, and the gardener. The first person I would hire would be a masseuse. She laughed and offered herself for hire. I was clueless as to how ominous that offer would become.

Rosa and I enjoyed a sexual relationship for the next few months. It was always at my apartment and she frequently arrived bearing gifts. In casual conversation I would mention I needed some jeans and the next time she came over she would bring a nice new pair of *Diesel* jeans. I asked how she knew which brand and size I would want. She said she looked in the drawer to my dresser. She observed me searching online for some running shoes and arrived two nights later with a pair of top-of-the-line *Asics Gel-Kayano.*

I was flattered by the showering of gifts, but somehow felt uneasy about accepting them. It was a strategy deployed by a sugar daddy trying to appease his mistress who was growing impatient with how much time he was spending with his wife or other girlfriend. Was Rosa my sugar mama? Was I becoming Rosa's boy toy? I asked her to stop bringing gifts and she claimed she just wanted to make me happy. I told her all it took was a back massage, so she abruptly pushed me to the floor and started kneading me like bread dough. I think Rosa was angered by my request to discontinue the gift parade and she decided to diffuse her wrath on my back. As usual, it felt amazing!

One week later she tried a different angle. Instead of bringing me an inanimate material gift, she decided to bring me a live one. And no, it wasn't a pet. I had joked with her about a threesome and how exciting it would be for me to watch her sharing herself with another woman. Men refer to this fantasy often and pretend to be joking so our girlfriends or wives don't get upset. But don't kid yourselves ladies, we are never really joking when we bring this up. Rosa was smart enough to know this and bold enough to make it happen. So instead of jeans or sneakers, I received a gift named Gabriella.

"Just living the dream!" reverberated through my head.

Rosa and I had fallen into a comfortable routine of massages, takeout food, and sex. We were lying in bed one night when she leaned over and tapped me on the shoulder. I was half awake, but she said she wanted to discuss something important. She rolled me over, sat on my hamstrings, and began her deep-tissue technique. I moaned with pleasure with each deep stroke. She began to explain her unique situation.

Every exotic dancer has a saga that led her to this maligned and dishonored profession. I had heard many varieties over the years, some believable and some utterly ridiculous. I had met a bright Yale undergraduate who rode the train from New Haven and danced at *Scores* to pay for college. I met an outrageously sexy, single mom from Florida who flew to New York one week each month and slept on a friend's couch to help support her two kids because her ex-husband was a deadbeat dad.

Many of the dancers in New York were foreigners visiting the city on rented time. They worked their asses off so they could take their bounty and their booty back to Hungary, Brazil, Russia, or wherever they called home. Not all the women in a gentleman's club fit the stereotype or deserve the stigma attached to dancing, especially in a market as lucrative as New York. Where else can one earn three thousand dollars cash in one night?

Rosa was no different. Her story was sad, and her situation was created by the misbehavior of a man she had once trusted. She had been married at the tender age of sixteen to an Australian oil executive when she was living in Caracas. He was thirty-one. Nine years later he abandoned her, trading Rosa in for her younger sister, and shockingly, with the blessing of Rosa's mother. These horrible circumstances caused Rosa to flee in disgust and shame, and she landed in Miami. She met another man in Florida marrying him two years later. She was only a few months away from gaining US citizenship when her new husband decided he wanted a divorce.

I knew exactly where this was headed, but I could never have foreseen the twists it would take in getting there. Rosa explained that her mother's sister hated her mother for what she had done to Rosa and how she had allowed this Aussie oilman to ruin their family. Rosa had always been the aunt's favorite niece. Her aunt also owned some valuable farmland close to Caracas that the government needed for a new super-highway. Rosa's aunt had become stricken with cancer and willed the land to Rosa in part to protest the despicable behavior of Rosa's mother. Rosa had recently completed the sale of the land, converted the currency, and placed the funds in a Miami bank account.

I had no idea how infatuated Rosa had become with me, but I was about to find out. She desperately wanted to become a United States citizen, but she apparently needed a husband to expedite the process. I had no idea what the immigration laws were, but it sounded logical. Rosa offered me one-hundred-and-fifty-thousand dollars to marry her! She even suggested signing a prenuptial contract allowing me to divorce her after two years with zero financial obligations provided she had gained U.S. citizenship.

I was dazed and confused. I had heard some crazy proposals, and I still receive emails from Nigeria informing me that I have inherited nine million dollars, but this was certifiably insane! The logical side of my brain questioned if such an agreement would be legally binding, not to mention the field day INS would have with it. How could I enforce a document that would incriminate me? I was sure it would cost me a substantial fine and possibly land me in prison. But Rosa wasn't done. There was more to her scheme.

She offered a second option to her outlandish proposal. Rosa desperately wanted a baby, so if I agreed to get her pregnant the contract would escalate to three-hundred-thousand dollars cash! Her proposal was preposterous. Or was it? Rosa could go to any sperm bank to review an extensive list of donors, and select someone for less than ten grand. Maybe I should be flattered? She was offering me fifteen times that amount.

Rosa was so nonchalant I thought I had been "punked".

"Where are the hidden cameras? Are you for real?" I asked.

She was puzzled, "No…no cameras *Papacito.* Really. Can we do this thing?"

I looked in her eyes and realized that she was completely serious.

"Are you out of your fucking mind?" was the question begging for an answer.

16

The Tasty Danish

Saturday June 25, 2005 7:31PM

It was a soggy, rainy night as I headed to a charity event in Sagaponack. The bash at Luna Farm was the first of many hosted throughout the summer in the Hamptons to raise money for many worthy causes. My pal, Ted, was running late because of traffic on the Long Island Expressway, so I planned to meet him at the event. It was held under a massive circus tent in the middle of a horse meadow. I had attended in previous years and it always attracted an upscale crowd with a sprinkling of B-list celebrities.

I arrived thirty minutes after the listed starting time and the tent was packed. I did an obligatory lap around the perimeter to get my bearings and gather a glimpse of the well-heeled crowd. It was a scouting mission to see what prey, if any, I wanted to pursue. I mimicked a lion on the Serengeti circling a herd of gazelles, but it was standard procedure when entering a large gathering, a technique that separated the skilled hunters from the novices. Some of the pretty ladies were seated at reserved tables while others mingled at the bar on the fringe of the parquet dance floor. I tactfully drifted along the sides of the tent, stalking the pack as I recognized some faces and eliminated possible targets.

The Hamptons crowd was always full of regulars, hipsters

in their thirties who had been renting share houses for a decade. But there was always a lot of turnover as well. A steady influx of fresh talent arrived each weekend whether the individual was signed up for a quarter share, a half share, or just crashing at a friend's place. That was one of the benefits of being in the Hamptons the entire summer; the crowd was constantly changing and being recycled. If you were involved in a fun share house with a desirable location and all the proper amenities, you suddenly had new friends you didn't realize you had in The City. Everyone's goal in July and August was to escape Manhattan on the weekends; people constantly angled for an invitation to the Hamptons.

I finished surveying the crowd and circled back to the main bar near the entrance where I chatted with an old friend and his crazy wife. They were Hamptons' regulars who didn't let their two-month-old newborn slow them down a step. They could both be described as party animals in a no-holds-barred kind of way. I had been a guest at their rentals over the years for a few after-hours parties. I'd been invited many times, but was cautiously selective on choosing when to accept.

The last time I had joined them for some pre-dawn cocktails, my friend's wife stripped naked directly in front of me at the pool, dived into the water, and coerced my date to join her. My date opted to dive in the deep end topless, much to the dismay of the three naked women splashing around in the heated pool as the steam smoothly drifted like fog across the water's top. My friend's wife chased my date all over the pool. She swam to the edge where I was sitting and flashed me a puzzled look as if to ask what's up with this crazy chick. I rose from my deck chair and whispered in her ear that my friend's wife had a thing for a hot woman with a sizzling body. My date hastily exited the pool as I wrapped her in a beach towel. She had no interest in any girl-on-girl action.

After hearing all about their new baby I realized I needed

a second drink so I headed straight for the bar. After snagging a vodka and Red Bull, I stepped back from the bar and unexplicably performed a complete one-hundred-eighty degree turn towards the entrance. I have no idea what motivated me to look in that exact direction at that precise moment. Maybe it was fate. Maybe I could see the bad poker face on the guy directly in front of me; he looked like a pathetic novice who had just been dealt a pair of pocket aces in a game of Texas Hold'em and was about to ejaculate. Maybe it was the tingling sensation of the heat singeing the back of my neck.

As I turned, my eyes converged on hers with the intensity and mathematical precision of a laser beam. I was gawking at her like a fifteen-year-old schoolboy. Now it was me who looked like the novice; my poker face had unexplainably abandoned me. I felt as if time stood still and all the people in the tent were frozen in suspended animation. The only thing that made it acceptable was that she was equally guilty. Her eyes never left mine for what probably amounted to ten seconds but felt like an hour. She had arrived with two girlfriends, and even as one of them tugged on her arm, she still remained firmly locked on my eyes.

She finally diverted her attention to the pesky friend as I searched for camouflage in the crowd. I was so embarrassed by my rookie maneuver! Staring at someone that long exceeded being obvious—it could have been construed as downright rude. But the flip-side was that she had stared just as long and just as hard at me, an abnormal occurrence for a woman of her stature. I rationalized my behavior based on her physical appearance. She was undeniably one of the most beautiful women I had ever seen during my tenure in the Big Apple. She was statuesque with light brown hair, piercing green eyes, and an elegance that radiated across an entire room, or a massive tent.

I didn't recognize her, but she was unmistakably a model. I assumed that she was incredibly successful at her craft, sporting such perfect symmetrical features along with her slim, toned physique. She wasn't a mannequin sporting the body of a twelve-year-old boy like the runway models, but looked more like she had just leaped off the pages of a *Victoria Secret* catalogue. With so many good-looking women in Manhattan it was rare to be so overwhelmed, but I was flat-out intimidated by her beauty.

As I shielded myself from her sight line, slipping behind two guys mired in trivial conversation, I noticed her glance back to the spot where our eyes first met. It was a critical observation and provided me with a glimmer of hope after behaving like such a rookie. I bellied up to the bar to order a third drink. It dawned on me that my friend, Ted, was still missing in action, but my thoughts were now obviously focused elsewhere.

I tactfully observed this striking woman as she navigated her way through the crowd. It was comical to watch her path; it perfectly mimicked mine in speed and direction. She was surveying the crowd in the exact same manner. Who was she looking for? I could only hope it wasn't a boyfriend or a date, but I knew the probability was high. A woman like her is rarely single, and never without a long line of potential suitors. I was usually too cocky to wait in any woman's queue, but for her I would have made an exception. I hadn't even met her yet and I was already conceding my dignity!

The mystery woman had almost completed her lap around the tent when I saw an old friend standing directly in her path. I strategically moved from the bar and cornered him, grabbing at some meaningless topic as an excuse to stand there for a few minutes. She saw me and also recognized the opportunity for an introduction. She was still walking with her two girlfriends but broke away and quickly approached me. As I saw her coming out of the corner of my eye I excused myself from the conversation.

"Hi, I'm Heather," she said with a flirtatious smile and an

unfamiliar accent.

I glanced at my pal to politely indicate our conversation was finished. He looked like he had been struck by lightning. The jaw-drop was measurable and his disbelief was amusing.

I introduced myself and told Heather I was so happy she stopped to speak with me. She then asked why I hadn't come to talk to her when she first arrived. Now I was frozen with fear, consumed by the proverbial deer-in-the-headlights sensation. I fumbled for an answer and the best I could do was to say that I didn't want to intrude on her and her girlfriends. What a lame response! I just hoped she wouldn't realize I was too chicken-shit to approach her that aggressively.

"Oh…how considerate of you," she sarcastically replied.

She and I both knew I had raped her with my eyes. But I reminded myself that she had visually raped me right back. I rebounded with a clever recovery.

"I was just playing hard-to-get," I laughingly replied.

I then gave her a more honest answer that was complimentary and cautious. I told her I wanted to wait a few minutes to gauge whether or not she was with someone at the party. This approach highlighted my experience and exhibited my gentlemanly nature.

"I never imagined a woman as stunning as you would be here solo," I said.

She smiled a heartfelt smile. I could tell she appreciated the honesty and recognized my compliment as sincere and not some horseshit pick-up line.

She then leaned over to tell her girlfriends she was going to the ladies room and asked me to escort her. I was thrilled with her request and recognized it was a perfect diversion to create some one-on-one time with me. As we headed for the restroom area I told Heather I detected a bit of an accent in her voice. She told me she was Danish.

"What a coincidence?" I responded. "I'm visiting

Copenhagen for the first time in mid-August."

She was euphoric and could not wait to tell me everything about her hometown. Her genuine enthusiasm for her country and her city was endearing.

I waited patiently for Heather by the ladies-room trailer door. As she exited she was approached by an older gentleman with an expensive camera around his neck. He had been hired by the promoters of the party to snap candid photos and splash them all over internet social sites such as *Gotham, Hamptons Magazine* and any other outlet that would post pictures of this fabulous event so the no-shows would feel badly about missing it. The photographer asked Heather about her trip to Thailand for the Miss Universe pageant, piquing my interest. I thought maybe I was hanging out with Miss Denmark.

"It was a tremendous experience, but I never imagined that being a judge would be so difficult," she answered.

The wheels in my head were spinning—a judge? Holy shit! Maybe she was a previous winner. Did I have a former Miss Universe on my arm? Was this another "pinch me I must be dreaming" moment? The photographer then asked if he could take our picture so Heather instinctively put her arm around me and struck a professional-looking pose. I just tried not to look like a complete shell-shocked dork.

After he got his photos he swiftly disappeared into the tent. He didn't want to miss a P. Diddy photo opportunity because he was engaged in small talk with us. Heather began asking all sorts of questions about me. It was the usual resume rundown as I tried to condense my entire life into sixty seconds. I asked her a few questions, but her answers were often curt as she evidently wanted to know more about me. I was thrilled with her level of interest, but tried not to be too verbose; nothing is more of a turn-off than someone who rambles endlessly about themselves. I finally stumbled upon two topics where Heather's answers were not brutally succinct. She loved discussing her family and Copenhagen.

It was refreshing to witness the pride Heather gushed for her hometown and feel the passion she had for her family. She had been in New York about ten years, but still appeared grounded by her Danish roots. It was refreshing because it's so easy to become hardened by the brashness and the anonymity one feels when living in New York. It doesn't matter who you are or where you're from, we are all small fish in a large pond on the island of Manhattan, and The City has a way of constantly reminding you of that fact.

Heather and I chatted away by the corner of the tent for the next thirty minutes. We were eventually interrupted by one of her girlfriends who came to drag her away. I asked Heather for her phone number and she asked for mine. I snuck in a request for her last name because there was already a Heather in my cell phone. How clever of me? Actually, I just wanted to Google her when I got home. I offered to take her to dinner sometime soon and she readily accepted. As I watched her walk away, a tremendous feeling of excitement permeated my body. I felt like I had just asked the Homecoming Queen to the prom.

"Of course! What the hell were you waiting for?" was her eager response.

I exited the tent like I was walking on air. After chatting with one of the most beautiful women I had ever met, I was exploding with self-confidence and oblivious to the fact that my friend, Ted, had never made it to the party. As I walked to my car I wasn't even sure where I was going! Making Heather's acquaintance had me in such a daze I didn't really care where I was headed.

When I returned to New York I tried to set up a date with Heather. I might as well have dropped by the White House and asked if President Obama wanted to check out a hot new sushi joint. She was impossible to connect with on the phone. She screened every call, and never answered. She would immediately call back, but her incoming line always registered as private. These are often two giant red flags indicating that the other person is hiding from someone. Either that or it is an illusion to appear busy, obsessively private, or mysterious. So at the outset things were a tad shady, and I was suspicious.

I performed a rudimentary background check on my new acquaintance, Heather, utilizing the power of the Internet. There were half-a-dozen major magazines where she had posed for the cover including *Elle, Vogue and Cosmopolitan*. I also discovered she had been selected as the top new model of the year by one of the world's most prominent modeling agencies, beating out Tom Brady's wife, supermodel Giselle Bundchen. Now I only needed three Super Bowl rings and a pair of Super Bowl MVP's to catch him.

She had been cast in a few movies, but seldom in a credited role. The beauty queens don't appreciate that serious acting is a skill that requires dedicated training and preparation. I keep wondering if I am ever going to meet an ex-model who wants to do something other than act. I did meet one who tried out for a spot on a S.W.A.T. team, but after failing to make the cut, she still pursued acting. I was bewildered as to why Heather's modeling career had started out so strongly and then seemed to fizzle. In my humble opinion I thought she was much better looking than Giselle. She still possessed a cover-girl face and a *Victoria's Secret* lingerie body, a lethal combination.

After playing one of the longest games of phone tag in my dating career, I finally met Heather at a place in midtown for lunch, a tiny hole-in-the-wall called *Chop It*. Heather was meticulous when ordering her salad, but based on her physical appearance I figured she was discriminating about what she consumed. She clearly treated her body as a temple, not an amusement park, and I respected her discipline.

It was good to finally see her again after a few weeks, but I became perturbed by her obsession about what was in her salad. She repeatedly interrupted our conversation to ask me if I could smell bacon bits mixed in her greens. I thought she was trying to purposely annoy me, but then I realized it was just her normal, self-centered behavior. She boasted about how she traveled frequently and apologized for her unavailability, as if it were a badge of courage. I told her I was intimately familiar with her job, proving my point by spinning the modeling lingo and using buzz words like go-sees, callbacks, tear sheets and bookings. It was a subtle attempt to let her know that I had dated other models. She almost seemed disappointed, nodding her head to acknowledge that I did 'get it', and rendering it unnecessary to explain herself further.

I told her my trip to Copenhagen was only about one month away. She made me promise we would have dinner before I departed on my month-long European adventure.

"My agency just booked me in Miami tomorrow morning and then they have me traveling to Paris for eight days."

"Great. Enjoy your trip. I'll call you when you return," I said without hesitation.

Once again she seemed irritated that I wasn't more upset about her being gone for ten days. I reiterated that I understood the intricacies of the modeling profession and looked forward to her return. I kissed her on the cheek as we said goodbye on the sidewalk. I walked away realizing that Heather was always looking for an edge when dealing with men. And I knew she sensed I wasn't mentally weak enough to give it to her. She was a woman who thrived on trampling confident, alpha male types.

Ten days later I called her as promised. She was impressed with my punctuality and my attention to details. I explained to Heather that when I say I am going to do something, I do it, and I have little tolerance for people who fail to deliver. I was hoping to get together, but she was back on the road to Los Angeles in two days. I asked her to reserve a date in her calendar when we could have dinner before my trip. She hesitantly agreed, but hedged herself.

"My schedule's crazy and could change at any moment," she said in an overly dramatic tone.

"That's fine," I told her. "Good luck in LA and be safe."

The circled date on the calendar finally arrived and I called Heather to confirm dinner. She hemmed and hawed because of some wrap party being held on the lower East Side for an independent film in which she had landed a small role. She then asked me if I would accompany her to the party and suggested we grab dinner afterwards. We rendez-voused at a place on Houston Street before walking to the soirée.

Heather explained a little bit about the movie and her small part. But she failed to mention that the film required some scenes with a large group of 'vertically challenged' extras. When we arrived I was somewhat surprised to be surrounded by almost two dozen 'little people', none taller than three-and-half feet. It gave the party a feeling of being under the Big Top or at a remake of the *Wizard of Oz.* I couldn't help but remind Heather that we first met under a circus tent so maybe this circus-like feeling was good karma.

"You have such a wonderful sense of humor," she commented while laughing.

We made the rounds at the party. Heather was like a politician at a pep rally, working the room, and searching for the all-important casting director. It was critical that she locate her and register a mental credit for making an appearance at the party. She was smart enough to know that schmoozing with the casting director could lead to future employment opportunities. Heather introduced me to the casting director as well and she seemed to take an interest in me. I could see out of the corner of my eye that Heather was annoyed. I think she felt like I was monopolizing her precious time, but I was just trying to be polite.

We left the party and began walking in a westerly direction. Heather instinctively grabbed my hand as we walked. I am not exactly sure why, but it was one of the few times I ever took special notice when a woman reached for my hand. After about five blocks Heather asked where we were going. I didn't have a clue, but quickly constructed an impromptu game plan. I told her I knew a cozy little French bistro in Soho. And although I hadn't made a reservation, the host was a friend who always took special care of me. I just hoped he was working that night and could hook me up in a pinch. I wanted to impress Heather with my big city swagger.

As we strolled into Raoul's on Prince Street I was relieved to see my friend Bowtie Bobby standing his post at the *maitre'd* station. I whispered in his ear that I needed a prime table in the private garden area for my special guest. He took one look at Heather and knew exactly what I meant. Half the heads in the restaurant had turned when Heather entered through the red curtains in front of the door. And it wasn't just the men. Her beauty transcended gender, and even a heterosexual woman couldn't help but stare and appreciate her radiant elegance. It was one of those moments where a man felt like a King, wishing everyone he knew could see him proudly make a grand entrance with such a glamorous Queen. I had to settle for one random fraternity brother I hadn't seen in almost a decade.

As I made arrangements with the host, I heard a familiar voice coming from the table to my right. Heather also spotted an old girlfriend having dinner at the front of the restaurant and excused herself to go say hello. The voice I recognized belonged to a former Cornell lacrosse and football player who was a year behind me in college. He was sitting with his back to the entrance so he did not enjoy Heather's angelic arrival. I tapped him on the shoulder and he was amazed I even recognized him. We chatted for a few minutes trying to cram in all that had happened to each of us in the past ten years. He was standing and facing the entryway to the restaurant. Suddenly his eyes grew wide with excitement. He looked like a six-year-old boy about to open his first birthday gift. He leaned in towards my ear to inform me that the hottest woman he had ever seen was walking straight towards us.

"I know. She's my date," I said without turning around.

He flashed a look of disbelief and then a sly grin gradually consumed his face.

"I always thought you were *The Man* in college. Good to see some things never change," he approvingly responded.

I introduced him to Heather and then both of us to his table of Merrill Lynch co-workers and clients. We followed the host's lead towards the private enclave in the back, through the kitchen area and out to the garden. Heather had been to Raoul's before, but she never had the privilege of dining in this intimate part of the restaurant. As we left my friend and his cronies, I smirked in a cocky delight as I knew the rest of their dessert conversation would focus on Heather. How did I know? Because if I were sitting at that table, I wouldn't have wanted to talk about anything else.

Bowtie Bobby sat us at the best table in the private garden. He had rolled out the red carpet and Heather knew it. I could sense that she was impressed—a difficult thing to accomplish with a woman like her. One doesn't have to be a rocket scientist to know how many big-swinging-dicks have tried to impress Heather since the day she first arrived from Denmark. I couldn't imagine all the dinners, gifts, private jets, and fancy yacht invites that had been thrown her way over the years.

Heather bragged about spending weekends at Trump's Mar-a-Lago compound in Palm Beach. She was well versed in being chased by fifty-five-year old men who promised to keep her dripping in Cartier jewelry and Carvelli couture. I just hoped she hadn't become one of those pathetic women, controlled by the tides of multi-millionaires flowing seasonally from Palm Beach, to Aspen, to the Hamptons, trailing in hot pursuit like a flock of seagulls. I was praying that at twenty-seven she had become bored and turned off by all the shallow men in New York attempting to buy her affection.

I did well financially, especially for a middle-class kid from Maine, but I couldn't compete with the massive wealth accumulated by some of the real estate tycoons, the media moguls, the Wall Street wizards, the Middle Eastern oil barons, and the spoiled members of the lucky sperm club who littered the Manhattan landscape. I was sure she had met many of them, and I was equally sure that many had attempted to seduce Heather with their wealth, their toys, and their empty promises. It is an unfair advantage, but no one ever said life was fair.

In competing for a woman's affection, the power of the purse often played a starring role. Many women in New York would publicly state that it didn't matter, but few actually believed it. For some of the ladies in the big city, whale hunting for a wealthy suitor was the single motivating factor behind their migration to New York. Why else would a woman want to pay $2200 per month to live in a lousy three-hundred square foot studio, ride the steamy overcrowded subways, and tolerate all the other challenges of living in Manhattan? They've all heard tales of past lottery winners and their spoils, so they sail into the city carrying their harpoons hoping to land a big fish. Amongst the whales it was easy to respect and admire the men who had built their fortunes from scratch. The lucky sperm club was the group that single men in Manhattan loathed the most.

Every time I met one of those sperm club chumps it urged me to consider entering politics, going to Washington, and dedicate my career to enacting a 100% inheritance tax. Conservative Republicans would break out in hives, but wouldn't that satisfy the spirit of the clause "all men created equal"? Let's all start with a bank account set to zero and make the game fair. Why should some newborns be instant multi-millionaires right out of the womb? What's fair and equal about that? Let's level the playing field in the great pursuit of companionship. It sounds Darwinian, but I think it will only strengthen the human race. Perhaps our notion of being civilized via probate and surrogate court proceedings only breeds mediocrity. I don't think bank accounts and dowries played a role in the mating choices of our earliest uncivilized ancestors. It was the evolution of the alpha male magnified in perpetuity.

Heather and I sat close to each other as we occupied the corner-booth table. She reached over and held my hand under the table at various moments during dinner. I rubbed her thigh and tickled her forearm a few times during our meal. It was the simplest form of foreplay, but it felt special with Heather. The food and the wine were fantastic. Raoul's was a neighborhood mainstay, irrefutably a top three Soho eatery for anyone in Manhattan who knew anything about fine dining.

Heather was fascinated about my trip to Europe and my itinerary. She gushed with excitement when explaining where I should go and what I should do in Copenhagen. She was an amateur artist so she broke out pen and paper from her purse and started drawing maps and symbols to represent touristy places that I needed to visit. She told me about Hamlet's Castle, the Viking Museum, and the Little Mermaid guarding the entry to the harbor. She drew pictures of a version of an ice-cream-cone type treat that had become a Danish trademark. I was staying in a section of the city called Nyhavn, close to the former home of Hans Christian Andersen, and she jotted down the names of a few restaurants I would enjoy that were close to my hotel.

She soon realized how overwhelmingly excited she was in pretending to be my tour guide and became embarrassed by her enthusiasm. I found her energy endearing and genuine. I loved someone who took pride in their roots. When she looked up from her scattered drawings and sketches, I leaned over and we shared a quixotic kiss. It was short and sweet. After all, we were in a public restaurant and I don't think PDA was commonplace for either one of us. But sometimes two people just cannot contain themselves, and I was happy to share one of those rare moments with Heather.

We embraced five more times throughout dessert. We both felt like a couple of innocent teenagers breaking the rules and enjoying every minute. She was a great kisser and paid me the same compliment. We were causing a bit of a stir in the usually refined and well-mannered private garden. The patrons were beginning to label us as the renegade and mischievous couple in the corner. Every man in that room was insanely jealous of me, and the thorny part was that their wives and girlfriends all knew it. Heather was such a desirable woman that even the other ladies around us probably offered their smitten partners a small ounce of amnesty. What power does a mortal man have in the presence of a Venus, a true goddess?

I asked for the check and was already nervous thinking about the ride home. My mind was racing through the possible scenarios and their outcomes. I had to make so many critical choices. Should we share a cab? Should I invite her to my place? Should I invite myself to her place? Should I get out of the cab and walk her to her door? If I ended up at her place, should I be aggressive or behave like a gentleman? These are all decisions that have to be made based on imperfect inputs such as body language, instinct, and experience. But the repercussions of a mistake could be costly. In this delicate situation if I said something inappropriate or acted disrespectfully, it might severely strain a blossoming and fragile relationship. This was like quarterbacking the two-minute drill in the Superbowl—one wrong move and game over.

I decided to jump in the cab with Heather and offered to drop her on the way uptown since her apartment was in the

East 30's, about halfway between Raoul's and my midtown pad. She didn't object and reacted in a manner that implied I executed the optimal first move in this little chess match. We shared some longer, more passionate kisses in the cab now that we were removed from the public gaze.

Once we pulled up to Heather's building I paid the meter and jumped out to walk her to the door. She looked a tad surprised, so I questioned my decision. We got to the door and embraced once more for a passionate kiss. She stopped, grabbed both my hands, and flashed me her alluring smile and her best bedroom eyes.

"I really want to invite you upstairs," said Heather.

I tried not to erupt with exuberance as that would have undoubtedly ruined the moment. Instead I acted suave and reserved, deserving an Oscar for my performance. And then she uttered the most lethal word a man can ever hear as he stands helplessly immobilized on a beautiful woman's doorstep.

She said, "But…," followed by a lingering and excruciating pause.

This is typically followed by a litany of excuses and most men have heard them all: "I have to get up early", "bad timing", "my apartment is a mess", "I'm too afraid of what might happen".

I will give Heather an enormous amount of credit. Her "but" was cunningly original and placed the onus squarely in my lap.

"If you come upstairs something wild and out of control might happen and I won't want to see you again," she claimed.

At first I looked puzzled, but then I realized exactly what she meant. She had shrewdly placed me in what behavioral scientists would label the prisoner's dilemma. Heather was essentially telling me that if I came upstairs and we engaged in something sexual, she would never be able to think about our relationship seriously. As tempting as she was physically,

I had no choice but to leave. I didn't want her to categorize me as a one-night stand. Initially I tried to convince her that she wouldn't feel that way. Gigantic mistake—never dictate to a woman how she is going to feel about anything. Heather brushed off my hubris and recognized it was my oversized ego talking.

I was impressed with her clever response. I think most guys would be fooled into one night of romance, thinking more would follow. But I wasn't going to underestimate Heather's resolve. I knew she meant what she said, and I definitely wanted to see her again. I kissed her one last time.

"Sweet dreams," I whispered in her ear before heading back to the curb.

She stood for a second behind the glass entryway and watched me as I tried to hail a cab. A famous sizzling scene from the movie *Body Heat* flashed into my head. The one where William Hurt grabs a chair off the front porch and hurls it though the glass next to the doorway, while a panting Kathleen Turner stands perfectly still in the hallway waiting for him to break into her house like a criminal and ravage her body. It was one of the sexiest scenes in the history of film and I wanted to recreate it so badly.

It took every ounce of self-control in my body to climb into the next cab that raced down her block. She was still in the lobby looking out towards the curb, but she had drifted closer to the elevator bank, almost removed from view. I think she was still testing my self-discipline. The entire cab ride I kept reviewing the decision in my head. I was ninety percent sure I had made the right call, but that ten percent of doubt was driving me insane. The fact that I was about to embark on a month-long trip to Europe and didn't know when I would see Heather again only complicated the situation.

When I returned from Europe I called Heather to share my joyful tales of Copenhagen. She left a voicemail telling me she was heading to South Africa and then to Europe, and would not be back in New York for almost six weeks. She apologized for being gone for so long, but explained it as a lifestyle imposition that accompanied her career choice. I knew extensive traveling was one of the liabilities of the modeling profession, but I had never courted a model with Heather's global demand.

Autumn came and went and the holidays were fast approaching before I finally got together with Heather again. I invited her to meet me for a drink at Nobu on 57th Street. She declined drinks telling me she had a meeting, but asked me to swing by her new apartment later. Once she had returned from Europe in October, we had difficulty connecting because she was dealing with the anxiety of finding a new apartment. It can be a daunting task in Manhattan because your life and all your choices, such as your gym, grocery store, dry cleaner, and even your dentist are often predicated on their location relative to your apartment. Heather had lived on East 35th Street for seven years, but was being overly dramatic about how she was struggling with the potential changes.

She also had been nursing herself back to health after a minor operation. She avoided the question when I asked her what ailment had required surgery. I had my suspicions, but would never want to appear preoccupied or pushy regarding medical issues. Heather told me she had an important eight-o'clock meeting, but would be home at nine o'clock sharp. I thought eight o'clock was an odd time to be having a meeting. And how could she be so sure it would end before nine o'clock? Once again something about Heather's private dealings seemed dubious.

I was excited to see her and brought my camera to share my pictures from Denmark. I arrived promptly at nine o'clock as she answered the door with a big smile wearing a simple white tee shirt and some jeans with her hair in a ponytail. I had never seen her in such a casual outfit with no makeup, but I honestly thought it was the best she had ever looked. Heather was such a natural beauty that fancy clothing and expensive cosmetics only masked her stunning features. Some women need those things to magnify their most brilliant feature or compensate for their ordinary appearance. Heather was blessed in that she just didn't need any help.

She gave me a big hug in the doorway and was excited to see me. I surprised her with some roses I had picked up at the corner grocer. I was trying to be suave and play it cool, but internally I was ecstatic. I really wanted to strip off my clothes and perform naked back flips onto her couch, but was worried about its inappropriateness. She led me to the sofa and was giddy to view my Denmark photos. Her face beamed with joy and pride as I scrolled through each Danish scene on my digital camera.

Once we finished the slideshow Heather must have been feeling a heightened closeness. She grabbed both my hands firmly and told me she had some private matters that she needed to share with me. I was overjoyed that she trusted me enough to unveil some of her dark secrets. I knew that whatever was about to follow was going to be difficult for her to discuss.

Heather and I had only known each other briefly, but I knew she had trust issues. I figured that given her extended time in Manhattan and being entrenched in the cutthroat world of high-end modeling, she had probably been burned a few times and had become withdrawn and guarded, almost jaded. A lot of people in New York City pledge meaningless and empty promises to extract whatever it is they want from you. The City can be sinister, once described to me as "colder than a nun's box on Good Friday", a twisted expression that I found irresistibly tasteless yet alarmingly accurate. Heather had undoubtedly experienced some of the frigid ugliness that New York had to offer.

She explained how her mother had unexpectedly died

when she was starting her ascent within the New York modeling ranks. The intense sadness of her loss and the pressure of her burgeoning career created a combustible situation. She turned to drugs and alcohol to escape depression and to curb her anxiety. Her career suffered as she spiraled out of control, consumed by these destructive vices. She was finally placed into a rehabilitation facility by a friend who discovered her one morning unconscious, reeking of alcohol, and slumped on her doorstep. Heather's meeting that evening was at a church on the corner of Park Avenue and 60th Street. It was an Alcoholics Anonymous meeting and explained why she had always avoided my innocent invitations to meet for a drink.

As her eyes welled up I leaned across the couch and gave her a hug. I could feel her arms squeezing me tightly. I was experiencing a sense of joy and responsibility as I gently rubbed the back of her head. I felt privileged that she trusted me enough to share these difficult aspects of her past, and I respected the fragility of her confession. I explained that I understood her plight because I had an alcoholic relative who never had the courage to confront those demons that she battled every day.

She confessed that she had feelings for me, but then explained why she would be a horrible girlfriend. It was awkward to have a girl suggest a relationship and then paint a laundry-list detailing all the reasons why I should not want to date her. I downplayed the situation by acknowledging that the timing wasn't right for us to date and that was okay. She seemed relieved that I could accept her shortcomings as I explained that we are all flawed. Sometimes the strongest relationships are built on the ability of two people to accept and overcome those flaws, a lesson I was gradually learning.

Heather was impressed with my insightfulness. I just laughed and told her it was my oversized ego that allowed me to be so patient. I knew it required a secure and confident man to even attempt a relationship with her. I accepted that one of the burdens of her attractiveness was to be constantly solicited, and even harassed by adoring men all over Manhattan. They were powerful, well-connected men who yearned for her affection for a variety of selfish reasons. I also explained that life is all about timing. I firmly believed in fate, and thought that if we were meant to have a meaningful, lasting romance then it would happen.

Heather commended me for my intellect and my maturity. I just smiled and said I was happy for her friendship. Suddenly she energetically sprang from the couch.

"I have something else I want to share with you," as she ripped off her tee shirt and exposed her exquisite, bra-covered breasts.

"What do you think?" she excitedly asked.

I wasn't sure if this was a trick question.

"They look spectacular," I answered.

For some reason she didn't seem convinced by my analysis.

"Do they look different?"

"I'm not sure. I don't think I've ever seen them from this vantage point," as I awkwardly fumbled for the words.

She then unhinged the back unleashing her exceptional, perfectly-shaped breasts and asked me to feel them. I surveyed the room in a manner suggesting I was looking for a hidden camera. Her request bordered on absurd. If a woman who has graced the covers of a dozen major fashion magazines asked you to feel her up, wouldn't you be just a tad suspicious? She laughed and grabbed my hand, placing it firmly on her left breast. It was reminiscent of Owen Wilson's character in *Wedding Crashers* being commanded by Jane Seymour's character to caress her new "bolt-ons".

"Be honest, how do they feel?" she asked.

I realized that her mysterious operation had been a breast augmentation procedure. I was shocked because from all the modeling pictures I had seen, they were already perfect. She was obviously panicking about her age at twenty-eight, and felt it necessary to do some remodeling. They looked and felt amazing, but it was so bizarre to be standing in the living room while a half-naked Heather insisted that I inspect her new breasts. I had fantasized about getting her unclothed, but not under these circumstances.

It was an odd evening that concluded with Heather pleading that I take a vow of silence about her breast enlargement. I just laughed because who was going to believe me?

The next few months followed a familiar pattern: phone messages, emails, and traveling. I was the guilty traveler, traipsing back and forth to Maine to watch my daughter's high-school basketball games every weekend. One Saturday afternoon in mid-February as I drove back to New York, Heather popped into my head so I gave her a call. Miraculously she picked up the call on the first ring and sounded excited to hear from me. I asked her if she had any plans that evening and we decided to meet for dinner. As soon as I hung up the cell phone I slammed the pedal to the metal.

Once back in Manhattan I felt like a teenage girl getting ready for a big date. I ripped through my closet trying to decide which shirt and shoes to wear and which belt matched my outfit. I was acting utterly pathetic, like one of the metro-sexual men that have flooded the social scene in New York. It was a behavioral classification that I despised, but I badly wanted everything to be perfect that night.

Heather and I met at Rue 57, a French bistro in mid-town close to her apartment. When I first arrived Heather was in a melancholy mood. She said she had been aggravated by an old friend while shopping downtown. I figured that something uncomplimentary was directed at Heather, but she didn't want to discuss it. By the time dessert arrived she seemed happier and more vivacious, sharing a funny Christmas story about her brother and father. Talking about family always placed her in good spirits.

Heather then asked me about what it would be like living in Maine. Was it a good place to raise a family? She inquired about the cost of living and asked me to describe what kind of a house we could live in for the five-thousand dollars per month we collectively spent on rent. I was gaining a sense of false hope listening to Heather talk about seaside cottages with dogs and children playing in the yard. I knew she was still clinging to the jet-setting lifestyle of her modeling career and her enchanting weekends in Palm Beach.

It was bitterly cold as we scurried back to the warmth of Heather's apartment on 58th Street. Once inside I removed her heavy jacket and hung it on the coat rack behind me. As I turned around I was met with a forceful embrace. She kissed me passionately, catching me by surprise, but I knew exactly what her body language meant. There was no need for dialogue or explanation. I began to slowly disrobe her as she gingerly back-pedaled towards the bedroom, our lips still locked in an unbreakable seal.

When we approached the side of her bed, only her black thong underwear remained. I performed the classic hands-free underwear removal maneuver, a technique where you lower the underwear almost to the knees using one hand while still engaged in a full kiss. Using your balance, you lift one leg, slide your foot between her thighs, and push her panties to the floor, where she easily steps out of them. A woman with a similar sense of poise and agility will reciprocate with the same precision.

We climbed into Heather's warm bed underneath the oversized puffy comforter. I had fantasized about this moment, but I was slightly disappointed right from the get-go. Heather obviously had not been on any bathing suit or lingerie shoots in awhile. Let's just say there was enough wool to knit a sweater when I gently slid my hand between her thighs. I was expecting freshly-waxed hardwood floors and had left my sickle at home.

I had unfairly placed Heather on such a high pedestal, that the actual romance couldn't possibly uphold the fantasy. It was disappointing, but that was my fault. I realized afterwards that I wanted the sex to be chart-breaking, like with my old girlfriend Taylor, but there is no denying chemistry and no substitute for a ravenous attitude. Sex with a new partner is rarely "off the hook" the first time because there is apprehension, there are undiscovered boundaries, and there is experimentation within the different erogenous zones. It usually requires time, effort and repetition to fully understand your partner's body and what positions, angles, and rhythms they enjoy most. If you are lucky enough to see fireworks the first time, buckle your seatbelt because it will only get better with repetition.

Imagine Tiger Woods on the 16th green during the Masters at Augusta. If he has a thirty foot putt for birdie he probably makes it twenty percent of the time. But if you gave him five practice putts from the same ball location where he can study the curvature, the thickness, and the moisture of the greens coupled with ball speed, he probably makes the same putt fifty percent of the time. Sex is no different from putting; it is all about muscle memory. And practice makes perfect!

Heather and I lacked physical chemistry; it was frustrating because I badly wanted it to be there, but it's something that cannot be forced. It is an intangible part of a relationship that either exists or it doesn't; if it's absent then the relationship is floundering on borrowed time.

Two months later I was heading to a cocktail party on the roof-deck of a penthouse near Heather's apartment. I thought it would be a nice gesture to invite her to the party since it was so close. She declined my invitation and began to lecture me again on why she would not be a good girlfriend for me. She mistakenly assumed my innocent invite was some desperate plea to date her. It's staggering to behold the hubris of some women in New York. I guess the persistent attention they receive from men clouds their judgment and their sense of reality.

I rudely interrupted her misguided ramblings to remind her that I had called about the party because some film-industry people would be in attendance. Her annoying rant and her general arrogance had become as irritating as a thrombotic hemorrhoid. I finally prescribed some "shut the fuck up" medication to counteract her gargantuan dose of self-importance and her inflated sense of desirability. I had been pushed to the brink.

"Listen sweetheart, it wasn't that good," was my cruel retort.

I think it had been an eternity since a man had taken a firm stand and not allowed Heather's undeniable beauty to devour his pride and curb his sensibility. I told her to take a moment to reflect on the fact that I had not called her since we had been intimate.

"If I wanted you to be my girlfriend, I would have called. I would have sent flowers. You just don't get it!" I exclaimed.

This reality check hit her like a two-by-four right between the eyes. She responded a day later by sending me a nasty email and we didn't communicate for almost a year. Sometimes a tasty Danish pastry becomes disgustingly stale. I was stunned that I found the *cojones* to dismiss Heather. But at the end of the day, regardless of how ridiculously good-looking a woman may be, you always have to have the resolve to move forward. One seemingly constant and unanswered question remained.

"Who's next?!"

17

KO'd by a Southern Belle

They say it happens when you least expect *it.* The *it* I am referring to is experiencing true love and finding your soul mate. *It* was completely unexpected when I reconnected with a young girl in the summer 1989 who would eventually become my ex-wife, and it happened again a few months after I met Lindsay.

Thursday March 15, 2007 8:59PM

I was attending a birthday party for a well-known Manhattan nightlife guy. He hobnobbed with everybody connected to the party scene in New York and had rented a popular night club called PM in the trendy Meatpacking District. I decided to attend with my friend, Brandon, knowing the party would attract the "beautiful people". Brandon and I enjoyed a few drinks, some savory appetizers, and great tunes spun by a well-known DJ. The soirée exceeded my expectations. We bumped into some old friends and made some new acquaintances.

The party had been raging for about three hours and the open bar was about to close. Brandon and I decided to do one more exploratory lap before leaving. Shortly after starting our leisurely stroll, a gorgeous blond began circling the party directly behind us.

"Don't worry. I'm not stalking you guys," the girl with the

golden hair yelled above the din.

We both laughed at her suggestion and recognized the ad hoc comment as an opportunity to introduce ourselves. Lindsay was a tall, elegant woman with a Southern drawl, an accent that I found insanely sexy. I loved her professional appearance; she had her blond hair tied in a bun and dressed like a career woman with a respectable job. It wasn't obvious as to whether she was more interested in Brandon or me.

After we adequately covered a few of those pesky resume questions, Lindsay talked about her allegiance to her alma mater, Auburn, and her passion for SEC football. She also bragged about how she was plugged into the SEC network in New York and knew a plethora of cute Southern girlfriends in the city. She was a skilled saleswoman and it was an effective pitch. Brandon and I sniffed an opportunity for us and our horde of bachelor buddies. My sister had attended the University of Alabama, so I knew how pretty and graceful southern belles could be. I had witnessed their tantalizing appeal first-hand at my sister's sorority, Alpha Chi Omega, while visiting Tuscaloosa.

As Brandon and I motioned for the door, I instinctively asked Lindsay for her cell number. We told her we had some nice single friends as well and thought we should organize a group outing. Lindsay agreed wholeheartedly to the idea. Brandon gave me a big high five outside the club. He said he had met a few Southern girls like Lindsay and that they always ran with a good-looking crew. He predicted that we had discovered a goldmine in meeting her. I felt like he was right, but I had no inkling how right he was.

Two freakish occurrences transpired over the next five days that were mind-boggling. Lindsay and I had met on Thursday night. It was now Saturday and the lease on my midtown apartment was expiring in a few weeks. I was determined to find a nice one-bedroom in Soho, a neighborhood where I had always wanted to live, but always found it to be inconvenient to my office. I had spent that Saturday morning with a real estate agent traipsing in and out of apartments all over Soho. It was noon and we were about to call it a day when she coerced me to visit one more place in the West Village. It was a cute apartment on Cornelia Street, but not exactly what I was searching for.

When we left the building I thanked the agent and realized I was starving from the morning's search efforts. There was a quaint breakfast place next door called Cornelia Street Café, so I popped in and grabbed a seat at the bar to order brunch. After the bartender took my order I surveyed the dining room and my eyes immediately met Lindsay's at a nearby table. Manhattan offers its millions of inhabitants over three thousand dining options so it was awfully rare to initially meet someone on a Thursday and coincidentally bump into them less than forty-eight hours later.

I approached her table and we both chuckled at our fortuitous reunion. She was dining with a girlfriend so I shared a brief hello and returned to my barstool. I quietly read the newspaper as I ate, but found myself sneaking a few undetected peeks at Lindsay. She was much more striking than I had remembered from the party. The lighting was always so inadequate in those places. The people you meet at nightclubs can look drastically different, almost unrecognizable, when you see them in broad daylight. She and her friend finished their meal and Lindsay took a roundabout path towards the exit to say goodbye before leaving. I appreciated the gesture.

Three days later on Tuesday morning I was hustling to a meeting in midtown at the Mandarin Oriental Hotel on Columbus Circle. I was traveling on the subway from Soho in an uptown direction on a rail line that I rarely took and it required a track switch at Times Square. I crossed the platform from the express track to the local side.

"Shaun. Shaun. Over here," I heard a faint voice cry out.

I was looking around unable to locate its origin. After a

train passed on the express track I heard the voice again, and standing across from me on the opposite platform was Lindsay, fashionably dressed, wearing a big smile, and delicately waving. I was shocked. Jokingly, I cupped my hands around my mouth like a bullhorn.

"Stop stalking me," I yelled across the tracks.

We both laughed and I told her I would call her later that night.

As I jumped on my train I couldn't help thinking there were cosmic forces at work. What were the odds of randomly bumping into this woman again on a subway line that I seldom ever ride? I was beginning to think that my beloved Irish grandmother was somehow intervening and sending me a heavenly message. Lindsay's surname was as Irish as a leprechaun, and my recently deceased grandmother had always wanted me to marry a nice Irish girl. She had always been the guardian angel in my life, and I was convinced that she was still watching over me from Heaven. Then I realized that Lindsay and I had first met two days before St. Patrick's Day. Now I was becoming rattled by all these intertwined cross-currents, spooky coincidences, and eerie improbabilities.

I called Lindsay later that evening. She and some girlfriends were going out to a place in Soho and wanted me to round up some of my buddies. Brandon and I gathered up three friends and went to rendezvous with Lindsay's clan of southern belles. The evening was fun, but nobody seemed to experience the lightning in a bottle connection. One of my friends was attracted to one of Lindsay's girlfriends, but she happened to be the only one that was already in a serious relationship. It seemed to always be the case in New York; the most desirable one was always unavailable. About a week later I received another casual invitation from Lindsay to meet her and three girlfriends at the Coffee Shop in Union Square. Brandon and I joined the girls for some afternoon cocktails. Her friends were cute, but I found myself more fixated on Lindsay.

A week later I fielded a call from Lindsay with a special invitation. She innocently asked me if I liked Bruce Springsteen. I told her that U2 and "The Boss" were probably two of my favorite musical acts. She was thrilled and offered to take me to a Bruce Springsteen tribute concert at Carnegie Hall. I wasn't even sure what a tribute concert meant, but I impulsively accepted her invitation. She explained that the show comprised thirteen different solo artists and bands, each performing their one favorite Springsteen song. It sounded like the ingredients for a memorable evening.

The show was brilliant. And at the end Bruce shocked the crowd! He had been lurking backstage unbeknownst to the audience. He miraculously appeared on stage and performed a couple of his classics, *Pink Cadillac* and *Rosalita*. It was a phenomenal performance that brought the house down. I repeatedly thanked Lindsay for letting me partake in such a memorable event. How many times, if ever, had The Boss played Carnegie Hall?

We were both hungry from all the excitement and decided to grab a late dinner at the nearby French bistro, Rue 57. Lindsay lived on West 16th Street, which was on the way to Soho, so after dinner we shared a cab and headed downtown. When we arrived at Lindsay's apartment, she unexpectedly dropped a bomb in my lap. I had about seven seconds to diffuse it or watch myself explode. She invited me upstairs to her apartment. I had to think fast and make a crucial decision. I knew by joining her I risked transforming our friendship into a courtship. Was I ready for that? Did I want to go down that road? Or did I want to maintain a friendly, platonic relationship? Seven seconds later I accepted her invitation knowing that there were potential consequences.

Lindsay's apartment was an oversized studio with spacious closets, a loft space, and high ceilings. Her décor was conservative, filled with antique furniture and vintage accessories, and loaded with family photos. She had pictures of her sister, her parents, her cousin, and her adorable newborn nephew, whom she always gushed over. It was a palpable display of how much she valued family, and the manner in which she discussed her baby nephew made it abundantly clear how much she loved children. It seemed incredibly judgmental and premature, but after two minutes in Lindsay's apartment I had concluded that she would someday make a wonderful mother.

She proudly explained who all the people were in each of the pictures as she cautiously invited me into her life. Lindsay explained what it was like growing up on a farm in rural Alabama. She had moved to New York City less than eighteen months earlier, but I was amazed at how well she had adapted to the frantic pace and daunting scope of the city. She leveraged her multiple networks to expedite the adaptation process. The crux of her job was to help enlarge Columbia University's war chest, also known as the endowment fund. Basically she asked wealthy alumni for seven-figure donations. She was a saleswoman and she excelled at her job.

After familiarizing me with her family and parts of her new life in New York, she sat down next to me on the couch. We instinctively kissed as if we had been dating for months. There was no cautionary hesitation, no awkward expressions, and no uncomfortable pauses. I knew this instantly changed our relationship, but I was at ease with our new situation. We were clearly attracted to each other, but we also both recognized that we had been pursuing active dating lives before our random introduction. Although both unattached when we met, we had been casually dating other people. As a general rule, anyone you meet in Manhattan who is both desirable and single inevitably has a few situations in their social life. The question became how much of it, if any, are they willing to abandon for you? Another barometer of where you rank is the cell-phone test. A "Manhattan-*ite*" can tell when they start to genuinely care about someone by their willingness to answer their precious cell phone when that person calls.

Lindsay and I vaguely discussed our dating situations that evening, and we were both comfortable with allowing things to progress naturally. If our affection for one another was strong enough and it matured, we both figured we would become exclusive. I left her apartment that evening excited about our kiss, but even more intrigued about our shared willingness to not force or rush the relationship. I loved the concept of letting something grow and mature before determining if it was meant to be.

Over the next few weeks Lindsay and I had a few impromptu dates. We had dinner in Soho and drinks with her friends. She introduced me to her most trusted male friend in New York and I introduced her to my wing woman, Banu. It still felt right as a casual relationship, but a few weeks later things unexpectedly moved into hyper drive. It was the first Wednesday of May and I was leaving on an early morning flight to Louisville on Thursday. The Kentucky Derby was Saturday and I was making my annual pilgrimage to Churchill Downs for the big race with a few of my college fraternity brothers. The ticket was purchased with frequent-flier miles so if I missed my flight it would be impossible to get rebooked. The limited direct flights to Louisville from New York had been sold out since January.

Lindsay had invited me out that evening with two of her girlfriends, so one of my single buddies tagged along hoping there might be a connection. I warned Lindsay that it had to be an early night because of my travel schedule. Unfortunately there was no love connection between my pal and either of her two friends, but Lindsay appeared to be in a party mood. She was drinking straight whiskey. We were all enjoying ourselves on the couches under the canopy of a trendy outdoor bar when I checked my Rolex and made a move for the exit. My intention was to leave them all there to continue having fun while I snuck away for a good night's sleep. Lindsay wouldn't let me pull "the Houdini." I sternly reminded her of my trip and she agreed to leave, but asked me to bring her home. I conceded because she was so irresistible when she batted her alluring "Betty Davis eyes", but I sensed an ulterior motive. When the cab pulled up to her building, she quickly paid the fare and asked me to come inside. The cab driver had turned the meter off before I could even tell him there was one more stop.

Lindsay coaxed me upstairs and started acting goofy and overly playful. I could tell by her body language where things were headed, but I was woefully unprepared to resist her calculated advances. I tried using the "I don't have any protection" excuse. I told her I couldn't stay the night because I had to pack and a car service was picking me up in the morning. Lindsay had a retort for all my objections. She was determined to seal the deal. I was the one being cleverly seduced, which was unfamiliar territory.

Lindsay had an incredible body covered by soft flawless skin, a tight muscular tummy, and firm legs from years of classical ballet and cheerleading. Her blond locks were sexy when she let them cascade down her back once released from her trademark bun. She took control and I enjoyed her surprisingly aggressive nature. Lindsay had always seemed so conservative, projecting the image of a sweet, passive and innocent lady when in public. Her aggressiveness was just one more pleasant surprise.

Lindsay was a passionate woman who loved kissing and the intimacy of gentle touching. She liked running her hands through my thick hair and pulling me tight to her body. She loved to snuggle in my arms and kiss my neck. I felt an overwhelming sense of guilt over the fact that I couldn't stay the night. I repeatedly apologized and promised her that running out the door was definitely not my style. I felt awful about the situation, and that was the reason I vehemently tried to resist her at the outset. Lindsay thought I had been joking because there was a solemn look of disbelief on her face as I got dressed to leave. Her disappointed expression only deepened my guilt. I was experiencing too much anxiety over packing and arriving at the airport on time. It was a sacrifice I deeply regret not making because it conveyed a horrible message.

The Kentucky Derby was one of my favorite events of the year. It was an opportunity to witness a great sporting event, soak up a glorious tradition, and bond with five esteemed members of my crazy college crew. There were plenty of parties, tons of celebrities, and high voltage energy all weekend. We usually had a group of about ten staying at one of the downtown hotels. We would hire a driver for the weekend to make it easier to get to the track and attend all the soirées.

The weekend was a roaring success. We enjoyed top-notch accommodations and great seats for both the Kentucky Oaks on Friday and the Kentucky Derby on Saturday. One of my college buddies had grown up in Louisville and attended St. Xavier High School. Most of his high-school pals lived locally so we had invaluable connections and some enviable invitations every year.

Although I felt guilty about leaving Lindsay's apartment that Wednesday night, the weekend was so busy I didn't give it much thought until I returned on Sunday. It bothered me that I hadn't spent the night. I felt like I had drowned our relationship just as it was starting to blossom. I couldn't go back and change what had happened, but I kept wishing that I could. It was inappropriate behavior and I knew it. I should have either stayed the night or prevented the evening from ever progressing to intimacy. And if I was so tormented, I could only imagine how perturbed Lindsay must have been by my abrupt departure. What the hell was I thinking?

Lindsay and I saw each other a few times in May as we

both got restless for the summer to arrive. She had signed up for a half-share in a house in Sag Harbor. It was going to be her inaugural Hamptons experience and my seventh straight summer, but my excitement level was high. I had experienced five different share houses, all in East Hampton, but this summer was going to be unique. Three friends of mine had begged me to participate in what could be best described as a "share boat" instead of the traditional share house. I was skeptical at first, but once I saw the size of the bedrooms and galley I became more enthusiastic. The expenses seemed reasonable when split three ways, so I optimistically gave the boat proposal the green light.

My two boat mates were ecstatic. They needed me on board because neither of them had ever spent any measurable time in the Hamptons and had no idea where to go, and even less of an idea on how to get there. I was their social director and default GPS for the summer, text messaging directions at all hours. Nothing is more difficult than trying to find a house party on an unlit back road in the Hamptons late at night. Without a knowledgeable guide, it's easy to spend hours driving in circles and cursing the darkness.

My business school classmate, Dan, had a Penn State fraternity brother who was in the early stages of a divorce. He lived in Palm Beach and had been in the yacht business for almost twenty years. He was a licensed boat captain and owned a fifty-foot yacht that he wanted to dock at Sag Harbor Marina for the season. It offered two full bedrooms, two full bathrooms, and a galley kitchen with a comfortable sleeping area. The boat could easily accommodate three couples on any given weekend.

By chance the marina was fairly close to where Lindsay was spending the summer. I was familiar with the share house she was renting and cautioned her about the frat-like antics that would occur there over the course of the summer. She was a Hampton's rookie so her poor choice was just a case of being uninformed. Based on my warning she wanted to opt out, but it was too late. The check had been cashed and refunds are seldom part of the deal when it comes to share houses in the Hamptons. I told Lindsay not to worry about her mistake; it was only eight weekends and she was more than welcome to spend some nights on the boat with me.

After the first weekend I was thrilled with my decision. The boat share concept was a towering home run! It was so peaceful being in the marina on the water. The subtle rocking motion at night was like being a baby rocked to sleep in a bassinette. The crisp fresh smell of the ocean air and the soft sound of water gently splashing against the hull was a soothing way to rise each morning. And all the boat owners at the marina were so friendly and accommodating. After seven seasons of being involved in East Hampton share houses, I realized I had done it all wrong.

The marina had some convenient amenities, and it was a short walk to Main Street in Sag Harbor, a place offering just about everything we needed. On Sunday of Memorial Day weekend we organized our first boat ride to Sunset Beach on Shelter Island. It instantly became our Sunday ritual. We would spend all day Saturday recruiting cute girls to join us for the Sunday afternoon cruise. It became a competition. Who could place the best-looking girls on the boat? I always had an unfair advantage because Lindsay had an automatic bid any weekend she was there. It was a picturesque thirty-minute ride through the bay to Sunset Beach. It was always romantic to watch the sun lazily disappear over the westerly tree tops across the water. Lindsay liked to share a kiss as we watched the majestic sunset.

On the third weekend of the summer, Lindsay was traveling. The boys and I hit an old Hampton's haunt, Cyril's, on Saturday afternoon. I unexpectedly met an adorable Texan named Noelle. She was statuesque with piercing blue eyes, sexy full lips, perfect teeth, and a dangerously inviting smile. I noticed her instantly as we stepped onto the gravel parking area in front of the infamous clam shack. And Noelle noticed me. I could tell when our eyes met that there was a mutual attraction. She made her way through the crowd towards me and we skipped any silly flirtatious drivel. She had grown up in Dallas, graduated from Yale, and worked at Goldman Sachs. Her resume was as impressive as her sizzling appeal. She liked my resume too. Our attraction grew stronger with each topic of conversation.

Now I had a serious dilemma. I wanted to connect with Noelle that evening, but I kept thinking about Lindsay. During Memorial Day Weekend, Lindsay had invited her cousin from Texas to join her. She wanted to be a good hostess so she reiterated that we were "on our own." I had a clarifying conversation with her to ensure she understood what that meant and that we were on the same page. As I replayed that discussion and recalled how engaging Lindsay had been with a few guys the prior weekend, I justified the idea of meeting Noelle that evening. Lindsay had tried to rationalize her suggestive behavior as simply helping her cousin meet some nice New York men. I had never accepted that flimsy explanation. At one point I became extremely annoyed by her behavior. I tried to disguise how upset and jealous I was because, just like in sports, "you never want to let them see you sweat."

Noelle invited me to a barbeque at her house in Amagansett. I grabbed the captain from the boat and we headed to the little gathering. We scoffed some burgers and swilled a few beers as the party was starting to unwind. Noelle was excited that I had shown up and quickly dragged me around the party to introduce me to her friends and housemates. One can gauge someone's interest in you by how enthusiastically they introduce you to their friends and relatives. It is always a telltale barometer of how proud someone feels about you as a companion.

Somehow Noelle coerced me into the laundry room just as we were about to leave for the next watering hole. Once we were in the seclusion of the washer and dryer, Noelle attacked me for a kiss. I didn't resist and couldn't help laughing when I realized we were hanging out with dirty sheets and towels. I had an uncomfortable twinge being with Noelle, but Lindsay and I had verified that we were both free agents, able to pursue whomever we pleased with no restrictions and no remorse. Noelle was aggressive, and if I hadn't moved towards the door, we might have dropped to the floor for a naughty roll in a pile of dirty laundry.

We joined the rest of the partygoers at Stephen's Talkhouse, an Amagansett mainstay and regarded as the best live music venue in the Hamptons. Noelle and I danced, sang along with the band, and took a break out back by the pool table. The Talkhouse was jam-packed, which was always the case on a Saturday in the summertime. At the end of the evening I drove Noelle back to her house. She wanted me to stay the night, but thought it would be inappropriate since she was sharing her room with a girlfriend. I wholeheartedly agreed and passionately kissed her good night, but promised her a reserved spot on the Sunset Beach cruise on Sunday afternoon.

When Noelle arrived on Sunday she was enthusiastic about hanging out on the boat. I had terribly underestimated how much women love big boats; it is a legitimate aphrodisiac. But the more I thought about the scarcity factor, the more it made sense. When we would arrive at Sunset Beach there would be five or six yachts anchored off the beach. The bar and restaurant area would be packed with over two hundred people. I would guess that maybe ten percent of the patrons had arrived via water, thus we had scarcity value. Who wanted to be amongst the other ninety percent who had to schlep there on a ferry and cross the island via car? Arriving on a fifty-foot yacht seemed a lot more exciting and unique.

Noelle brought along a few of her housemates as well. They all had a great time enjoying the open water, some cocktails, and the VIP feeling of cruising into Sunset Beach on a water taxi from the yacht. I think Noelle romanticized me as a bonafide rock star that Sunday. Somehow the components of that day created a glorified image of what I was all about. Deep down I was still just a beer-and-football-loving guy from a simple place who didn't give a shit about impressing anybody. My accomplishments in life spoke volumes and could not be enhanced nor diminished by a fancy yacht rental.

When the boat returned to Sag Harbor it was almost nine o'clock so I offered Noelle a ride back to the city. My relationship with Noelle progressed at warp speed and I had neither the control nor the inclination to stop it. It was summer time, and I was rightfully pursuing the fun part of the "fun in the sun" slogan that signified those three cherished months.

Lindsay took some time off from work during the July 4th week. We had the boat to ourselves for a few nights before the boys arrived for what was guaranteed to be a weekend of debauchery. Lindsay and I thoroughly enjoyed our forty-eight hours of solitude on the yacht. We made love on the stairs leading up from the galley while the stars and the moon shined down on us from above. The seawater made its familiar and soothing splashing noises against the boat's hull. It was a deliciously romantic night.

The second evening Lindsay was treating me to a fancy dinner at a new steakhouse in East Hampton. While at her house in Sag Harbor gathering a few things she got cornered by a housemate requesting a ride into town. I was surprised to find Brandi in the backseat when Lindsay arrived at the marina. When Brandi's friend changed plans and she got blown off, we were burdened with a third wheel for dinner. To ease her own discomfort she invited another girlfriend to join us. As we sat down I scratched my head and wondered how dinner with

Lindsay had become a table for four.

The evening hinged on outrageous when Brandi decided to solicit my opinion on an unusual subject. After ordering my meal Brandi tapped my arm.

"Do men like their asshole fingered when they're getting a blow job?" she asked.

It was an unusual question, especially from someone I had known for five minutes and who had shamelessly crashed my dinner at this upscale restaurant. I answered the question without skipping a beat, and then looked at Lindsay as if to ask where the hell she dug up this crazy chick.

The next weekend Lindsay was back in the Hamptons, and fortunately, Noelle spent the weekend elsewhere. I realized that seeing both of them was going to be impossible. My dilemma was that I honestly enjoyed spending time with each of them. They were intelligent, sexy, Southern, and incredibly fun to be around. They both made me feel ten years younger. After maintaining a relationship with both of them for a month, it was mid-July and a nondescript girl approached me at Cyril's.

Lindsay was spending that weekend on Fisher Island, a secluded island off the Connecticut coast, while Noelle was in Texas visiting her folks. I was hanging out with the boys and sipping an ice-cold Mud Slide. I had no idea who this girl was, but she approached, asked my name, and scampered away as she whipped out her cell phone. About five minutes later my cell phone rang and it was Lindsay. I instinctively smelled a disaster brewing so I didn't answer the call. Lindsay had left a message saying it was urgent that I call her. I knew the jig was up. Somehow the meddling girl in the parking lot had connected the dots and squealed on me. Or had she? Had I done anything wrong? I was forthright with Lindsay about both of us being free agents. The more I thought about it, the less I hesitated to return Lindsay's call. I had nothing to hide and no need to apologize.

I called Lindsay and she predictably confronted me about Noelle. I readily admitted to the connection and was quick to reference our conversation about not being attached. She said she remembered it, but somehow it felt different when it was dropped like a bomb from ten thousand feet into her lap. The intrusive girl in the parking lot knew Lindsay through one of her male friends and also knew Noelle in a roundabout way. Once she became privy to my involvement with both women she couldn't leak the information fast enough. Some girls just love to meddle in other people's affairs and gossip about people they hardly know.

My birthday was in three days and Lindsay had already arranged a special dinner in Tribeca. After our conversation I was confident I would be dining alone. It was a painful reality, but I was responsible for the situation and readily accepted the consequences. I began scanning the Cyril's crowd. Sadly, "on to the next one" was my mantra, and like a seasoned competitor, I never dwelled on the losses.

Miraculously, Lindsay called me late on Monday night and asked if I was still available for Tuesday's dinner. I was ecstatic that she was willing to rebook. She treated me to one of the finest restaurants in all of Manhattan, Bouley. The conversation was awkward at first, but we both handled the situation like mature adults. She admitted that I had been honest and aboveboard in where our relationship stood and its parameters.

"Listen buddy, if you hadn't been honest in admitting what was going on, you would have never heard from me again," she firmly stated.

It was a case of honesty being the best policy. In that spirit I called Noelle to explain the situation and how things had now changed. She understood and couldn't have handled the complex circumstances any better. Thankfully Noelle and I are still good friends.

As we enjoyed our fabulous meal, Lindsay basically said our

relationship was finished unless I was willing to accept some major rule changes. I enjoyed Lindsay's companionship too much to let her go, and that night I realized how much she truly meant to me. She said the only way that we could continue would be as an exclusive couple and asked me to think about it. I didn't flinch when she asked for a commitment. Five seconds later I told her I happily accepted her new terms and was excited to call her my girlfriend. Quite frankly, my willingness to forego the remaining "fun in the sun" scared the shit out of me. Lindsay had managed to pierce the armor around my heart.

The remainder of the summer, Lindsay and I became inseparable. We attended polo matches and enjoyed the nightlife in Southampton at places like Pink Elephant, Dune, and Madame Tongs. We went to house parties together. Whenever she went out with the girls or I went out with the boys, we always made arrangements to rendezvous later in the evening. I vividly remember being surrounded by vodka bottles and women one Saturday night at the Pink Elephant. I knew Lindsay was on her way to meet us. She peeked around the French doors searching for me on the crowded deck, and the moment I saw her captivating smile, a euphoric and warm sensation filled my body. The more time I spent with her, the more I wanted to be by her side. The boys on the boat were growing restless with my attachment to Lindsay, but I didn't care. I was falling in love with her and there was nothing anybody could do or say to stop it. I was so happy!

The first weekend in August I had to drive my daughter back to Maine after hosting her and a girlfriend for a fun-filled week in the Hamptons. I had invited Lindsay to take the trip up to Maine with us. We were due for a weekend away from the hustle and bustle of the Hamptons. She caught the train out to Bridgehampton on Thursday evening, where I picked her up and the four of us enjoyed dinner at Nick & Tony's in East Hampton. I was excited to have Lindsay meet my daughter, my parents, and experience the sights of my treasured hometown. Lindsay had never been to Maine so she was also excited about the weekend getaway.

Lindsay's visit was a smashing success. We enjoyed perfect weather and a smorgasbord of tasty meals with plenty of fresh Maine lobster prepared in scrumptious dishes. My parents were enamored with Lindsay from the moment she crossed the threshold of the front door. When she flashed that Southern charm coupled with her soothing drawl my father was smitten and became putty in her hands. She reminded my parents of all the sweet and adorable young ladies in my sister's sorority at 'Bama.

On Saturday my father loaded us into his convertible BMW and we embarked on a guided tour of Portland, soaking up all its picturesque waterfront scenery. Lindsay was overwhelmed by the beauty of the rustic and rugged Maine coast. On Saturday night Lindsay nonchalantly whispered in my ear to thank me for bringing her to Maine. She added that she could envision herself living there someday; it was a statement that had serious overtures and caught me totally off guard. As I dissected her comment, I realized that she was subtly telling me she would follow me anywhere.

There was an annual concert on a floating barge in East Hampton that Sunday called the Barcelona party. I made a tactical error in suggesting we head back early Sunday morning to make it onto the boat for the afternoon festivities. Lindsay was enjoying Maine and wanted to stay the extra day. She had only been there for thirty-six hours, but I was selfishly determined to return for the concert. Lindsay was irritated by my decision and wanted a vacation from the Hampton's hoopla.

The concert turned out to be a fun and worthwhile event, and we cruised to Sunset Beach afterwards. The boys got shit-faced, picked up some sloppy bimbos, and partied all night on the boat while Lindsay and I tried to sleep so I could rise early on Monday and transport her back to the city for work. It became an ugly, sleep-deprived night, and Lindsay chastised me for not staying in Maine. I had no rebuttal for her unhappiness, and in hindsight, I too wished we had enjoyed the tranquility of Maine for one more day.

Labor Day came and went as Lindsay traveled to Alabama to visit her family while the boys and I wrapped up the summer in style as the social scene moved to fall. September was always a great month in Manhattan. The tourists vanished and everyone returned to the city from the beaches, the mountains, and the lakes. Lindsay and I attended a black-tie charity event at the Central Park Boathouse that first Friday night. It was a lavish affair with over a thousand guests. We strolled through the crowd as if we were the King and Queen of the Prom and Lindsay looked so devastatingly beautiful. That evening I finally appreciated that Lindsay exhibited a classical, Grace Kelly type of elegance. I was so proud to have her on my arm and it dawned on me how lucky I was to be dating such an extraordinary woman.

Friday September 14, 2007 3:42PM

We enjoyed a getaway weekend in Newport, Rhode Island en route to a friend's wedding. Lindsay was overwhelmed by the majesty and the glamour of the Newport mansions. She had never experienced the opulent remnants of the Gilded Age. And she was thrilled to learn that one of Cornelius Vanderbilt's grandsons had married Alva Smith who was originally from Mobile, Alabama. Alva Vanderbilt became a driving force in the suffrage movement culminating in the passage of the 19th Amendment, guaranteeing women the right to vote. Alva and William Kissam Vanderbilt constructed one of the most magnificent mansions in Newport, Marble House. It was located just down Bellevue Avenue from another stately Vanderbilt property, the Breakers, Newport's crown jewel, and perhaps the most palatial home ever built in America.

It was on that Saturday evening that I made a eureka discovery. Lindsay and I had enjoyed an appetizing meal at the West Deck and enjoyed a few cocktails on Bannister Wharf. It was an unseasonably cool mid-September evening, so we headed back to the house. The cold temperature had triggered the heating system, making the house uncomfortably warm. I had forgotten to pull down the shade on one of the windows and the curious moonlight peeked into our bedroom, softly illuminating one side of Lindsay's beautiful face. I slowly reached over with my index finger to gently wipe away a few small beads of sweat that had accumulated in the tiny crease on the side of Lindsay's regal nose.

Lindsay suddenly reached for my hand.

"Quit it!" she exclaimed as I snickered at her embarrassment.

She was obviously self-conscious about her tiny imperfection. She blushed and then she laughed bashfully, allowing me to encroach on her vulnerability. I told her how much I loved her cute little dew drops as I reflected upon some of my own deficiencies. As Lindsay and I spooned and the moonlight danced off the windblown tree branches, I was enlightened by how intimate and how valuable imperfections could be in defining a relationship.

I awoke the next morning hoping to expose another quirk that made Lindsay so completely adorable to me. I absolutely loved her southern accent and there was one silly word that for some reason provided me with foolish joy, yet caused Lindsay tremendous consternation. I guess I never fully understood how much of a dirty word "pussy" is considered in Alabama. The first few months she refused to ever say it, but we cracked that barrier during a night of unbridled passion and uninhibited sexual commentary. After that episode I would look at Lindsay with a fiendish smirk and playfully beg her to say pussy.

She would usually respond, "Quit it! I'm not sayin' it."

Then her cute little-girl grin would consume her face.

She would quickly blurt out, "Pussy," while looking around the room as if to verify that no one else was listening.

I would laugh hysterically and she would giggle like a baby being tickled.

She sprung up in bed that morning and shouted, "Oh my God! What have you done to me? What is my sister going to think?"

"What the hell are you talking about?" I inquired.

"In less than six months you've convinced me to wax my privates, and now y'all have me sayin' pussy twice a day."

I was laughing uncontrollably at Lindsay's dire revelation.

The week after our Newport excursion another monumental event occurred, and it was eagerly greeted by another one of my catastrophic fuck-ups. It was Wednesday morning and I had spent the night at Lindsay's apartment. The office where I traded stocks was located two blocks away on Fifth Avenue. Lindsay was busy showering while I made the bed and got myself dressed. There was some economic data being released at 8:30AM that would affect some of my positions, so my mind was already focused on that day's market activity. As I passed by the bathroom to leave, I knocked to give Lindsay a kiss goodbye. She opened the door all wet and naked as she wrapped herself in a towel. She looked incredibly gorgeous with her glistening skin and her damp hair pulled back. I leaned over the bathroom threshold and gave Lindsay a soft kiss wishing her a good day at work.

"Have a great day too, honey. I love you!" she responded.

It was so unexpected and I was so absorbed in my own thoughts that I almost didn't even hear it. Neither one of us had ever said the "L" word.

By the time I realized the magnitude of what she had said,

and my lack of a response, I was halfway to the elevator. Why the hell was I thinking about CPI data? Should I go back? Should I skip the market opening and make passionate love to her on the bathroom floor? Should I knock on the door, kiss her, and tell her the same thing? Maybe I should have gone to the corner store, bought a rose, and ambushed her with an "I love you." Any of these possibilities would have been exponentially better than what I did—nothing. The moment was forever lost. With the World Series on the line I took a called third strike and left the bat on my shoulder. I choked. What a fucking moron! And I couldn't help but ask myself, why does this woman tolerate my sorry ass?

At the end of September Lindsay asked me to accompany her on a business trip. She was heading to Paris and Athens for a series of important meetings and wanted me to join her. At the back end of her trip she planned a four-day weekend on Mykonos in the Greek Islands. It sounded like a great adventure and I was enthusiastically on board. I was going to fly to Paris, rendezvous with Lindsay at her hotel, and return to New York from Athens. We were both excited about the eight-day, three-city excursion. Unfortunately the trip marked the beginning of the end. Everything seemed to go wrong.

The first night I arrived in Paris, I made arrangements for us to go to visit a nightclub that was managed by my Parisian friend, Victoria. Once we arrived at the club Lindsay began drinking heavily. I urged her not to get drunk so we could enjoy some sightseeing on Sunday morning before departing for Athens. Lindsay did not heed my warning, and instead became completely intoxicated. When we left the club it was freezing outside and it took an hour to hail a cab ride back to the hotel; Paris is on the junior varsity squad when it comes to late night transportation.

The next morning Lindsay wasn't getting out of bed for anything. She couldn't even make it downstairs for the breakfast buffet. Not only was she hung over, but she was also feeling the effects of an oncoming cold. I had warned her repeatedly the night before, but she just kept taunting me while throwing back the whiskey. Her developing cold intensified throughout our trip. The weather in Athens was brutally hot and the weather in Mykonos was also strange. The wind was gusting at about twenty miles per hour from the moment we landed until the day we left. Even the locals said it was unusual. To compound my misery, I received a frantic voicemail from my investment advisor; my biggest investment position was spiraling downward while we were trying to shelter ourselves on the beach from the swirling winds. The trip was disastrous.

Two weeks after we returned to New York, Lindsay asked me to stop by her apartment. I could tell by the stern tone in her voice she had something serious on her mind. I had felt coldness growing between us since we returned and had a strong idea where the conversation was headed. Lindsay voiced her concerns about liking me too much, the emotional inequality in our relationship, being afraid of getting hurt, and protecting her heart. Once again, I made a colossal mistake by attacking her instead of empathizing and soothing her anxieties.

I assumed a defensive stance by lashing out and accusing her of repeating a familiar pattern. By the age of twenty-six Lindsay had been engaged twice and ran away both times. Oddly, she feared commitment, which was so typically a male issue in relationships. After my divorce I had always proceeded with caution, and knowing Lindsay's past, I worried about her unwillingness to take a vow. Her parents had been divorced when she was young, and both had endured tumultuous relationships while she grew up. Those troublesome exposures created a lasting impression. Watching her sister initiate divorce proceedings that fall after two years of a rocky marriage was enough to push her over the edge. The result—I got whacked with the old "it's not you, it's me" cliché.

My natural reaction was to act unsurprised, as if I had expected everything she said. Lindsay's two busted engagements had raised a red flag at the outset, but my inflated ego told me that I was different. She had fled from the other two because those chumps couldn't match my *je ne sais quoi.* I rationalized that she just needed a break and would eventually come to her senses. She would realize how perfect we were for each other.

I escorted her out of the apartment and down the tree-lined block as she headed to the Coffee Shop on Union Square to meet a girlfriend. As Lindsay crossed Fifth Avenue I watched her cute ass shake and smugly told myself that she would soon return. I had seen this act before and "they" always came back. Why would this time be different?

The weeks passed and we shared an occasional text message or a meaningless email, but it was becoming clear that she was trying hard to move forward. My sister visited in mid-November and we were heading to a friend's party that I knew Lindsay would be attending. It was an opportunity to introduce them, even though one attended Alabama and one went to Auburn, a bitter rivalry. Aside from their hatred for each other's alma mater, Lindsay and my sister got along splendidly.

"Lindsay absolutely adores you," my sister reported back to me.

"Then what the hell is she doing without me in her life?" I asked in frustration.

The winter brought basketball season, which kept me distracted for the next three months. It was my daughter's junior year and her team was one of the pre-season favorites to win the Class A state girl's basketball title. As predicted they finished as the number two seed at the end of the regular season, but they got beat at the buzzer in the semi-final game. I can remember watching my daughter and her teammates collapse to the floor, slumped over in agony as if a team of snipers had shot all five of them simultaneously from the rafters. Their reaction was so precise it seemed choreographed. It's heartbreaking to watch your kid pour her heart and soul into something only to end up a few measly seconds short in pursuit of her dream.

With the basketball season finished, I turned back to the other heartbreak in my life, my growing loneliness and my unending thoughts about Lindsay. Solitude and confinement are side effects of living in Manhattan where it often seems that everyone has their own agenda. When you live in The City you accept it, but this was a different kind of imprisonment. Lindsay was on my mind all the time. It was freakishly odd, but I couldn't stop thinking about her.

I would hear a song by Lynard Skynard, the band who performed *Sweet Home Alabama*, and I would think of her. I would see a random woman on the subway with blond hair tied in a bun, the way Lindsay always wore it, and I would think of her. I would see a magazine cover with Kate Hudson, a celebrity that some people thought Lindsay resembled, and I would think of her. I would turn on HBO and *Crazy in Alabama* with Melanie Griffith would be playing. I would turn on ESPN and there would be a report about Nick Saban and the turnaround he was engineering with Alabama's football program. Lindsay had consumed my thoughts and it was maddening!

After twelve years of searching for a lifelong partner in all the wrong places, I had let a truly amazing woman slip away. The worst part was that she did all the work—she found me! She pushed for a more meaningful relationship. She fell in love with me, the dreadfully flawed honeymoon junkie. As April arrived I was still constantly thinking about the joyous times spent with Lindsay and how genuine it felt. The image of a future together with some adorable children became increasingly vivid. Sometimes I would stare in a trance, mesmerized by how I could almost touch my thoughts of us together in imaginary romantic settings. How had I let that dream fall by the wayside?

I began thinking about all the traits and adjectives on

my silly checklist that represented the attributes of the perfect woman. Lindsay had exhibited so many of those qualities. What the fuck was I thinking? And who the hell was I to think I deserved perfection? Does the Perfect Woman really exist? The answer was resoundingly no. Who's perfect? We are all flawed. I came to the revolutionary conclusion that when selecting a life partner one has to identify their flaws and then decide if you can accept or maybe even embrace those imperfections. It took me forty years to figure this out. For a guy who claims to be pretty smart, I can be a remarkably slow learner. I think I may qualify as relationship retarded. Maybe it's a side effect from years of being a honeymoon junkie.

The one thing that stood out in my mind about Lindsay was a question that I always asked myself about every woman I ever dated. The answer was vital and at the core of every relationship I ever seriously analyzed. What kind of mother would she make? To me that was often one of the most important functions a woman ever performed. I was blessed with the manner in which my ex-wife raised my daughter after my unplanned absence. But I knew that when I married her. I felt tenderness in Lindsay's heart that told me someday she would become a magnificent mother.

I always slept well at night knowing that my daughter was under the watchful and caring eye of my ex-wife. I was sure no harm would come to her, and that she would grow into a morally upstanding and responsible young lady. I envisioned Lindsay performing that precious duty with the same steadfast dedication. This was not always a quality I observed in all the women I had dated. Some were selfish or self-absorbed, and I doubted they would sacrifice or develop the mental perseverance to be a great mother.

As I reflected upon my revelations and their implications, I realized that Lindsay was so unmistakably *the one*. But how was I going to get her back? The only time I had tried to regain the affection of a previous lover was with my ex-wife. My record was short on experience with one glaring loss, a life-altering defeat. I realized I needed to make some serious changes. I had to identify my flaws and address my addiction. I needed rehabilitation.

I checked my foolish pride at the door and begged Lindsay to join me for Sunday brunch at her favorite spot, Cornelia Café. That little rendezvous led to a bowling alley date and then a dinner date. By mid-May I had mustered up the courage to ask her back into my life. I vowed I would do anything to win her back, including becoming a farmer in Alabama if that is what it would take. I told Lindsay I had experienced an epiphany after reflecting upon the last decade of my life and finding it to be disturbingly shallow and unfulfilling. I had invested way too much time chasing the honeymoon high and advancing my Wall Street career. I felt emotionally bankrupt and uncomfortably numb. The one thing that saved my soul from the darkness was the love in my heart for my daughter. She was my beacon of hope and proved I was capable of something wonderful.

Lindsay's body language, her demeanor, and her heart all screamed that she wanted me back in her life. I could feel her wanting to say yes. She then admitted that she had fallen completely in love with me last summer, and even had fleeting thoughts of marriage. Her confession only added to my torment. I could still sense there was an internal conflict raging in her soul; an insurmountable wall was rising, brick by brick, between her head and her heart.

She declined my emotional plea, and for the first time since that fateful car ride in December of 1994, I was once again totally devastated. I was left to wallow aimlessly in my loneliness, clueless in my search for answers. Why wouldn't she want to be reunited? Her rejection felt like a crushing punch to the jaw, forcefully delivered by a heavyweight champion. And as I lay knocked out on the canvas of the ring, I had forgotten how severe the pain could be.

I had taken a chance and exposed my heart, desperately hoping to win back this extraordinary woman. You can heal a bruised ego or mend ruptured pride, but as much as you try to shield your heart, regardless of how good you are at doing it, you realize that no one is invincible. There is no medicine, no therapists, and no specialists that can heal the wound. We are all so incredibly vulnerable. Love is life and life is love. Both can be taken from you in a split second, and usually when you least expect it. Either way, I must wholeheartedly agree with Alfred Lord Tennyson.

"'Tis far better to have loved and lost than to have never loved at all."

18

The Long Journey Continues

The question begging for an answer is what have I learned from this amazing, disjointed, and unplanned expedition. At twenty-eight I appeared to be the guy who had everything in the game of life, including direction and purpose. I had been a top student, a gifted athlete, attended prominent schools, and worked for the most prestigious firm on Wall Street. I had a gorgeous wife and doted on my loving daughter. I loved and I lost, but I rebounded with a gritty resilience in The City that demands nothing less than mental fortitude. Life moved on.

I crawled out from a mountain of graduate school debt and the financial strain of divorce to enjoy the jetsetter lifestyle. I lived on a top floor of a concierge building overlooking Central Park and in a nineteenth-century brownstone in Boston's best neighborhood. I summered on the beaches of East Hampton, Nantucket, and Newport, and even lived on a yacht in Sag Harbor. I drove expensive cars and assembled a wardrobe filled with quality labels. I regularly attended marquee events. And I dated a plethora of beautiful women, some of which blossomed into meaningful relationships.

A Quixotic Quest

Although I still haven't found *the one*, I continue to search. I forge ahead, waking each morning with the hope of meeting my rightful soul mate. I am an eternal optimist who refuses to concede and am determined to explore the vastness. My true love is lurking somewhere out there in the random chaos of life. I love my daughter, my family and my country. I know there is an abundance of love in my heart that waits patiently to someday become a roaring flood.

I have traveled great distances, like a nomadic hunter traversing the tundra searching for sustenance, hoping to encounter true love. I thought I found *it* in my early twenties, but *it* crumbled like a dam with a hair-line crack. The water dripped slowly at first until the backlog of pressure crushed the foundation and all was lost.

Upon getting divorced in 1995 I had no idea what a raucous journey lay ahead, just as I am uncertain now about what is on the horizon. It has been a spectacular and adventurous ride for which I am divinely thankful. I have been blessed to meet so many intriguing women, each one contributing something to my composition, hopefully making me a better man.

Confident or Cocky?

I had always been highly self-confident as a teenager, teetering on that feeling of invincibility that many young people experience. I succeeded in the classroom and on the playing fields where each new achievement reinforced that confidence. My self-esteem was severely deflated following my separation and eventual divorce. When I looked in the mirror I only saw myself as even more pathetic. I magnified the negative and staggered onto the narrow ledge of depression.

Time heeled the damage and my self-confidence was gradually repaired, but with each relationship it grew closer to arrogance. I amplified my positive attributes leading to an inflated sense of desirability. I entered a frightening state of mind where no one was good enough, yet I felt I deserved to find perfection.

In my misguided search for Nirvana I became addicted to the chase and the blissful early stages of the relationship-building process, but certainly not because I was hoping to carve a notch on my belt. Quite the contrary—my mentality was that quality far outweighed quantity or the sophomoric bravado of chest-pounding conquests. I was not interested in silly games of catch and release. I typically wanted to date the one girl in the room that everyone else desired. Why?—because everybody else couldn't be wrong. Or could they? I developed the charisma and regained the confidence to repeatedly make that date happen.

"Shaun, you're too good looking," a wise friend from Newport quipped ten years after my divorce.

He claimed I was aging like a fine wine and suggested that was my curse.

I always accepted his joke as flattery, but there was a somber undertone to his jest. The *real* curse was the anguish that lingered after the painful separation from my only child and the failure of my marriage. Although I craved the perfect woman, I repeatedly pursued flawed partners to cleverly avoid the vulnerability that accompanies true love.

I was so frightened by the pain of being unceremoniously dumped that I shielded my heart. I concocted shrewd excuses to avoid ever getting too close. I cowered behind flimsy justifications such as geography, a turbulent past, age, a celebrity birthday party, a love-child, and even haunting ghosts!

When love finally found me, I was too self-absorbed to recognize *it*, to nurture *it*, and to reciprocate *it* properly. I had become so cautious and guarded with my emotions. I vowed never to mislead anyone, and I refused to confess love as an obligatory response if someone else told me that they loved me. That was the beginning of my demise with Lindsay, but my mind was too clouded to realize it. My ego had become a mighty dam trapping my emotions behind a rock-solid façade.

When I finally pledged my love for her it was too late. Irreparable damage had been strewn across the relationship.

Orwell & Kerouac

It may sound contrite, but fifteen years ago all I really wanted was a white picket fence, a BMW, a golden Labrador, and the 2.5 kids that conformed to some asinine image manufactured by Madison Avenue and packaged as the yuppie lifestyle. That was the course I charted when I got married by candlelight next to a boundless ocean in 1991.

During the fall of 1994 I languidly climbed aboard the 5:55AM train in Harrison each morning dressed in my company-issued khaki trench coat like all the other Wall Street zombies. I was surprisingly content to be amongst those corporate sheep. My mundane routine reminded me of one of the most influential advertisements ever created—the *Apple Computer* ad introducing the *MacIntosh* that aired during the 1984 Super Bowl. Its singular showing undeniably heightened its legendary impact. The ad was a clever Orwellian depiction of Big Blue, IBM's well-crafted nickname, acting as Big Brother and preaching conformity to the robotic line-workers. Perhaps my ex-wife was analogous to the renegade woman who hurled a sledgehammer at the screen, smashing the Wizard—the controller of the Matrix, and liberating the brainwashed laborers.

In a twisted sort of way, maybe I owe my ex-wife a measure of gratitude for my freedom, and for allowing me to experience this convoluted journey of exuberance and self-discovery. In the late 1950's Jack Kerouac went *On the Road* to find meaning. I did what any recently divorced guy would do—I dusted myself off and tried to jump back on the relationship bike. Instead, I stumbled upon an unhealthy addiction that I never even realized existed.

I am certain I would still be a Wall Street stiff, cringing under my desk in fear of a pink slip, if not for the arduous decision by my ex-wife to leave me. I would still be looking ahead and grinding it out to achieve some silly milestone, such as twenty years of service, like a prisoner fulfilling a sentence. If I were still married, I am sure I would be flabbier, my wardrobe would be boring, and by now my wife would have issued a death sentence for my balls, forcing me to get my pipe crimped. When retirement arrived, there would be a farewell dinner, a shiny new Rolex, ice for my nuts, and hopefully a plump nest egg with a fancy country club membership.

My ex-wife once begged me to return to Maine to become a teacher and a football coach. I was a freshly-minted MBA burdened by sixty grand in student loans and thought she was insane. But maybe she was partially right. Maybe I was too focused on success and numb to my own happiness. I guess I had something to prove and felt the need to remain in Manhattan and claim my stake.

The Wolf and my Drug

I cannot imagine all the trouble I could have stirred up for the past fifteen years if I had completely immersed myself in the New York party scene. I am sure my stories would have been a lot raunchier, more sordid, and quite pathetic. But I always maintained too much respect for my body and for my job to pump myself full of drugs, deprive myself of sleep, or hitch a ride in the self-destructive fast lane. There are some on Wall Street who drive that express lane to the high-life, who compromise the rules, and who abandon their integrity to become filthy rich. They are seduced by the pursuit of the Manhattan lifestyle, much like the Bud Fox character in the movie *Wall Street*.

The Street is littered with legendary stories of corporate

abuses committed in the den of thieves: a trader sending an intern to Miami on a G5 to pick up stone crab at Joe's for lunch, or an investment banker flying a Bichon Frise to Ohio for a coiffure appointment. A few years ago there were headlines about midget-tossing on a drug-filled yacht with traders from Fidelity Investments and Credit Suisse. One of the traders, a former neighbor of mine in Boston, was eventually fired by Fidelity.

Other players ordain themselves as The Wolf of Wall Street, get incoherently drunk or high, and crash their private helicopter on some poor bastard's manicured lawn in East Hampton at four in the morning. Many Wall Street professionals have the means to perform these obnoxious escapades, but only the reckless few perform such lewd and idiotic acts of overindulgence. A few bad apples can easily taint the entire industry.

Luckily I was never one of them. Goldman Sachs taught its new associates about these ridiculous abuses by showing us original articles documenting the tomfoolery, and strongly emphasizing there was no quicker way to get fired from the firm. Ask Jim Cramer. He explained how an inappropriate photo projecting him as a "big swinging dick" got him axed from Goldman in his book, *Confessions of a Street Addict*.

The golden rule was to always ask how it would look if what I am doing right now was plastered all over the front page of the *Wall Street Journal*. Somehow, tossing a midget while surrounded by high-end call girls and a pile of blow on a fancy yacht didn't seem quite as humorous. Ask Fidelity Investments and my former neighbor.

America has assumed its position as the world's superpower for the moment and every empire claims its Rome. New York has garnered the title of America's grandest city so I used to joke that I lived and played in modern day Rome. And like the gluttonous Romans, I gorged on fine food, trading commissions, and beautiful women. Manhattan is so often romanticized in magazines, television, and cinema. But danger lurks in the form of temptation and a cult-like theme of ravenous consumption. Like an indulgent king, the more you get the more you want. With unlimited offerings, one can become eternally unfulfilled and constantly wondering, where is my next big score?

My guilty pleasure was meeting and pursuing a lot of accomplished, interesting, and breathtaking women. And the more I met, the more I wanted to meet. Female companionship became my drug of choice. When I got divorced, my closest male friends were married and living the suburban lifestyle that I had briefly enjoyed. I scrambled to replace them with a potpourri of female companions. Some of these women were purely friends, some were "friends with benefits", and some were ex-lovers turned confidant. They filled a gaping void that I never even realized existed.

I had spent my formative years in high school and college hanging out with teammates and my fraternity brothers. The only time I ever spent with a female was with a girlfriend punching a time clock invariably motivated by sex. I never understood or appreciated what a terrific resource a woman could be simply as a friend. Ironically, that myopic view undoubtedly contributed to the failure of my marriage.

At a minimum, I spent two months courting and dating every woman in this book except for the college intern who temporarily earned me the nickname, the Barber. My addiction arose from feasting on the newness of a relationship. In the early stages of any new connection there is always the euphoric bliss, the "honeymoon stage", which can effortlessly endure for a few months. But the instant those feelings of harmony and paradise began to fade, I was searching for my next fix.

And where did the honeymoon junkie go to satisfy his craving? The best places to meet interesting ladies always seemed to be the chic new restaurants or the boutique hotel bars. In my shameful pursuit of the beautiful crowd I knew they always had to be one step ahead of the masses, so any place trendy was instantly a Mecca for the models, and the wannabe posers they dragged in their wake. But not exactly havens or proven training grounds for great mothers-to-be. In hindsight I should have centered my quest for *the one* at church, the grocery store, or one of New York's world-class museums. I am sure those locales would have been much more suitable hunting grounds.

Side-effects of Addiction

I am the self-proclaimed "King of the Idiots" for not eradicating this addiction and marrying at least two of these phenomenal women. I can only blame myself. I had the self-discipline to avoid so much of the danger in Manhattan, but I was overcome by the curse of the honeymoon junkie. My old wound caused bad choices. As much as I wanted the perfect woman I repeatedly sought flawed partners to limit the likelihood of ever becoming emotionally anchored.

Love at first sight?—it can start the fire, but love is a shared experience that grows from a tiny kernel. That first glance, first touch, first laugh or first kiss can become the seed. I planted many seeds, but the pain of my divorce blocked out the sun and closed the valves to my heart.

My honeymoon addiction left me lost in the fog and oblivious to the lighthouse. Every night I went out in Manhattan my goal was to meet one woman interesting enough to make "the list", a scrolling database of potential partners. The list always provided a sea of options whenever I began to lose that honeymoon feeling.

I had forgotten the benefits of monogamy and how to be singularly focused on a relationship. At the first hint of trouble, the search for a replacement was automatically triggered. I had stumbled into an abyss as powerfully gripping as a black hole. Could I ever escape and return to the place I once was? Could

I relocate to suburbia with a new wife and start a second family? Or had I become obsessed with the hunt? Had I become comfortably numb willing to let keepers like Lindsay or Laurie slip away? It was a disturbing realization that even my daughter recognized and begged me to fix. She desperately wanted me to find *the one* and settle down.

Death and the Afterlife

As time passes and I reflect on my life, most of it doesn't seem to matter as much anymore. The love I have for my daughter and my family grows in importance with each passing day. We never know where the end lies, but we all comprehend its inevitability. The only thing that really matters is love. That is the only currency worth anything when that day on your tombstone arrives. Love is the only thing that you get to take with you.

I read a book that proposed a theory on the afterlife. It suggested a city, a sort of way-station, where souls gather after death. It's described as a waiting room where we are to remain for as long as someone on Earth has a memory of us. Those fleeting thoughts become our life support while we wait for Judgment Day. I fell in love with the concept, and its premise encouraged me to reconnect with the Church after a two decade hiatus. My beloved grandmother passed in the summer of 2006 so part of my motivation was to selfishly breathe life into her memory. I hope God forgives me.

A wise man once told me that you could judge a man by how many people attended his funeral. The people who love, honor, and respect you will always find a way to make an appearance. A crowded funeral is the ultimate barometer on how meaningful that dash was—the one sandwiched between the two years serving as bookends on the shiny piece of granite planted above your earth-covered box.

Perfection

I often get asked two simple, straightforward questions by the women I've dated and pursued.

"What exactly are you looking for in a woman? How would you describe the perfect woman?"

I think the answer to those magical questions is equally as simple and universally accepted. As a generalization most men want essentially the same thing—a woman who embodies the social eloquence of Grace Kelly, the culinary artistry of Martha Stewart, and the sexual ambition of Jenna Jameson. If you package that with a certain level of intellect and cerebral curiosity – *Voilá!* You may have found Nirvana! And Cindy Crawford got accepted at Northwestern, proving that brains and beauty are not mutually exclusive! One more reason to never compromise the search.

A Grace Kelly imitation will inflame a man's pride. A Martha Stewart impression exploits the old wives' tale that "the best way to a man's heart is through his stomach." And mimicking Jenna Jameson's insatiable sexual appetite will guarantee that a man never has the energy or the desire to stray from the cave. Most men yearn to be with a woman who will somehow make them a better man, someone who challenges them to achieve greatness in their life. An all-star wife can often become that life coach who motivates a man to be the best that he can be.

The second part of the question hinged on describing perfection. It simply does not exist. Trust me. I have been tirelessly chasing it for fifteen years. No one is perfect. We all have flaws, and more importantly, flaws can be a beautiful thing. In a relationship the onus is upon each person to identify those flaws and make a truthful judgment on whether or not they can tolerate, accept, and even come to admire those imperfections.

Another part of the equation that is vitally important to me pertains to children. Every time I dated someone I repeatedly asked myself the same question.

"What kind of mother do you think she would be?"

Does she have the patience and is she willing to make the sacrifices that are prerequisites for that most difficult job? The answer to that question was always a crucial ingredient in the evaluation process. Nothing has brought me more joy in my lifetime than my daughter so when I find *the one* I hope God will grace us with children.

"Will you ever get married again?" was also a frequently asked question.

Shortly after my divorce and still burdened by the pain embedded in my memory, I was bitter, constantly questioning the institution of marriage and the advent of monogamy. Like some liberal eccentric who was pondering crazy conspiracy theories, I would ask myself who invented marriage? The church. And why did they invent it? Money. Who else benefited? The government. What did they gain? Order among the populace. It sounds almost too simplistic, but these are fairly logical motivations.

To answer the question, I actually now pray at church each Sunday for marriage. I beg God to help me find *the one* knowing that it is the only remedy for a honeymoon junkie. And when I find her I never want to think, or even hear that dreadful phrase.

"The honeymoon is over."

Epilogue: A Possible Sequel?

In the last fifteen years I have enjoyed relationships that lasted as long as eighteen months and as short as a month. I have been fortunate to experience more than the ones documented here. There have been other interesting and accomplished women in my life: a former Miss Slovakia, a Tufts dental school student, the daughter of the founder of a prestigious Wall Street firm, a Betsey Johnson designer, and a hedge fund manager from the now-defunct Bear Stearns.

My "hedgie friend" from the mid-90's is now mired at the epicenter of a landmark insider trading case involving wire tapping, an informant, executives from IBM, McKinsey and Google, and a billionaire hedge fund manager from Sri Lanka. I was even idiotic enough to appear on a ridiculous reality television dating show titled *Seducing Cindy* featuring internet bikini babe and two-time *Playboy* cover girl, Cindy Margolis. That escapade represented the pinnacle during my age of foolishness. I wanted to save some material for a sequel if this book becomes a rousing success.

Acknowledgements

"No man is an island" and I certainly did not complete this journey without the help and the patience of many people from so many different corners of my world. I would like to begin by thanking my biggest supporters in life who religiously cheered me on from little league baseball bleachers and a crowd of 20 through college football games at Cornell and a crowd of 20,000—Brian and Marti Hawkins and my sister Sarah Hawkins Cox. Once again they shouted encouragement as I staggered to the finish line at the publishing house and I am forever appreciative of their sacrifices, their love, and their support.

I would like to thank Kristine Lombardi, someone I met briefly at a business school classmate's wedding in 1996. She works in the publishing business and enthusiastically volunteered to become my best pen pal for the last eighteen months as this book evolved through all its stages. She was with me electronically the entire way providing invaluable advice, keen suggestions, and knowledgeable opinions.

Like so many great ideas, the foundation for this book began as scratches on the back of a cocktail napkin. A friend urged me to write a story about my escapades on the Manhattan dating scene. I argued vehemently against the idea and jokingly asked, "Who wants to read *The Adventures of Fuckleberry Hawk?*" After laughing at the hypothetical title I slowly became convinced that my story was an entertaining journey from the despair of divorce to the thrills of being a jet-setting bachelor. That persuasive friend was Chris Smith, a fellow "Maine-iac", who I met in Manhattan. He is the one I credit with challenging me to find the platform that would make *Honeymoon Junkie* viable. He became a constant bulletin board of guidance since he had done the bulk of the legwork in preparing his book, *The Modern Medusa*, for publication. His insights into the business aspects of publishing were critical.

I would like to thank my former boss at Goldman Sachs in Boston, Fred Clough, for his thoughtful evaluation when the book would have been best described as a disjointed collection of relationship failures. His pertinent and thoughtful observations definitely improved the book.

When my writing was complete I had a bloated manuscript that needed some editing assistance. Novice writers have a tendency to be verbose and I was not immune to that common *faux pas*. I called upon the valedictorian of my father's high school class and still his best friend from high school, Peter Lysaght (Cheverus '63 & Dartmouth '67). Peter sacrificed part of his summer vacation and time spent on the beach at the family compound in Pine Point to help me trim the fat and eliminate some of my rambling rants. I also received invaluable editing assistance from a neighborhood friend, Ellie Chase. She performed the pain-staking task of locating and correcting my numerous grammatical miscues.

I would like to thank Tony Richard who saved me from the dreadful task of becoming computer-savvy and designing a website. Tony was a bulldog in getting everything done on time and under budget. He is a graphic designer and provided the wizardry behind my website, my book cover, and my layout.

I want to make a special mention for Charles Heskett. He was introduced to me back in 2004 by an old football teammate and fraternity brother from Chicago, Brent Felitto. Charles is a Harvard MBA, a Bowdoin graduate like my father, and a diehard Red Sox fan and was the first to read my initial version. When the book resonated with Charles it gave me the encouragement I was looking for because he perfectly fit the demographic of the target market for my story. The Chuckster is also the guy who introduced me to Chris Smith, his best pal from Bowdoin College.

I want to thank my high school English teacher, Margaret Mary McCann, who recognized a glimmer of talent and has always prodded me over the years to pursue my writing abilities. I was too busy being a football player, a Dad, and a Wall Street executive to ever carve out the time and expend the energy to write. Her encouragement always echoed in the far reaches of my head and I am glad I finally made the time to write this book. If nothing else it was a therapeutic exercise.

There are so many others to thank in so many ways for reaching out and having an impact on this book. Many friends from my hometown of Portland have been so supportive and exuberant for this book to be completed. There were days when their infectious enthusiasm helped me to regroup and "to get the ball into end zone" one more time. Lastly, I owe a debt of gratitude to all the wonderful women who were crazy enough to date me and who ultimately became the foundation for my story.